A2
Science in Society

Project directors:
Angela Hall
Robin Millar

Editors
Angela Hall
Andrew Hunt

Contributors
Nan Davies
Anna Grayson
Angela Hall
Jonathan Holmes
Andrew Hunt
Emma Newall
Nick Owens

Expert advisers

We are grateful for the advice we received during the planning stages of the A2 Science in Society course from teachers and a number of expert advisers including: Emm Barnes, University of Manchester; Peter Finegold, Isinglass Consultancy Ltd; David Gooding, University of Bath; Baroness Susan Greenfield, The Royal Institution; Sir Roland Jackson, The British Association for the Advancement of Science; David Kirby, University of Manchester; Sir John Krebs, Jesus College, Oxford; Ralph Levinson, Institute of Education; Dean Madden, National Centre for Biotechnology Education; Professor Lord May of Oxford, Merton College, Oxford; Steve Miller, University College London; Jonathan Osborne, King's College; Michael Reiss, Institute of Education; Lynne Symonds, The Association for Science Education; Jon Turney; Martin Westwell; Stephen Webster, Imperial College; Emma Weitkamp, University of the West of England; Jonny Woodward, University of Leicester.

We also acknowledge with thanks the advice from those who read and commented on draft chapters in this book: Paul Bowers Isaacson, Nuffield Curriculum Centre; Peter Long, University of Bath; Emma Meaburn, Institute of Psychiatry, King's College London; Angela Melamed, Nuffield Curriculum Centre; Marcus Pembrey, Institute of Child Health, University College London; GlaxoSmithKline; Iain Stewart, University of Plymouth; Kathleen Taylor; John Zajicek, Peninsula College of Medicine and Dentistry.

www.heinemann.co.uk

✓ Free online support
✓ Useful weblinks
✓ 24 hour online ordering

01865 888080

Heinemann

Heinemann is an imprint of Pearson Education Limited, a company incorporated in England and Wales, having its registered office at Edinburgh Gate, Harlow, Essex, CM20 2JE. Registered company number: 872828

www.heinemann.co.uk

Heinemann is a registered trademark of Pearson Education Ltd

Text © The Nuffield Foundation, 2009

12 11 10 09
10 9 8 7 6 5 4 3 2 1

British Library Cataloguing in Publication Data is available from the British Library on request.

ISBN 978 0 435654 65 8

Edited by Tim Jackson
Designed by Wooden Ark
Produced by Tek-Art
Original illustrations © Pearson Education Limited 2009
Illustrated by Tek-Art
Picture research by Alison Prior
Cover photo/illustration © dino4/iStockphoto (main image);
Barbara Strnadova/Science Photo Library (butterfly)
Printed in China (CTPS/01)

Websites
The websites used in this book were correct and up-to-date at the time of publication. It is essential for tutors to preview each website before using it in class so as to ensure that the URL is still accurate, relevant and appropriate. We suggest that tutors bookmark useful websites and consider enabling students to access them through the school/college intranet.

Contents

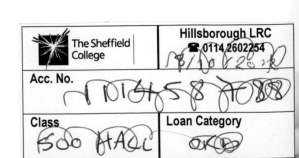

Acknowledgements

The editor and publisher would like to thank the following individuals and organisations for permission to reproduce photographs:

p1 TR Bubbles Photo Library/Alamy; p1 M Fan Travel Stock/Alamy; p4 Anatomical Travelogue/Science Photo Library; p5 BSIP Roux/Science Photo Library; p8 David Nicholls/Science Photo Library; p9 Kay Roberts/GlaxoSmithKline; p10 Simon Fraser/ Science Photo Library; p11 Kay Roberts/GlaxoSmithKline; p13 TR Science Photo Library; p13 BR Alexander Myers/Alamy; p16 Science Photo Library; p17 Wendy Wilson; p19 BSIP Mendil/Science Photo Library; p21 AFP/Getty Images; p22 Getty Images; p25 Jim Varney/Science Photo Library; p26 Will & Deni McIntyre/Science Photo Library; p28 Andrew Fox/Corbis; p29 Digital Stock; p30 Image State/Alamy; p32 Digital Vision/Punchstock; p36 David Parker/Science Photo Library; p39 TL Alex Bartel/Science Photo Library; p39 BR Anna Grayson; p40 Helen Everson; p48 ALSPAC; p51 TR Jupiter Images/Bananastock/Alamy; p51 BL Hulton Archive/Getty Images; p52 LWA-Dann Tardif/Corbis; p61 TL David Palmer; p61 BR Angela Hall; p65 iStockphoto/ Nikolay Titov; p66 Tissuepix/Science Photo Library; p67 TL Gusto Images/Science Photo Library; p67 BL US National Library of Medicine/Science Photo Library; p69 Dr Andrew Schwartz/Pittsburgh University; p71 TL The National History Museum, London; p71 TR The Natural History Museum, London; p71 BR William Ervin/Science Photo Library; p72 Great Ape Trust of Iowa; p75 Tek Image/Science Photo Library; p76 Deco/Alamy; p77 Mehau Kulyk/Science Photo Library; p82 Paul Thompson/ UCLA School of Medicine; p84 Anna Grayson; p90 Photo Edit Inc/Laura Dwight; p92 Emotiv Systems; p93 Ian Hooton/Science Photo Library; p95 Professor JC Hebden/ Biomedical Optics Research Laboratory/University College London; p98 TR Corbis; p98 M Jeremy Walker/Science Photo Library; p103 Corbis; p104 AFP/Getty Images; p110 TL Jonathan Holmes; p110 TR Jonathan Holmes; p113 TR Eye of Science/Science Photo Library; p113 BL Dr Iain Robertson; p115 Rob Mulvaney; p116 Rob Mulvaney; p120 Jonathan Holmes; p121 Dr Alan Haywood/University of Leeds; p122 Dr Alan Haywood/University of Leeds; p126 Jonathan Holmes; p128 Dennis Cox/Alamy; p129 Martin Shields/Alamy; p133 TR Metro/Photoshot/Universal; p135 TR Angelo Calvalli/ Zefa/Corbis; p135 M Greenshoots Communications/Alamy; p136 BL Juice Images/ Corbis; p136 BR AFP/Getty Images; p142 John Wilkinson/Ecoscene/Corbis; p145 London Aerial Photography/Corbis; p148 Jeff Morgan Farming/Alamy; p150 Sellafield Ltd; p151 Lucy Watson/Sellafield Ltd; p158 Getty Images; p159 TR Suzanne Plunkett/ PA Photos; p159 B AFP/Getty Images; p160 AFP/Getty Images; p163 Martin Bond/ Science Photo Library; p166 Anna Grayson; p167 T Jim Varney/Science Photo Library; p167 B Nic Delves-Broughton; p169 Anna Grayson; p172 Cyril Ruoso/JH Editorial/ Getty Images; p174 Angela Hall; p176 TL Gail Shumway/Getty Images; P176 TR Stephen Frink Collection/Alamy; P179 Michael Martin/Science Photo Library; p183 John Foster/Science Photo Library; p184 T Geological Survey of Canada/Science Photo Library; p184 B Geoscience Features/Landform Slides; p187 Brian Bowes/Science Photo Library; p191 Georgette Douwma/Getty Images; p192 Sinclair Stammers/Science Photo Library; p194 David Noton/Getty Images; p196 Sven Torfinn/Panos Pictures; p197 Hulton Archive/Getty Images; p198 Peter Long; p199 Peter Long; p202 Gualtiero Boffi/Shutterstock; p203 Frans Lanting/FLPA; p204 Jurgen & Christine Sohns/FLPA.

Thanks are due to the following for permission to reproduce illustrations:

Fig. 1.34: EMCDDA (2004), *Annual report: the state of the drugs problem in the European Union and Norway*. European Monitoring Centre for Drugs and Drug Addiction, Lisbon. **Fig. 2.13**: © Irving Gottesman (1994), used by kind permission.

Fig. 2.15: Caspi et al. (2005). Moderation of the effect of adolescent-onset cannabis use on adult psychosis by a functional polymorphism in the catechol-O-methyltransferase gene: longitudinal evidence of a Gene X environmental interaction. *Biological Psychiatry*, 57 (10), pp.1117-1127. Fig. 3.19: © Roger Dooley, used by kind permission. Fig. 3.25: Gazzaniga, M.S. (1998). The split brain revisited. *Scientific American*, 279 (1), pp.35-39. Fig. 4.3: Ruddiman, W.F. (2001). *Earth's climate: past and future*. 1ˢᵗ ed. W.H. Freeman and Company, New York. Fig. 4.9: © Oak Ridge National Laboratory, used by kind permission. Fig. 4.19: IPCC (2001), *Climate Change 2001: Working Group I: The Scientific Basis*. Prepared by Working Group I of the Intergovernmental Panel on Climate Change. Figure 2.20. Cambridge University Press. Fig. 4.23: IPCC (2001), *Climate Change 2001: Working Group I: The Scientific Basis*. Prepared by Working Group I of the Intergovernmental Panel on Climate Change. Figure 15. Cambridge University Press. Fig. 4.28: IPCC, http://www.ipcc.ch/about/how-the-ipcc-is-organized. htm. Accessed 3ʳᵈ December 2008. Fig. 4.29: IPCC (2001), *Climate Change 2001: Working Group I: The Scientific Basis*. Prepared by Working Group I of the Intergovernmental Panel on Climate Change. Figure 3.12. Cambridge University Press. Fig. 4.36: Stainforth, D. et al. (2005). Uncertainty in predictions of the climate response to rising levels of greenhouse gases. *Nature*, 433 (2005), pp. 404. Fig. 5.6: *Key World Energy Statistics* © OECD/IEA, 2008. Fig. 5.11: DTI (2007), *Meeting the energy challenge*. Figure 5.1.1, pp.129. Reproduced under the terms of the Click-Use Licence. Fig. 5.14: IPCC (2005), *Special report on carbon dioxide capture and storage*. Prepared by Working Group III of the Intergovernmental Panel on Climate Change. Figure 5.14. Cambridge University Press. Fig. 5.19: DEFRA. Reproduced under the terms of the Click-Use Licence. Fig. 5.24: BERR, *Energy Trends June 2008*. Reproduced under the terms of the Click-Use Licence. Fig. 5.25: Marine Current Turbines Ltd. Fig. 5.26: United Nations Development Programme (2000), *World Energy Assessment: energy and the challenge of sustainability*. Figure 9.3. Fig. 5.32: BERR, *Renewable Energy Strategy Consultation 2008*. Reproduced under the terms of the Click-Use Licence. Fig 5.33: BERR, *Renewable Energy Strategy Consultation 2008*. Reproduced under the terms of the Click-Use Licence. Fig. 5.35: DTI (2007), *Meeting the energy challenge*. Figure 2.2, pp.49. Reproduced under the terms of the Click-Use Licence. Fig. 6.11: *New Scientist*, used by kind permission. Fig. 6.18: Courtillot, V. and Olson, P. (2007). Mantle plumes link magnetic superchrons to phanerozoic mass depletion events. *Earth and Planetary Science Letters*, 260 (2007), pp.495-504. Fig. 6.24: © Richard W. Hughes (2007), http://www.ruby-sapphire.com/madagascar_ruby_sapphire.htm. Fig. 6.26: John Vucetich. Fig. 6.30: Millennium Ecosystem Assessment. Fig. 6.40: Martyn Gorman. Fig. 6.41: Martyn Gorman.

Thanks are due to the following for permission to reproduce copyright material:

Fig. 1.18: Home Office, http://www.homeoffice.gov.uk/drugs/drugs-law/Class-a-b-c/. Reproduced under the terms of the Click-Use Licence. Fig. 1.19: Home Office, *Home Office Statistical Bulletin 04/05*. Reproduced under the terms of the Click-Use Licence. Page 22: Quote reproduced by kind permission of Stephen Fry. Fig 4.14: Met Office, http://www.metoffice.gov.uk/research/hadleycentre/obsdata/. Reproduced under the terms of the Click-Use Licence. Fig. 5.7: *Key World Energy Statistics* © OECD/IEA, 2008. Fig. 5.17: Health and Safety Executive. Reproduced under the terms of the Click-Use Licence. Fig. 5.18: Health and Safety Executive. Reproduced under the terms of the Click-Use Licence.

Foreword

This book covers the topics in the second year of the *Science in Society* course leading to a full A-level qualification. The book is complemented by outline schemes of work, activities, case studies and weblinks on the project website (www.scienceinsocietyadvanced.org).

The specification, book and website have been developed by the Nuffield Curriculum Centre in close collaboration with the University of York Science Education Group. David Baker of the Awarding Body AQA helped to guide the work on the specification with Paul Bowers Isaacson, Andrew Hunt and Angela Melamed. In developing the course and teaching resources we have benefited greatly from advice given by many teachers, together with expert advisers from universities and other research centres.

We would like to thank our co-authors and advisers for their contributions to this book. We are also indebted to Liz Marchant, Claire Gordon and Sally Woods of Heinemann for their support and expertise as well as Maja Melendez and Jo Oladejo at the Nuffield Curriculum Centre.

We are also very grateful to the Trustees of the Nuffield Foundation for their encouragement and financial support.

Angela Hall
Robin Millar

The A2 topics

There are just six topics in the A2 *Science in Society* course. You are going to learn new science explanations and explore ideas about science in the fields of neuroscience, genetics, climate change, energy resources and biodiversity. These are complex areas of frontier science where our knowledge is changing in the light of new evidence. They are interdisciplinary topics in which you will consider policy issues from national and international as well as personal perspectives.

Science explanations

In the AS course you learnt to make sense of and apply well-established science explanations that you had met before in introductory science courses (such as GCSE). In the A2 course you will learn about new science explanations, but only in as much detail as is needed to understand the important issues as well as an informed member of the public, journalist or lawyer might. This is a course to prepare you to make sense of what scientific experts have to tell us about ourselves and our environment.

How science works

In the A2 course you will add depth to your understanding of how science works and how it impacts on society. You will meet statistical concepts to make your interpretation of scientific data more rigorous. In the context of climate change you will also learn about the importance of dynamic modelling in complex situations. Considering policy decisions about scientific issues gives you a chance to explore methods such as cost-benefit analysis that can help to inform decisions. In general you will become more sophisticated in your analysis of information and the arguments you put forward to support your opinions.

Studying the course

This book covers the topics in Unit 3 of the A2 *Science in Society* course specification. The questions in each chapter highlight the important ideas and explanations. They are helpful starting points for discussion. As you carry out your own enquiries into the key issues, this book will be one of the sources of information you can refer to. Interpreting a range of documentary evidence related to each topic from a variety of sources will be important preparation for the case studies used in the assessment of Unit 4 of the course.

The course specification, together with specimen examination papers, are all available from the Awarding Body AQA. The latest information is available on the AQA website (www.aqa.org.uk). You will find a commentary on the questions in this book on the website (www.scienceinsocietyadvanced.org) where you will also find links to other websites with up-to-date and authoritative information about the issues which feature in the course.

Chapter 1

Cells, chemicals and the mind

Figure 1.1

Scientists use mirrors to find out when children reach new levels of self-awareness. Young babies do not recognise themselves in a mirror. Not until they are 15–20 months old do their brains develop sufficiently to see themselves in their reflection.

- How and why do chemicals affect our brains?

- Is there any clear distinction between legal and illegal drugs in terms of what they do to the brain?

- Should research into diseases of younger people, such as depression, take precedence over research into diseases of older people, such as Parkinson's disease and Alzheimer's disease?

- How can we tell if someone is mentally ill?

- What is society's attitude to mental illness? Should it change?

- Should we use drugs to improve learning, memory and concentration?

Figure 1.2

Our brains have to do remarkable things which we often take for granted when taking part in skilful athletic activities.

The Sheffield College
Hillsborough LRC
Telephone: 0114 260 2254

1.1 The brain, nerves and neurotransmitters

Everything you do, including a very simple task like typing your name on a keyboard, involves your brain in a huge act of coordination that takes just a fraction of a second. Millions of nerve cells within the brain act together to produce signals and transmit them along nerve cells, causing your fingers to move in the correct way.

Our brains and nervous system sometimes let us down: we drop things, forget things or trip up, for example. Some days we seem to make more mistakes, perhaps because we are tired or distracted, and there are times when we feel sad or even depressed. People differ in their memory, moods and coordination, so it is not always easy to tell when someone is developing a disease of the nervous system.

Neuroscience is the study of the nervous system and provides an insight into how the brain functions in health and disease. By investigating the way the brain functions when healthy, scientists can begin to unravel the mysteries of the brain in a diseased or altered state. They can also discover drugs to treat diseases. The research also helps to explain why taking drugs recreationally can alter mental states and sometimes damage the nervous system.

Scientists are still at an early stage of understanding how the brain works, which means that in neuroscience we see 'science in the making'.

Nerve cells

The technical name for a nerve cell is a neurone (Figure 1.3). Neurones are the basic units of the nervous system. There are about 100 billion (10^{11}) neurones in the human brain. Each one is connected to hundreds of others giving about 10^{14} interconnections in total. The interconnections between nerve cells are called synapses.

Figure 1.3

Two neurones joined by a synapse. At one end of each neurone is the cell body, which contains the nucleus and all the other features of a typical cell. Branching structures called dendrites protrude from the cell body, and gather incoming signals. An axon, which can be very long, carries impulses away from the cell body towards the dendrites of other neurones, or to muscles. An axon links to the dendrites or the cell body of another neurone via one or more synapses.

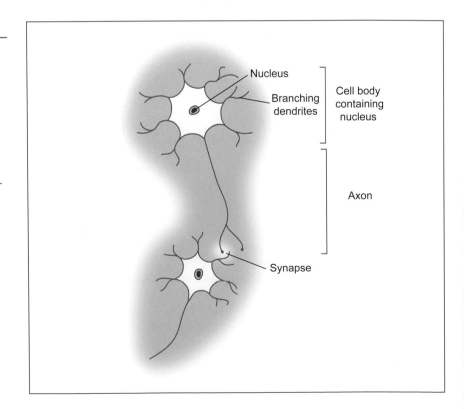

Nerve impulses travel like waves over the surface of the body of neurones and along axons. The waves are electrical signals that arise when tiny channels open in the cell membrane allowing ions (electrically charged atoms) to move in and out of the cell. An axon or dendrite can carry over 100 impulses per second, at a speed of up to 100 metres per second. Nerve impulses provide constant communication between the nerve cells in the brain and throughout the body.

The cell body of a neurone integrates the information arriving at its many dendrites, and sends signals to other neurones via its single axon. A neurone in the cerebral cortex (see Figure 1.6, page 5) has up to 100 000 synapses on its dendrites. Some of the synapses excite the neurone, making it more likely to send a signal down its axon. Other synapses inhibit the neurone, making it less active. The overall effect of all the incoming information determines the output of the cell body. The axon may connect to other neurones in the brain, or it may go out of the brain to control a muscle or gland.

Synapses and neurotransmitters

Nerve impulses do not pass directly from one neurone to the next. Instead, the signals cross synapses by means of a chemical neurotransmitter. Neurotransmitters are released from one neurone and diffuse across a tiny gap to the next neurone (Figures 1.4 and 1.5). On reaching the next neurone the neurotransmitter molecules join to receptor molecules, making the receiving neurone more active or less active than it was before.

About 50 different neurotransmitters are used in the human brain. They are small molecules that can pass quickly across the synaptic gap. Some neurotransmitters are mainly excitatory and others mainly inhibitory, but their specific action depends on the receptors they bind to in different brain cells.

Key terms

A **neurone** consists of dendrites, a cell body and an axon ending at a synapse.

Dendrites receive chemical signals from other neurones. The cell body integrates the incoming signals.

Axons transmit signals from the cell body to synapses on the dendrites of other neurones.

Synapses are the junctions between nerve cells.

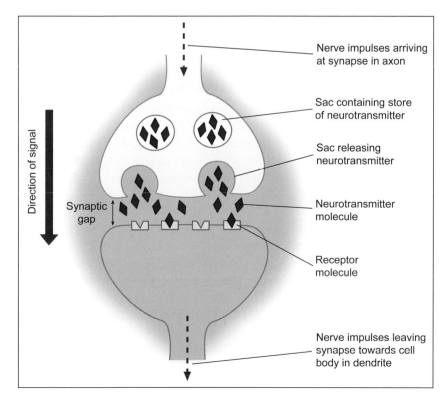

Direction of signal

Nerve impulses arriving at synapse in axon

Sac containing store of neurotransmitter

Sac releasing neurotransmitter

Neurotransmitter molecule

Synaptic gap

Receptor molecule

Nerve impulses leaving synapse towards cell body in dendrite

Figure 1.4

Schematic diagram of a synapse. Nerve impulses arriving at the end of the axon of the upper neurone (yellow) cause the release of neurotransmitter molecules into the tiny synaptic gap. The neurotransmitter molecules move across the gap and dock with receptor molecules in the dendrites of the lower neurone (orange). By docking with receptors, the neurotransmitter causes nerve impulses to be generated in the receiving neurone. The neurotransmitter's shape allows it to fit into the receptor molecule like a key in a lock. After the signal has been carried across the synapse, neurotransmitter molecules are very quickly either broken down or are reabsorbed into the neurone that released them. This highly schematic diagram is not to scale.

Figure 1.5

Computer-generated image showing neurones and synapses. Notice the neurotransmitters on the receiving surface of the synapse.

Neurotransmitters are synthesised in the cell body, and are transported to synapses along tiny tubules inside dendrites and axons. A single brain axon can be many centimetres long, so the place where a transmitter is made can be some distance from the site where it acts.

The first neurotransmitter to be discovered was acetylcholine. This is the neurotransmitter between nerve axons and muscles. The main neurotransmitter that excites neurones in the brain is glutamate.

There are two inhibitory neurotransmitters. These are GABA and glycine. Inhibitory neurotransmitters help to bring precision to nervous activity in the brain by suppressing activity in some neurones while other neurones are excited.

Other neurotransmitters have a more gradual effect than the excitatory and inhibitory neurotransmitters. Examples of this kind of transmitter are dopamine, serotonin and noradrenaline. Acetylcholine also acts in this kind of way within the brain.

The structure of the human brain

The human brain is highly complex. No two brains are exactly alike, and everyone's brain is changing all the time as the synapses between their neurones are modified under genetic control and by the environment (see Chapter 2). Figure 1.6 shows some of the main structures and functions of the parts of a typical human brain, seen in cross-section.

The human brain has about four times the volume of that of a chimpanzee, one of our closest living relatives. The part that shows the greatest difference is the cerebral cortex, which is relatively much larger in humans than in any other mammal.

The relative size of different brain regions provides evidence about the aspects of behaviour that are most important to a species. Some animals, such as whales, have brains that are larger than a human brain, simply because they are large animals. Much of the extra brain size in a whale is to control all their muscle fibres, so it does not make them more intelligent.

The pattern of connections between neurones in the brain constantly changes. New synapses form in response to experience while others disappear when not used.

Questions

1 Suggest reasons why it is hard for scientists to investigate the human brain and find out how it works.

2 Suggest reasons why society allocates large sums of money to fund brain research.

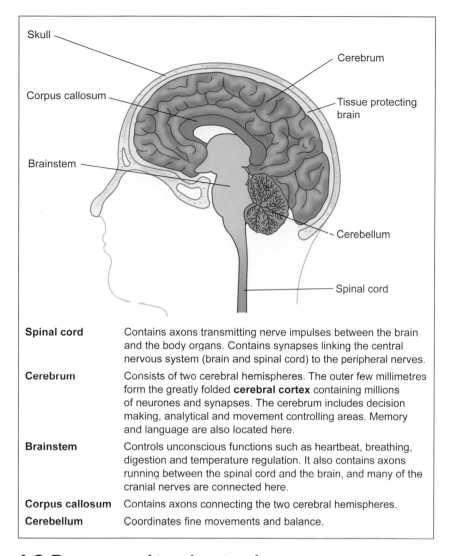

Figure 1.6

The main parts of the human brain and their functions (not to scale).

Labels on diagram: Skull, Corpus callosum, Brainstem, Cerebrum, Tissue protecting brain, Cerebellum, Spinal cord

Spinal cord	Contains axons transmitting nerve impulses between the brain and the body organs. Contains synapses linking the central nervous system (brain and spinal cord) to the peripheral nerves.
Cerebrum	Consists of two cerebral hemispheres. The outer few millimetres form the greatly folded **cerebral cortex** containing millions of neurones and synapses. The cerebrum includes decision making, analytical and movement controlling areas. Memory and language are also located here.
Brainstem	Controls unconscious functions such as heartbeat, breathing, digestion and temperature regulation. It also contains axons running between the spinal cord and the brain, and many of the cranial nerves are connected here.
Corpus callosum	Contains axons connecting the two cerebral hemispheres.
Cerebellum	Coordinates fine movements and balance.

1.2 Degenerative brain diseases

Parkinson's disease

The use of drugs to treat the symptoms of Parkinson's disease is one of the success stories of neuroscience. However, success is partial because there is no cure and the benefits of the drugs decline with time. The study of the disease has helped scientists to learn more about the importance of neurotransmitters and their effects on brain functions.

Symptoms of disease

If you hold your hand out to read your wrist watch, you may find that your hand is not perfectly still: there will almost certainly be a very small degree of vibration. Holding your arm in one position requires your brain to do a lot of unconscious calculation. The muscles above and below the elbow are both contracting just enough to hold the joint in balance, taking account of the weight of the arm and anything you are holding. Any movement leads to an automatic correction in muscle tension. We usually take our control of posture and movement for granted, but this can begin to fail in people affected by Parkinson's disease. This is a disease named after Dr James Parkinson who, in 1817, wrote an *Essay on the Shaking Palsy*.

Figure 1.7

A man reading a newspaper with trembling hands due to the effects of Parkinson's disease.

Figure 1.8

The characteristic appearance of a person with Parkinson's disease. Walking occurs with short quick steps, and the patient can become rooted to the spot.

Parkinson's disease is a neurodegenerative disease. This means that it is not a disease caused by infection, but rather that it is caused by the breakdown of neurones, leading to the gradual loss of their function. It is the second most common neurodegenerative disease, after Alzheimer's disease.

Parkinson's disease usually develops in people aged 50 or over, though there are some early-onset cases that tend to run in families. The mean age of onset is about 65, affecting about 1% of the overall UK population.

One of the early signs of Parkinson's disease is shaking or tremor of the limbs, often appearing first in one arm, when the arm is resting. At this stage the patient is still able to carry out voluntary movement in a normal controlled way. However, as the disease progresses, movement becomes slow and the limbs feel stiff. There can be a pause between the patient deciding to move and being able to get going. Walking characteristically occurs in small rapid steps, with a stooping gait. Activities such as dressing become difficult, and the patient may go on to have problems with talking, writing and even swallowing. After several years, there can be cognitive decline and dementia, but the disease is not immediately life-threatening.

Dopamine

What characterises patients with Parkinson's disease is that they respond to treatment by the drug levodopa (sometimes written as L-dopa). Levodopa reduces the tremors and stiffness seen in the disease. Levodopa is thought to work by helping to restore the levels of the neurotransmitter dopamine in the dopamine production centre in the brain.

The nerve cell bodies in the dopamine production centre produce dopamine. Long axons supply the dopamine to synapses across many different brain areas. Deterioration of the cells that produce dopamine is one of the main causes of the symptoms of Parkinson's disease.

Question

3 Give examples, from parts of the body other than the brain, to illustrate the difference between an infectious disease and a degenerative disease.

Figure 1.9

Dopamine produced in the brainstem is transmitted to different regions of the brain. Its effect depends on where it is in the brain.

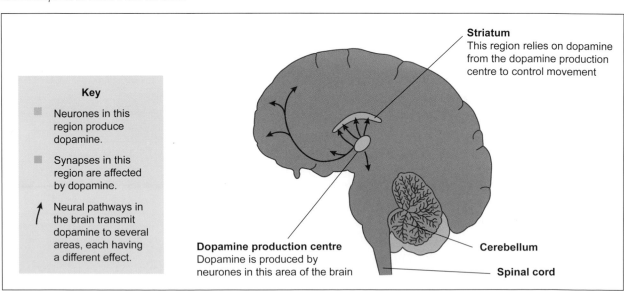

Key

- Neurones in this region produce dopamine.

- Synapses in this region are affected by dopamine.

↑ Neural pathways in the brain transmit dopamine to several areas, each having a different effect.

Striatum
This region relies on dopamine from the dopamine production centre to control movement

Dopamine production centre
Dopamine is produced by neurones in this area of the brain

Cerebellum

Spinal cord

Dopamine is essential for the normal control of movement, and also has a major role in the reward pathway of the brain (see page 12). The drug levodopa is able to enter the brain, where it is converted into dopamine, restoring the neurotransmitter and helping to reduce the symptoms of the disease. The dose of levodopa prescribed is delicately balanced: too little does not control the symptoms of Parkinson's disease, but too much can produce excess dopamine in the brain, causing unpleasant and disturbing side effects, including muscle spasms, depression and psychosis. The dosage needed varies with each patient and is largely a matter of trial and error.

The brain has a very good blood supply, but many substances are unable to pass from the bloodstream into the brain. This is because there is a membrane around the blood vessels in the brain that prevents selected molecules and ions from passing between the blood and the brain cells. This blood-brain barrier helps to protect the brain from toxins or psychoactive substances in the blood. Drugs must pass this blood-brain barrier in order to reach the brain.

Questions

4 Is it correct to say that the drug levodopa is a cure for Parkinson's disease?

5 Suggest the steps a doctor might follow to confirm a diagnosis of Parkinson's disease.

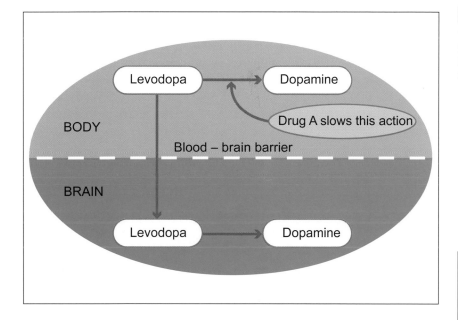

Figure 1.10

The conversion of levodopa to dopamine. Some levodopa is changed into dopamine by body (non-brain) cells before levodopa reaches the brain.

Dopamine is unable to cross the blood-brain barrier, but levodopa is able to do so. Levodopa enters the brain and is then converted into dopamine by brain cells (Figure 1.10). This is the main reason for prescribing levodopa rather than dopamine itself. Another reason is that outside the brain, dopamine causes side effects such as vomiting.

An alternative to using levodopa as a treatment for Parkinson's disease is to prescribe a drug that mimics dopamine, and has the same effects at synapses.

The tremors and stiffness of Parkinson's disease are well controlled by levodopa or dopamine mimics in the early years of the disease. Long-term treatment works less well. Levodopa pills are usually taken at intervals throughout the day. This leads to phases of high and low concentration of dopamine in the brain, which can upset the natural rhythm of the cells that make dopamine. In time the dose of levodopa has to increase if it is

Questions

6 Drug A in Figure 1.10 is commonly prescribed to patients on levodopa to slow the change of levodopa to dopamine outside the brain. Explain why taking this drug increases the amount of dopamine in the brain.

7 a) Explain why taking a dopamine mimic helps to reduced the symptoms of Parkinson's disease.
b) Give one other property that a dopamine mimic must have if it is to reduce Parkinson's disease symptoms.
c) Suggest reasons why taking a dopamine mimic may help to avoid the side effects that levodopa treatment causes.

Questions

8 Suggest why the total number of people affected by Parkinson's disease is expected to double by 2030.

9 Suggest how a more even dose of levodopa could be provided for a patient with Parkinson's disease.

10 People with Parkinson's disease must inform the Driver Vehicle Licensing Agency (DVLA) and their car insurer about their condition. What criteria should be used to decide whether or not a patient should be denied a licence?

still to be effective. This causes side effects caused by high and variable levels of dopamine in the brain.

There is an urgent need for better treatment for Parkinson's disease, as it affects so many people worldwide. The disease has profound costs for individuals and societies, since 15 years after diagnosis, about 40% of patients with the disease are in long-term care homes. The prevalence of the disease is expected to double by 2030.

Deep brain stimulation

After a time, some patients with Parkinson's disease find that treatment with levodopa does not prevent episodes of uncontrollable tremors. This can seriously disrupt their lives.

One solution is deep brain stimulation. Surgeons control the problem by inserting electrodes, about 1–2 mm in diameter, into the brain through the skull. Most of the successful effects have been achieved by implanting the electrodes close to a part of the brain that helps control complex movements. The electrodes are attached to an electrical pulse generator attached to the chest, rather like a heart pacemaker (Figure 1.11).

Electrically stimulating these deep brain areas with high frequency electrical pulses reduces abnormal neurone activity, preventing excessive tremors. This is a high risk technique and can cause brain haemorrhage, heart attack, fits or infection. It is only suitable for around 5% of patients with Parkinson's disease. It is very costly and does not slow the progress of neurone loss. However, the technique has been extremely beneficial for some patients and has been effective for as long as 8 years.

Questions

11 No research studies of deep brain stimulation have been carried out with healthy volunteers. Suggestions reasons why this is so.

12 There is some evidence from animal studies that deep brain stimulation can enhance memory and attentiveness. In time it might be shown that this surgical procedure could improve brain power.
a) Should research into the use of deep brain stimulation to enhance cognitive ability be funded?
b) Who should be allowed this treatment on the NHS?

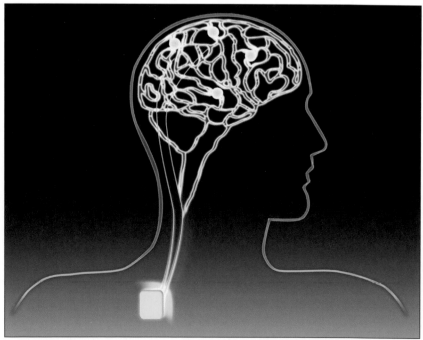

Figure 1.11

Deep brain stimulation is achieved by connecting electrodes in the brain to a pacemaker placed under the skin. The pacemaker sends regular electrical pulses to the brain.

Beyond levodopa

Until recently it was widely believed that levodopa itself could damage the cells that make dopamine. For this reason levodopa prescription was delayed for as long as possible. More recent studies suggest that patients receiving early levodopa treatment may do better than controls who received it later. Although levodopa may not harm these cells, it does nothing to slow their degeneration. In order to slow or prevent neurone degeneration, scientists need to find out what causes the degeneration to happen.

The causes of Parkinson's disease are still largely unknown. Genetic factors play a part, particularly in some of the early-onset forms of the disease, appearing in people aged under 40. Normally, however, onset of the disease seems to be more influenced by environmental factors than by genes.

The lack of any clear genetic link has switched attention to environmental factors. Post-mortem examinations of the brains of people who have had Parkinson's disease find unusual deposits, called Lewy bodies, in the neurones of 90% of patients, both in the substantia nigra and in other brain areas. It is possible that Lewy bodies are caused by environmental toxins, and that they cause or are a sign of neurodegeneration.

Newer drugs are aimed at slowing the damage to the cells that make dopamine caused by environmental factors or by harmful substances made inside the brain cells themselves. There are several different drugs under clinical trial that are designed to protect neurones, but so far no drug has been found that slows the progression of Parkinson's disease.

Research into new drugs to treat degenerative brain diseases

Ayesha Ahmed is a scientist who works in the field of drug discovery for the pharmaceutical company GlaxoSmithKline (GSK). She belongs to a team that is developing new drug treatments that might improve the quality of life for many people. She specialises in a range of neurological and psychiatric diseases.

In order to understand how and where a potential new chemical might act, biologists need to investigate the mechanism that causes a disease in the brain and the surrounding pathways. By targeting specific points in these pathways, chemists can design and make molecules that will hopefully go on to become drugs (Figure 1.12).

Ayesha studied biomedical sciences at university. As a result she became fascinated by how the brain works, and took a particular interest in neurodegenerative diseases. She learnt about the action of drugs in the pharmacology course. This introduced her to the way that drugs can act on receptors in the brain. She studied drug dependence and the many factors involved. For example, in alcoholism there are biological, neurological and psychological factors as well as genetic factors.

Before starting her research career, Ayesha took a year out in America at the Massachusetts General Hospital, working with post-mortem brain tissue of people who had Alzheimer's disease, Parkinson's disease and Huntington's disease. She was looking at the biochemical and enzyme changes in these tissues. Then she began research work studying Alzheimer's disease that led to a doctoral qualification (PhD).

Questions

13 What would you want to know about the presence of Lewy bodies in the wider population before concluding that they are connected with Parkinson's disease?

14 If the presence of Lewy bodies is linked to Parkinson's disease, why is it still uncertain whether Lewy bodies cause Parkinson's disease?

15 A possible new drug X was tested in mice, and seemed to protect neurones against toxins. The drug was then used in human clinical trials. The drug was given to a sample of patients with early Parkinson's disease and a matched sample of patients with the same disease was given levodopa. Brain scans were used to compare the survival of the cells that make dopamine in the two groups. Substantia nigra cells were found to survive better with drug X than with levodopa. Explain whether this study demonstrates that drug X successfully protects neurones.

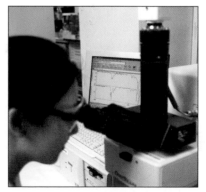

Figure 1.12

A member of the drug discovery research team in a laboratory of the pharmaceutical company GSK.

Ayesha explains some of the personal background that motivates her as a research scientist: "I have a disabled younger sister and this probably sparked an interest in how the brain works. This led to my exploration in neuroscience, particularly neuropharmacology and psychology, which I have found fascinating. Also, being of Bengali origin, there are diseases that seem to be more prevalent in our community, such as diabetes, heart disease, and high blood pressure, so again the genetics and epidemiology of these conditions is interesting."

Ayesha's own expertise is in Alzheimer's disease, but the company works on a variety of neurological and psychiatric diseases. Alzheimer's disease is the most common of a group of diseases classified as dementias. It is a progressive neurodegenerative disease characterised by a gradual loss of short-term memory at first, leading to general impairment of thinking, reasoning and perception.

The key question is what causes these diseases. There is no single cause. Some may be genetic, so you might have a genetic mutation that causes the formation of an abnormal protein resulting in normal physiological processes not working (Figure 1.13). Life experiences can be a factor – there is a suggestion that dietary and lifestyle factors may be involved in Parkinson's and Alzheimer's, as well as chronic stress and severe head injury. Of course, just getting older is the greatest risk factor.

As Ayesha explains: "In Alzheimer's disease there is a build up of two abnormal proteins we call amyloid and tau. We don't know exactly why, but something triggers a deposition of these proteins, particularly in the hippocampus and cortex regions of the brain. These parts of the brain are involved in memory and higher thought processes. The accumulation of the proteins impairs cellular function and causes cell death, particularly of the important neurones.

"Psychiatric diseases such as schizophrenia and depression can be induced by a whole combination of factors including alterations in brain structure, levels of neurotransmitters (serotonin and dopamine), genetics, childhood factors and complications at birth. There is evidence that schizophrenia has a genetic association as it is passed down in families. Also, if an identical twin raised separately from its sibling develops schizophrenia, there is a 50% chance that their twin will do so too.

"Schizophrenia is classed as a severe mental disorder characterised by delusions, hallucinations, psychosis, paranoia, disorganised thinking, perception and speech, as well as physical agitation. Onset of symptoms typically occurs during young adulthood. It has been observed that there is an increase in the neurotransmitter dopamine, and treatment is often with antipsychotic drugs that either inhibit dopamine release or suppress dopamine function.

"Depression is characterised by deep, long-lasting feelings of sadness or despair. Often levels of the neurotransmitter serotonin are markedly lower than normal in people suffering from depression. Drugs that maintain higher levels of serotonin by preventing the breakdown of this neurotransmitter are used as one form of treatment. Other drugs maintain or increase levels of another neurotransmitter, noradrenaline (which is also involved in mood).

"At present the main treatment available on the market for Alzheimer's disease is a drug that inhibits the breakdown of the neurotransmitter called

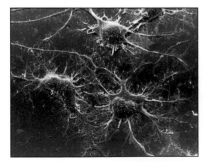

Figure 1.13

A coloured scanning electron micrograph image of cells used in research into Alzheimer's disease. These cells have been genetically engineered to produce a protein which then forms the protein amyloid. Plaques of amyloid are found in the brains of people with Alzheimer's disease.

acetylcholine that is involved in learning, memory and attention. Now that we understand that there is an accumulation of amyloid protein, the ideal scenario would be to inhibit the formation of this protein. In order to do this we need to understand the pathway of how amyloid is formed and then try to design a chemical compound that can act somewhere along that pathway.

"To find the right molecule we have to work with chemists. We can give them details of what the receptor site is like, so they can create a compound that is designed to fit the receptor and block it. We work with the chemists to help them understand the receptor structure.

"Once the compound is synthesised we carry out experiments to see if it really does block the receptor – this is first done *in vitro*, and this is the main part of my work. We use radioactive isotopes to see how well a new drug binds to the receptor. The radioactivity helps us to keep track of what happens to the molecules. If we find that our test compound binds effectively to the receptor site, then the chemists file a patent on the molecule and its structure.

"The big challenge for drugs that act on the brain, either for neurological or psychiatric disease, is to get the drug into the brain. This is because of the blood-brain barrier that prevents large proteins and cells crossing from the bloodstream into the brain. This can make it difficult for drugs to reach the desired site of action.

"Before the drug can be tested in humans, experiments must be carried out *in vivo*, in other words on animals such as mice, rats and fruitflies. This is always done in the most humane way possible and all experiments are strictly regulated by the Home Office and UK legislation.

"After this, if the drug looks hopeful, clinical trials start. These are very tightly controlled and regulated. The whole research and development process can take between 10 and 15 years. As a patent on a new medicine generally lasts for 20 years, this only leaves five to eight years before it runs out, which is an important factor in the business.

"Even if we can identify the receptor and create a molecule that binds to the receptor it is unlikely that the new drug will have a single effect. This is because receptors are often involved in several biochemical pathways. As a result, all drugs have side effects – which is something we always need to account for when considering drug action and pharmacology.

"People sometimes ask what would happen if healthy people took these drugs – would it give a brain boost? There is some evidence that some cognitive-enhancing drugs that are being tested for Alzheimer's disease might help memory in people who don't have the disease, but this has yet to be fully tested. Drugs used to treat depression have very little abuse potential as it takes about 2–4 weeks to see the beneficial effects plus they have side effects such as sleepiness and the potential to increase anxiety.

"I like the science in my work, analysing and interpreting the data. I also like the people I work with. You get some really interesting, friendly personalities who are passionate about the science and really believe in what they are doing in terms of helping patients. My dream drug to discover would be one to treat Alzheimer's disease. It is such a debilitating disease, and a drug that worked well would really help a lot of people. It would improve the amount of quality time for patients and their families. To see that for patients would be a reward in itself for me."

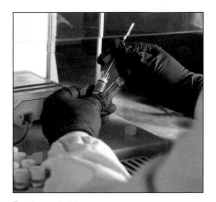

Figure 1.14

Preparing samples for analysis while developing new drugs.

Questions

16 Why do scientists need a theory of how the brain works in order to be able to design drugs to treat brain diseases?

17 What type of interdisciplinary collaboration does the research to develop new drugs benefit from?

18 Explain the main difference between *in vitro* and *in vivo* testing of drugs.

19 Why do scientists in pharmaceutical companies often publish their main findings as patents and not as papers in academic journals?

1.3 Recreational drugs and the brain

Many people use drugs to change their state of consciousness. They may use stimulants to help them to stay awake or sedatives to calm their nerves. Others choose to take drugs that seem to offer new types of mental experiences or that help them to forget their everyday troubles – at least for a short time. Scientists have discovered that all these drugs work by interacting in various ways with the neurotransmitters in the brain.

Taking medicines in a way not recommended by a doctor, or in such large quantities that they become a danger to health, are two of the ways in which people misuse drugs. Alcohol and tobacco are examples of drugs that are commonly misused even though they are not illegal. Obtaining and using illegal drugs – those that have been banned by law – is another type of misuse.

Drugs and dopamine

As well as its role in controlling movement and coordination, dopamine acts as a transmitter across several brain areas. There are also different related types of synaptic receptor to which dopamine can bind. The fact that there are around 35 000 dopamine producing neurones in the brain and each one has up to 100 000 synapses suggests that dopamine has varied and widespread functions as a neurotransmitter.

Scientists have found that dopamine has great significance in drug taking and drug addiction because it is involved in the reward pathway in the brain. This pathway originates in the brainstem and extends into the prefrontal cortex. It is activated when people seek a reward or are motivated to do something.

Three interconnected regions of the brain are known to be involved in the reward pathway: the dopamine production centre, the nucleus accumbens, and the prefrontal cortex. The neurones of the dopamine production centre produce dopamine, which is released in the nucleus accumbens and in the prefrontal cortex (Figure 1.15). These particular pathways are activated by a rewarding stimulus, and make us feel good. Almost all recreational drugs raise dopamine levels in the nucleus accumbens.

Key term

A **reward** is an environmental change that makes it more likely that a behaviour pattern will be repeated.

Figure 1.15

Dopamine pathways in the human brain. Note that all these structures occur in both sides of the brain.

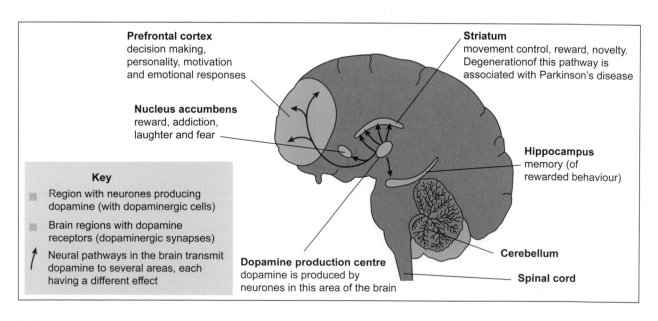

Prefrontal cortex
decision making, personality, motivation and emotional responses

Nucleus accumbens
reward, addiction, laughter and fear

Striatum
movement control, reward, novelty. Degeneration of this pathway is associated with Parkinson's disease

Hippocampus
memory (of rewarded behaviour)

Cerebellum

Spinal cord

Dopamine production centre
dopamine is produced by neurones in this area of the brain

Key

- Region with neurones producing dopamine (with dopaminergic cells)
- Brain regions with dopamine receptors (dopaminergic synapses)
- Neural pathways in the brain transmit dopamine to several areas, each having a different effect

Experiments with animals have helped scientists to understand the reward pathway. In an experiment, carried out in the 1960s, rats were trained to press a lever to receive a small electrical pulse via an electrode into their nucleus accumbens. They repeated the lever pressing behaviour over and over again for hours, because the end result was pleasurable (Figure 1.16). Analysis of the rats' brains showed that dopamine was present in greater quantities in the reward pathways after the experiment.

Further research has confirmed that drugs interfere with the way in which our brains send, receive and process information. Drugs that are used by an individual to seek pleasure have an effect on the dopamine reward pathway.

The dopamine reward system is present in all mammals and has the function of rewarding behaviour that helps survival and reproduction, for example feeding, drinking and sexual behaviour. It makes such behaviour pleasurable and therefore likely to be repeated.

This pathway is very significant because humans, and other animals, indulge in activities that they find rewarding. Parents of young children, for example, adopt a technique of rewarding good behaviour to encourage their child to behave well. This is called positive reinforcement. A child tends to repeat behaviours that lead to a reward. We all repeat things that make us feel good.

Dependence, tolerance and addiction

Regular use of legal drugs can lead to dependence that may not be seriously harmful. People who drink coffee or cola drinks can become dependent on the caffeine these drinks contain and suffer headaches and nervousness if they do not maintain a regular intake of the drug.

Drugs tend to have less effect the longer people take them. A bigger dose is then required to have the same effect. This reduced effectiveness is called drug tolerance. The brain tends to adapt to repeated doses of a drug by making its synapses less responsive. This can happen through a reduction in the number of receptor molecules. Tolerance can also happen because less transmitter is released into synapses. Tolerance is one aspect of addiction. The drug user craves higher doses of the drug in order to bring back the effects experienced when it was first used.

Drug addiction is characterised by repeated failures to stop drug use despite prior resolutions to do so. It is an uncontrollable, compulsive craving, with the addict seeking and using drugs even in the face of adverse health and social consequences. There is a widely held view that some people are more susceptible than others to drug abuse and drug addiction. Social, cultural and family factors must all play a part, and there are also likely to be genetic differences in people's susceptibility to drug abuse.

Figure 1.16

Rat pressing a lever, causing stimulation of its brain via an electrode.

Question

20 Give examples to show how parents and teachers can use rewards to encourage good behaviour.

Key terms

Drug users become **dependent** on a drug when they suffer unpleasant physical or psychological withdrawal symptoms if they stop taking the drug.

People are **addicted** to drugs when they have lost control over drug taking. Addicts continue to take drugs compulsively despite harmful effects on health and social relationships.

Figure 1.17

Sherlock Holmes used addictive drugs, especially a 7% solution of cocaine. This was not illegal in Victorian England.
Dr Watson called Holmes a 'self-poisoner' and Holmes admitted that the drug was harmful.

Figure 1.18

The action of cocaine on the neurotransmitter dopamine in a synapse. Cocaine blocks dopamine transporters, leaving more dopamine in the synapse. This leads to more signals being transmitted by the receiving neurone, giving the feelings of a cocaine high. Within an hour, more than half of the cocaine is removed from the synapse, so a cocaine high does not last very long.

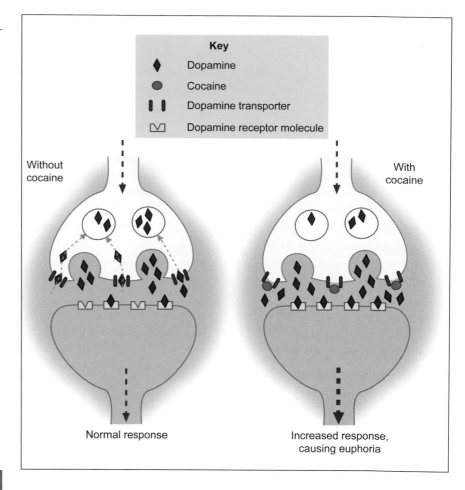

Questions

21 Why do people choose to take drugs even when they know about the risks of addiction and possible effects on health and wellbeing?

22 What methods do people use to try to stop smoking by managing or overcoming an addiction to nicotine?

23 Why has the abuse of alcohol by younger people become a big issue in recent years?

24 New knowledge about the biological basis of addiction has had little impact on the discovery and development of better ways to help addicts. Suggest reasons why this is so.

25 Should addiction be regarded as a mental illness or as a self-inflicted condition that is the result of bad choices in particular social circumstances?

Scientists have established that many drugs of abuse work directly or indirectly by affecting the transmission of dopamine across synapses in the nucleus accumbens (Figure 1.18). Some drugs mimic neurotransmitters whereas others block receptor molecules. Still others alter the way that neurotransmitters are released or inactivated.

Cocaine, for example, blocks the dopamine transporters that normally remove dopamine rapidly from synapses shortly after it has been released. The result is that dopamine molecules remain in the synapse. This produces prolonged and enhanced stimulation of the receptor neurone.

Prolonged use of drugs can lead to damaging changes to nerve cells and brain systems. This is an example of the way that addictive drugs distort the way the brain works. A growing understanding of the effects of drugs on neurones has led to addiction being viewed as a type of mental illness rather than a matter of individual responsibility.

Drug classification

Illegal drugs are classified as A, B or C, where Class A drugs are the most harmful and addictive. Different classes of drugs carry different penalties for possession and dealing. Some scientists and health workers argue that this classification system is flawed and does not take enough account of the harm caused to a person or to society by a particular drug.

Some drugs, classified as illegal, may be prescribed by doctors. They are then legal if they are prescribed for use, for example in pain relief or to relieve the symptoms of certain medical conditions. For example diamorphine (heroin) is prescribed as a very strong pain reliever, and cannabis is thought to help people with multiple sclerosis. Prescribed drugs are often misused, however – someone for whom they are not intended may take them, or they may be taken in the wrong way.

Drug type	Example	Possession	Dealing
Class A: these are considered to be the most dangerous to health.	Ecstasy, LSD, heroin, cocaine, crack, magic mushrooms, amphetamines (if prepared for injection).	Up to 7 years in prison or an unlimited fine or both.	Up to life in prison or an unlimited fine or both.
Class B: also dangerous to health but not as much as Class A drugs.	Amphetamines, cannabis, methylphenidate (Ritalin), codeine in concentrations above 2.5%, dihydrocodeine.	Up to 5 years in prison or an unlimited fine or both.	Up to 14 years in prison or an unlimited fine or both.
Class C: the least harmful of the three classes.	Benzodiazepine including valium and rohypnol, some painkillers, gamma hydroxybutyrate (GHB), ketamine, anabolic steroids, liquid ecstasy.	Up to 2 years in prison or an unlimited fine or both.	Up to 14 years in prison or an unlimited fine or both.

26 Give examples of the ways in which the illegal use of recreational drugs can cause harm to:
a) individuals
b) societies.

27 Countries may adopt one of these three principles when formulating policies to regulate recreational drugs:
- Governments should prohibit and seek to eliminate drug use because it is inherently bad.
- Governments have a responsibility to protect the life and health of citizens so the aim should be to minimise the harm caused by drug abuse.
- Individual freedom to take drugs should not be limited except where it can be shown to cause harm to other people.

a) Which of these principles underpins drug policy in the UK?
b) What would be the consequences of adopting either of the other principles?

28 What contribution does science have to make to the development of drug policies?

Figure 1.19

Illegal drugs are classified under the Misuse of Drugs Act 1971, which can only be changed and added to by the Home Secretary. This table shows penalties for possession and dealing of illegal drugs.

Cannabis

Classifying cannabis

Class A drugs have the greatest addictive potential and therefore lead to an increase in crime and social unrest. The adverse effects to society of cannabis misuse are less clear-cut. Indeed cannabis has been used as a medicine for thousands of years. It was made illegal in the UK in the 1920s, after an Egyptian delegate at an international drugs conference in Geneva suggested that its effects were as dangerous as opium. In 1968, however, a Home Office report into its effects concluded that there was no evidence that its use led to violent crime, aggression or antisocial behaviour or that it led to dependence or psychosis.

Figure 1.20

The main drugs used by people in the 16–59 age range (2005/6). The data comes from the British Crime Survey.

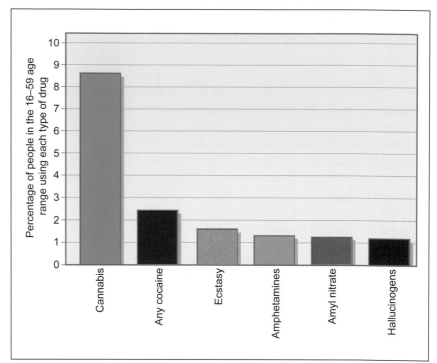

Figure 1.21

Cannabis plants growing in an illegal nursery. The plants seen here are skunk, a particularly potent form of the plant.

Questions

29 Comment on, and suggest reasons for, the pattern of drug use among 16–59 year olds shown in Figure 1.20.

30 The House of Commons Select Committee on Science and Technology has criticised the Government for using drug classifications as a means of 'sending out signals' rather than simply classifying drugs on the basis of harm. Why is there a potential conflict between scientific evidence and political pressures when it comes to drug classifications?

In January 2004 cannabis was downgraded from a Class B to a Class C drug in the UK to free up police resources to fight hard drugs such as cocaine (Figure 1.20). This reclassification was in response to a report arguing that UK drugs policy should focus on tackling the problems caused by heroin. The UK government's tactics turned to reducing the availability of Class A drugs. The approach was based on targeting the supply of drugs, locally, regionally and internationally, through effective policing, increasing intelligence sharing between the agencies involved, and confiscating the proceeds of drug trafficking.

However, some evidence of a link between cannabis abuse and mental ill health, particularly schizophrenia, resulted in calls for a change in the classification of cannabis. In 2005 the Advisory Council on the Misuse of Drugs examined all the new evidence on the harm caused by cannabis and outlined its findings in a report to the government. On the basis of this evidence, the Home Secretary decided that cannabis should remain a Class C drug, stating that this classification was supported by the police, and most drugs and mental health charities.

In January 2009 the government announced the reclassification of cannabis as a Class B drug. This decision was taken as part of its drug strategy and in response to public concern about the potential detriment to mental health caused by taking cannabis, particularly the stronger types like skunk (Figure 1.21).

Some argue that the government's attitude to cannabis is guided by political interests and does not take enough account of peer-reviewed scientific evidence. In a letter to the Advisory Council on the Misuse of Drugs, the Home Secretary Jacqui Smith wrote "Any final decision on the classification of cannabis will be consistent with our aim of reducing the harm caused by drugs, and ensuring that people – especially young people – are aware of the risks of using them."

Cannabis and multiple sclerosis

Professor John Zajicek is a clinical academic, which means he both cares for patients and carries out research (Figure 1.22). He is a neurologist and so deals with all neurodegenerative diseases, but currently specialises in multiple sclerosis (MS). Following reports from patients that smoking cannabis – illegally – improved the symptoms of MS, he has been carrying out medical trials to see if the drug really does work to relieve the symptoms of the disease, or if it might even slow the progression of the disease.

Figure 1.22

Professor John Zajicek.

Multiple sclerosis

Multiple sclerosis (MS) is the result of damage to the protective covering surrounding nerve axons, called the myelin sheath. If this insulating sheath is damaged, nerve impulses do not get to and fro between the brain and the rest of the body.

Multiple sclerosis can affect people in different ways. Symptoms, as the disease progresses, include pain, weakness, numbness, bladder disturbances, poor balance, blindness, memory problems and fatigue. Multiple sclerosis tends to affect young adults and can progress at very different rates. No one knows exactly what causes the disease, or whether it is genetic, environmental or caused by an unknown pathogen. An immune response and inflammation is known to be involved, where the white blood cells attack the protective myelin layer. As well as damage to the myelin sheath and membrane around the nerve cells, the disease leads to a build up of hardened scarred tissue in the brain. 'Sclerosis' means 'hardening'.

Professor Zajicek works in a part of the new Peninsular Medical School in Plymouth. Plymouth is where the very first medical trial took place, in the eighteenth century, when a ship's doctor, John Lind, set out to find a cure for scurvy. He gave several different treatments to separate groups of sailors, including sea water, vitriol (dilute sulfuric acid) and oranges and limes. The first cannabis trial was similar, in that 667 people with MS were divided into three groups and each given different medication:

- The first group had a placebo.
- The second group had a synthetic cannabinoid called delta-9 tetra-hydro cannabinol, or THC for short. This drug was already licensed as an antinausea drug for cancer patients.
- The third group had capsules of whole extract of cannabis. The natural plant contains 60 different cannabinoid chemicals. Any success with this treatment over THC would need to be followed up to see exactly which chemical was active.

Professor Zajicek explains: "We did not want them to smoke the drug as that would have been both unhealthy and illegal, so they all received identical white capsules. Unfortunately, because of the known effects of cannabis, causing euphoria, many people realised that they were on the real thing rather than the placebo. To try to minimise this effect, we had an assessor who was completely independent and did not talk to the patients or to me, the treating physician."

After 15 weeks, some patients reported improvements, particularly in pain relief and bladder disturbance. Patients who were not in wheelchairs could walk faster. But, there was a disappointment – measuring muscle stiffness using the best available means before and after the 15 weeks showed no real difference.

Professor Zajicek continues: "We then gave people the option to continue for a year, and then we did see more differences, particularly when we measured muscle stiffness, which had reduced considerably. This long-term improvement suggests that it wasn't just the symptoms that were being treated, but that something was happening to slow the progression of the disease. This effect seemed more pronounced in the THC group."

This sounds like a breakthrough, but for Professor Zajicek it was time to start thinking about another long-term clinical trial, and also time to consider how cannabis affects the brain and how it might work. As he says: "Believe it or not, our brains are full of cannabinoid receptors. In fact one of the commonest receptors in the brain is the cannabinoid receptor. We do not really know what these do, but we think they have a role in neurotransmitter release. So, if you smoke cannabis it locks onto these receptors. This alters the release of neurotransmitters causing a number of different reactions.

"One theory is that the cannabinoid receptors are important in the development of the nervous system and in protecting the nervous system as you get older. Cannabinoids might increase the number of connections between neurones. Now that might sound like a good thing, but there is evidence that it may be a bad thing when you are in your teens and there is an association between excessive cannabis use and schizophrenia."

Professor Zajicek would not touch recreational cannabis himself because of the link with mental illness, and the difficulty of controlling the dose, regardless of the legal status of the drug. When asked if it is addictive, he says: "Probably not in terms of developing tolerance and needing to take increasing doses for the same effect, as with alcohol and cocaine. But, you might be able to develop a tolerance to it and some people have a 'cold turkey' effect if they stop taking it."

There are some interesting laboratory results from *in vitro* experiments too. Cannabinoids can protect against programmed cell death, where DNA signals cells to commit suicide after a certain time. It could be that cannabinoids help prevent a state where too much of the neurotransmitter glutamate excites nerve cells to death. It might help reduce damage from free radicals and it can certainly reduce inflammation.

The next trial is testing the cannabinoid THC rather than the natural cannabis extract, and will be longer. "We want to test if we can slow the disease with THC over 3 years," explains Zajicek. "We also want to test safety over the long term and to develop better ways of testing our results."

Brain imaging will also be used to see if the patients' brains reduce in volume – and here, Professor Zajicek comes up with a chilling fact: "At the age of eight our brains are at their maximum size, and after that they shrink. So, whatever you do in the way of drinking and drugs accelerates that."

Questions

31 a) What are the key features of a well-designed clinical trial?
b) Why did the design of the first trial of THC and cannabis extract on MS patients have to be modified?

32 Why was it important, as the programme of research developed, to have a theory on how cannabis affects the brain and how it might work?

33 What does Professor Zajicek mean by the term 'cold turkey'?

1.4 Mental illness

Mental illness is common but much less well understood by the public than infectious diseases, heart disease or cancer. As a result, people who are mentally ill can find that they are treated with suspicion or even fear.

Mental illness can cause controversy among experts too because of disagreements about the classification, causes and treatments for the various conditions that cause distress. In some circumstances it can be a serious disadvantage for someone to be classified as being mentally ill. In other circumstances a diagnosis can bring benefits because the person concerned becomes eligible for support and treatment. This is illustrated by attention deficit hyperactivity disorder (ADHD). Parents in some countries press for their children to be classed as suffering from ADHD, even where the diagnosis is borderline, because of the special attention and help their children will receive as a result. In some parts of the United States, pressure from parents means that up to a fifth of all children are diagnosed with the condition, which is a much higher proportion than is found in most parts of the world.

Question

34 What practical disadvantages can people face if they are diagnosed as suffering from a mental disorder?

Attention deficit hyperactivity disorder (ADHD)

Children with ADHD are typically hyperactive, inattentive and impulsive. Their behaviour greatly hinders their progress at school.

About 5% of schoolchildren in Britain have been diagnosed with ADHD, and it is much more common in boys than in girls. Severe ADHD can be very distressing. A child with ADHD is often bewildered by the effect their actions have on others, and simply does not know how to change.

Parents and teachers may find it difficult to cope with such challenging behaviour. Without diagnosis and treatment, individuals can become isolated and disaffected and have poor academic attainment. The boys tend to be accident prone, drop out of school early, drift from job to job and show an attraction to risk.

Thus early diagnosis is essential if a child is not to suffer academically and socially. Some studies have suggested that a significant percentage of convicted prisoners – 30% or more of those convicted of serious offences – may have untreated ADHD. The characteristics of the condition often appear well before school age and continue throughout life.

However, in her book *The Sexual Paradox*, published in 2008, psychologist Susan Pinker notes that such boys can sometimes develop into 'extreme men', becoming athletes, criminals, inventors and sometimes multi-millionaires. Being novelty seeking, energetic and easily bored can sometimes lead young men with ADHD to set up businesses and projects that are very successful.

Figure 1.23

Brothers suffering from hyperactivity bouncing on a sofa.

35 If one member of the family has ADHD it is likely that it will also affect another member. Explain what this suggests about the causes of ADHD.

36 Explain why it is much more difficult to diagnose a mental condition such as ADHD than an infectious disease such as chicken pox or measles.

37 'Diagnostic creep' describes the process by which the language used to describe a condition widens to give a broader definition of what counts as illness. Explain how the process can turn social issues into medical conditions requiring treatment by doctors.

38 What might a doctor say to reassure parents that they are not to blame for their children's diagnosis of ADHD?

So, despite being diagnosed with ADHD as children, people with the condition can be very successful adults. The dull environment and enforced immobility of the classroom is very different from the open spaces and need for hard physical work that our ancestors experienced, and in which we presumably evolved. Yet children with ADHD are widely prescribed drugs to help treat their 'condition'.

Diagnosing ADHD

In 1845 the physician Heinrich Hoffman published a poetry book about children and their characteristics. His poem 'Fidgety Philip' accurately described a child we would now recognise as having ADHD. However, 57 years would pass before Sir George Still described a group of children with impulsive behaviour in a series of lectures to the Royal College of Physicians.

There are no specific laboratory tests for ADHD. The diagnosis is made by a child psychiatrist, an educational psychologist or a paediatrician. The expert bases the diagnosis on a set of descriptive criteria as defined in either the American Psychiatric Association's *Diagnostic and Statistical Manual of Mental Disorders* (DSMM), or its European counterpart the ICD.

The clinician observes the child closely and gathers evidence from parents, teachers and other adults in contact with the child. Sometimes special psychometric tests are used to explore the child's mental processes. In making the diagnosis, other mental disorders such as anxiety or depression must be ruled out.

Causes of ADHD?

As yet there is no clear understanding of the causes of ADHD. It is clear that both genetic and environmental factors are important. It is likely that a number of genes, rather than a single gene, are involved. Research has focused on genes involved in dopamine pathways in the brain; in particular the gene that codes for the transporter molecules in neurones that are responsible for removing dopamine from synapses (see Figure 1.18, page 14).

Brain imaging studies have pinpointed areas of the frontal lobe in people with ADHD that have a decreased metabolic activity compared to people without ADHD symptoms. A decrease in metabolic activity is also seen in the basal ganglia, a part of the brain responsible for movement.

Research carried out at the Cognition and Brain Sciences Unit in Cambridge has suggested that a phenomenon called 'left neglect' can contribute to the development of symptoms of ADHD in some children. The study suggests that children with ADHD simply stop noticing things that happen to their left, especially when they are carrying out boring activities. This phenomenon has long been seen in adults with severe right-sided brain injury. The researchers showed that even in non-ADHD children an element of 'left neglect' crept in when they were bored with their tasks, but not as quickly as in ADHD children. The right side of the brain, which controls the left side of the body, is heavily involved in keeping us alert. When given stimulant medication, ADHD children's left neglect fell to the same levels as those without ADHD. Children with ADHD may be misdiagnosed as having dyslexia, leading to inappropriate treatment.

Treatment of ADHD

Ideally an effective treatment plan for children with ADHD involves a combination of approaches that can include psychological therapy, behaviour management, counselling, a change of diet, educational support and medication. However, the resources available are seldom ideal, so there is an increasing reliance on the use of drugs.

The main drug used to treat ADHD is Ritalin, a type of amphetamine. Ritalin makes children calmer and more attentive. Prescription rates for Ritalin vary from about 30 per 1000 to 140 per 1000 children in different health regions of Britain. In the USA there has been a much higher rate of diagnosis of ADHD and prescription of Ritalin than in Britain, but Britain is now catching up. The National Institute of Clinical Excellence (NICE) has issued guidelines saying that only the most severely affected children in the UK should be given Ritalin – around 1% of school-aged children.

Ritalin is thought to work by raising the levels of dopamine in the brain, perhaps compensating for a natural deficit. However, Ritalin's exact mode of action is not fully understood. The treatment is controversial because it involves the medication of children, whose diagnosis is a matter of judgement. In the USA there have been recent lawsuits against the makers of Ritalin and the American Psychiatric Association, claiming that they conspired to promote the disorder ADHD to increase the market for the drug. The cases were dismissed. However, some clinicians doubt the reality of the condition and the desirability of medical intervention.

Like all drugs, Ritalin has some side effects, including psychosis, mood swings and difficulty sleeping, which have some parallels to the side effects caused by Parkinson's disease medication.

Questions

39 Should the child have the final decision about whether or not to take Ritalin for ADHD?

40 Suggest reasons why doctors prescribe Ritalin at different rates in different regions of Britain.

41 Suggest possible changes in a synapse that that could lead to a deficit of dopamine.

42 Explain why it is not unexpected that there are similarities between the side effects of levodopa and the side effects of Ritalin.

Figure 1.24

Artworks in a classroom in a school in Washington, DC. There are 330 pupils at this special school. All have been diagnosed with learning disabilities, including attention deficit disorder. There are four times more boys than girls. A third of the pupils take drugs such as Ritalin.

Figure 1.25

Stephen Fry, who suffers from bipolar disorder.

Depression

In a 2006 BBC television documentary, the actor and comedian Stephen Fry talked about his own experiences of suffering from a severe form of depression known as bipolar disorder (sometimes called manic depression). Fry describes walking out of a West End play, *Cell Mates*, in 1995, and spending two hours sitting in his car contemplating suicide. After fleeing to Belgium he was eventually diagnosed as having bipolar disorder, giving him an explanation of the violent mood swings he had experienced throughout his life.

When asked why he made the programme he replied:

"I'm in a rare and privileged position of being able to help address the whole business of stigma, and why it is that the rest of society finds it so easy to wrinkle their noses, cross over, or block their ears when confronted with an illness of the mind and of the mood – especially when we reach out with such sympathy towards diseases of the liver or other organs that don't affect who we are and how we feel in quite such devastating complexity."

Depression affects one in every six people in Britain at some stage during their lives. About one in twenty people experience clinical depression. It is estimated that one-tenth of the population is depressed at any one time. Children, teenagers and adults of all ages, backgrounds and ethnic groups may be affected. About 2% of all children in the UK under the age of 12 experience depression; that is around 180 000 children.

Depression varies in its severity. Often the disabling aspects of the condition are the feelings of worthlessness, hopelessness and self-hatred. The black cloud of depression leads to an inability to cope with daily life, which is known as clinical depression. It has been estimated that by 2020 clinical depression will be second only to heart disease in its effect on society.

Diagnosis

Clinical depression goes beyond sadness and upset. This does not mean, however, that people with milder symptoms are not depressed: an individual may experience mild depression for many years and so diagnosis is important, whatever the severity. A diagnosis of depression by a doctor is based on the following criteria:

- How serious it is: mild depression is likely to have some impact on daily life; moderate depression is likely to have significant impact on daily life; severe depression renders daily activities almost impossible.
- Physical symptoms: loss of interest; loss of pleasure; weight gain or loss associated with a changed appetite; loss of energy and extreme tiredness; feelings of guilt; poor self-esteem; problems sleeping; agitated behaviour; difficulty making decisions; difficulty concentrating; thoughts of death and thoughts of suicide.
- Psychotic symptoms: hallucinations or delusional behaviour may occur.

Questions

43 What is meant by stigma? Suggest why a stigma is attached to mental illnesses more than physical illnesses.

44 Why are there no accurate figures for the number of people in the population who experience depression?

45 Women are twice as likely to experience clinical depression as men. Some argue that this statement is biased. Why might they think so?

Whilst depression can be classified according to its severity, it is also important to note that there are different types of depression. The mother who has just given birth to a beautiful child, surrounded by family and friends may not be able to respond to her child but may feel that she has to put on a brave face. She may feel exhausted all the time, find it difficult to fall asleep yet when she wakes feel too tired to cope with life. She may be irritable, anxious and very tearful and her sense of time may be distorted. These are the symptoms of post-natal depression. As many as 15% of women experience this type of depression in their baby's first year.

Manic depression or bipolar disorder affects 1% of the population at some time in their lives and usually first affects a person when they are in their late teenage years. It is characterised by extreme mood swings, together with altered thought patterns, emotions and physical health. The illness recurs at intervals. However, there are successful comedians and other creative people afflicted by bipolar disorder. Between depressive phases they seem able to be exuberant and creative to an extent that might not be possible if they did not suffer from the condition.

Seasonal affective disorder (SAD) describes people who become depressed at particular times of the year, especially in the late autumn or winter. The symptoms are many and varied. They can include sleep and eating problems, a lack of energy for everyday tasks, anxiety and other changes of mood.

Causes

A number of environmental factors are thought to influence whether or not a person becomes depressed. One well-documented example is physical activity. Depression is negatively correlated with physical activity: people who exercise more tend to be less depressed. A correlation, positive or negative (see box, page 24), does not necessarily mean that one factor actually causes the other. In this particular case it could be that exercise reduces depression or that people do not exercise because they are depressed – both being examples of causation. However, there may be a third factor that causes both depression and the tendency not to exercise.

A large scale study of the links between exercise and depression was carried out over 11 years by psychologists at the University of Amsterdam, and published in 2008 in *The Archives of General Psychiatry*. The study looked at 5952 twins, 1357 fraternal siblings and 1249 parents. Participants were aged 15–50 years, and used self-report questionnaires to measure their mental state and amount of leisure time exercise. There was a statistically significant (but small) negative correlation between exercise and depression in both cross-sectional and longitudinal analysis of the results. However, analysis of the identical twin pairs did not show that the twin who exercised more showed less anxiety and depression than the twin who exercised less.

Questions

46 Suggest reasons why the diagnosis of clinical forms of depression can often be delayed or missed altogether.

47 What are the changes in winter that might lead to seasonal affective disorder?

Key terms

A **cross-sectional study** looks at a range of data collected at one particular time, for example comparing reported levels of depression and exercise from a single questionnaire from a sample of people.

A **longitudinal study** investigates changes over a long period of time – from days to years, for example analysing how depression changes as people increase then decrease their levels of exercise over many months.

A result is considered **statistically significant** if tests on the data show that it is unlikely to have occurred by chance alone. A statistically significant result allows scientists to claim that an experimental effect they are trying to measure is real.

Question

48 What conclusions can you draw from the results of the Amsterdam study into the link between exercise and depression?

If something happens only when a factor is present, scientists say that there is a correlation between the factor and the outcome. If one variable increases (or decreases) steadily in value as the value of another variable increases, this is even stronger evidence that the two variables are correlated.

If both variables increase together, the correlation is positive. If one goes down as the other goes up, the correlation is negative.

A correlation coefficient is a measure of the strength of a correlation. The values of a correlation vary in the range +1 for a perfect positive correlation to –1 for a perfect negative correlation. A value of zero indicates no correlation. Figure 1.26 gives examples of some correlated variables.

Variable 1	Variable 2	Correlation coefficient
Body fat in obese children	Sum of measurement of six skin folds	+0.80
Lung cancer mortality in a range of countries in 1950	Cigarette consumption per capita in 1930	+0.74
Degree of atherosclerosis in Framingham heart study in 1979	Level of blood cholesterol	+0.36
Exam marks for a group of students	The weight of the students	0.00
A score from a mental health questionnaire – the lower the score the better the mental health	Score on a test of sense of humour	–0.48

Figure 1.26

A correlation can occur by chance, especially with small samples. A correlation that is unlikely to be due to chance is said to be statistically significant.

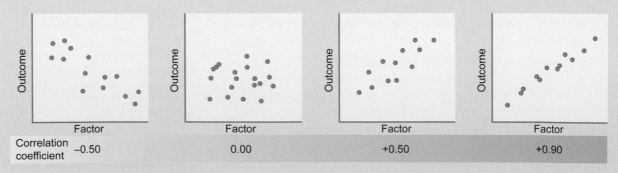

Correlation coefficient	–0.50	0.00	+0.50	+0.90

Figure 1.27

Scatter graphs showing different degrees of correlation.

A correlation between a factor and an outcome may suggest that the factor is the cause of the outcome but it does not prove that there is a causal link. The factor could be the cause of the outcome, but both could be caused by another factor.

Depression often runs in families and this suggests that individuals have an increased risk of developing depression as a result of their genetic make up. However, there is likely to be an environmental component as well: members of the same family are likely to live together in similar circumstances and acquire common learned behaviour.

Recent research nonetheless points to the involvement of a number of genes in depressive illness and in particular the ways in which these genes interact with one another.

Treatment of depression

People with mild depression may opt for a number of self-help techniques, which include a healthy diet, finding someone to talk to about their problems, herbal medicine and physical exercise. For people with more severe depression, drug treatments and even electroconvulsive therapy are used.

It is generally accepted that depression is linked to altered levels of neurotransmitters in the brain, particularly serotonin, dopamine and noradrenaline. Antidepressant drugs are intended to increase the activity of the neurotransmitters associated with mood, notably serotonin. Selective serotonin reuptake inhibitors (SSRIs), such as Prozac, are widely prescribed for depression. As with all medicines they come with the risk of side effects that range from blurred vision and constipation to sexual problems and aggression. The benefits of any treatment must always therefore be weighed against the risks. Some psychoactive drugs, such as MDMA (ecstasy), greatly increase the levels of serotonin in synapses, but MDMA is too powerful a stimulant for the treatment of depression.

Anyone with a mental health problem must make sure that they consider the risks as well as the benefits of any proposed treatment. Antidepressant drugs may be helpful in treating moderate to severe depression but some people may not respond to them. Even if they do find some relief from their symptoms, the side effects may leave them feeling worse overall. It's important for an individual to have access to information about their proposed treatment as well as information about alternative treatments or therapies, in order to make an informed decision about the best treatment.

Questions

49 Give an example of a situation where there is a correlation between a factor and an outcome but no causal link.

50 Research has pinpointed a gene mutation that disrupts the brain's biological clock – what might be the significance of this in different types of depression?

51 Explain why it is important that antidepressants designed to affect levels of serotonin should be highly selective in terms of their precise action.

52 If someone takes an antidepressant drug and it makes him or her feel in a better mood, does this mean that the person is suffering from clinical depression?

53 a) What questions should a patient with depression ask the doctor before deciding to start treatment with a drug?
b) Why is it important that a person with depression should fully understand the benefits and risks of a proposed drug treatment?

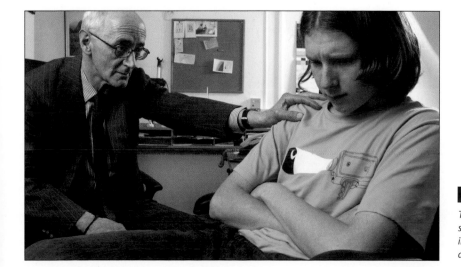

Figure 1.28

Treatments for depression depend on its severity and likely causes. Treatment may include talking therapies and antidepressant drugs.

54 Suggest why lithium reduces depression in some people but not others.

55 In 2006 there were 31 million prescriptions for antidepressants in Britain including 631 000 for children. Suggest three possible reasons for this very high rate of prescribing antidepressants.

56 a) Suggest reasons why CBT can be a longer lasting treatment for some patients than treatment with drugs.
b) Suggest one other benefit of CBT over drug treatment.

Mood stabilisers, for example compounds containing lithium, have been used to effect in the treatment of bipolar disorder and are used together with antidepressants to treat severe depression. They work in part by increasing the synthesis of serotonin. Some patients are greatly helped by lithium but others are not.

Drug treatments for depression are common, but they are not the only approach. Cognitive behavioural therapy (CBT) is a talking therapy that aims to help the patient alter the way events are perceived and to change their behaviour. Patients are helped to think more positively, particularly about themselves, and to challenge their own negative thoughts and beliefs. Cognitive behavioural therapy is provided by a fully trained and qualified health practitioner. It is more expensive than drug treatment, as there are high labour costs involved. However, CBT can be very effective for patients with mild or moderate depression. It can be longer lasting than drug treatments. Cognitive behavioural therapy can have side effects, in the sense that some patients find it upsetting to face up to the realities of their condition.

Electroconvulsive therapy (ECT) is a controversial treatment that involves giving the patient an electrical shock to the brain. It is usually used either as an emergency treatment or when an individual has not responded to drug treatment. Some patients have found it very successful in treating their severe depression, whilst others have reported serious side effects that include memory loss.

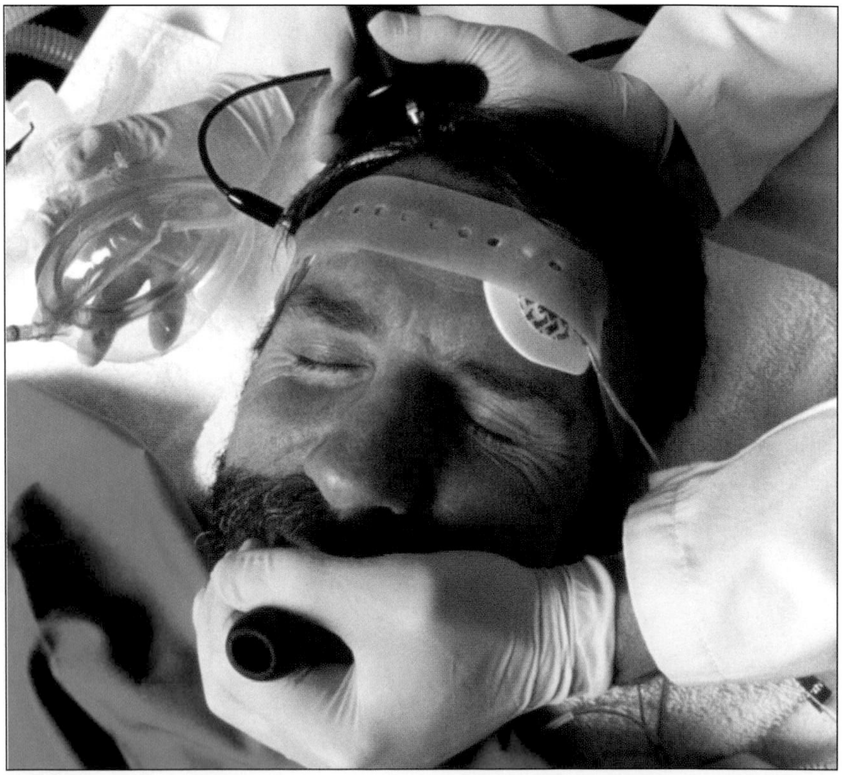

57 NICE recommends that ECT 'is used only to achieve rapid and short-term improvement of severe symptoms after an adequate trial of other treatment options has proven ineffective and/or when the condition is considered potentially life-threatening'. This advice has been welcomed by patient support groups. However, the Royal College of Psychiatrists in 2005 criticised these guidelines as being too restricting. Explain possible reasons for these differing views about criteria for ECT.

Figure 1.29

Electroconvulsive therapy. Electrodes are placed at two positions on the skull and an electric current is passed briefly through the brain. The patient is under anaesthetic with a muscle relaxant. The way ECT works is not understood, but it can bring long-lasting improvement in some intractable cases.

1.5 Enhancing brain performance with drugs

Therapy or enhancement

Drugs originally developed to treat illnesses such as ADHD, excessive sleepiness (narcolepsy) and Alzheimer's disease are increasingly being used to enhance performance in people without these disorders.

Figure 1.30

Headlines for stories about non-medical uses for neurological drugs.

At first sight there is a clear distinction between a therapy to treat disease and a treatment to enhance performance in someone who is considered normal and healthy. However, a closer examination shows that there are contexts in which it is hard to be precise about the difference.

The definition of what counts as good health changes with time. In the past the 'absence of disease' was taken as the guide to healthiness. The World Health Organization has proposed a much more demanding definition of health as 'complete physical, mental and social well being'. This wider definition of good health has implications for society as the average age of the population rises in countries such as the UK, while new medical treatments develop. People who would once have accepted it as a normal part of growing old that they become more forgetful, or show other signs of mental decline, now see these changes as conditions for which there should be medical treatment.

Questions

58 Which socially acceptable drugs do people use to improve concentration or to keep awake while studying?

59 Which of these aspects of cognitive ability would you most like to be able to improve by taking a drug: concentration and attention, learning and memory, speed of processing new information or decision making and planning?

60 a) If there were a drug to help you learn better would you want to use it when studying?
b) What would you want to know before even considering taking such a drug?

61 Apart from taking drugs, what other methods do people use in attempts to improve their cognitive abilities?

62 a) Give an example from sport to illustrate the difference between therapy and enhancement in the context of physical activity.
b) Show that it can be difficult to make a clear distinction between therapy and enhancement in the context of sport.
c) Why is the use of some drugs for enhancement banned in sport?

63 Is there a difference in principle between enhancing performance in a maths exam by using a calculator or by taking a drug to speed mental processing?

64 Two people have the same cognitive ability but one is apparently healthy while the other is affected by a known disorder that affects the brain. On what basis might one person be given a drug to improve their mental performance but not the other?

Questions

65 Suggest reasons why scientists might choose to research the effects of drugs on the cognitive abilities of healthy volunteers.

66 Are people 'better than well' if they take a drug that makes them perform more effectively than their normal capabilities?

67 Why do the armed forces supply modafinil to people involved in sustained military operations?

68 What do you need to know about the details of a research study into the use of a drug such as modafinil to enhance brain power before deciding whether or not to take the findings seriously?

69 a) People lose their medals in sport if tests show that they have used performance-enhancing drugs. Is it cheating to use drugs to enhance cognitive performance?
b) Should people be stripped of academic qualifications if there is evidence that they have used drugs to help them do better in exams?

Figure 1.31

Are students under so much pressure to perform that they are now resorting to performance-enhancing drugs?

Drugs to enhance brain performance

Many of the drugs to treat mental disorders act by altering the balance of neurotransmitters in the brain. Scientists have carried out research with these drugs in healthy volunteers in order to learn more about the way in which drugs can affect performance. Some of this research has suggested that the drugs can not only be used to treat disease but also to enhance the cognitive abilities of people in good health.

This research is still at an early stage, so it should be interpreted with care. Effects observed under controlled laboratory conditions may not be seen in ordinary life. The brain is complex and long-term side effects may not be a problem at first. There is also the danger that a drug that improves performance in one way may at the same time harm other aspects of cognitive performance.

Modafinil

Modafinil was originally developed and used as a sleep-regulating drug, to improve wakefulness in people with narcolepsy. It is a non-amphetamine drug that has been shown to significantly increase wakefulness and reduce the severity of symptoms when compared to a group given a placebo. Unfavourable side effects from taking modafinil can include headaches, dizziness, blurred vision, depression and suicidal thoughts.

Modafinil's use has now widened. Military personnel are taking the drug to stay awake and alert for as long as 40 hours without feeling the need to sleep. This is not a new practice: soldiers have taken amphetamines for many decades, but modafinil reportedly offers similar benefits without some of the severe side effects associated with the earlier drugs. Whilst the immediate side effects from using the drug may be less serious, medical professionals are concerned about the long-term effects on the body of sleep deprivation caused by the drug.

There are some reports that modafinil is being used by university students, particularly during the period leading up to and including examinations. Moreover, there is a suggestion that modafinil enhances short-term memory. Systematic research studies have produced

contradictory findings. Although one placebo-controlled study has shown that adult, male volunteers do better on some tasks such as recalling sequences of numbers and recognising patterns seen before; another study found no statistically significant difference in any cognitive tests between those given the drug and a control group given a placebo.

Antidementia drugs

Donepezil is an example of a drug developed to help people with Alzheimer's disease, and which can enhance 'normal' performance. The drug blocks the action of the enzyme that breaks down the neurotransmitter acetylcholine in synapses. Donepezil helps with the behavioural symptoms of Alzheimer's disease by lifting the patient's confidence, improving mood and drive, and reducing delusions and hallucinations.

Researchers at Stanford University published the results in 2002 of their study of the effects of donepezil on flight simulator performance. Two groups of pilots (18 men with a mean age of 52 and age range from 30 to 70) received seven 75-minute sessions of training in a flight simulator. Immediately after the training, half of the pilots began a 30-day course of donepezil and the other half a 30-day course of a placebo. At the end of the 30 days the pilots were tested in simulated emergency situations. The donepezil group was found to have retained the skills and information from the earlier training far better than the placebo group.

Questions

70 a) Comment on the sample of pilots chosen for the study.
b) What conclusions can be drawn from the results of the study of the effects of donepezil on pilots?

71 What reasons are there for believing that the demand for drugs to enhance cognitive abilities is likely to grow?

Figure 1.32

Pilots in a flight simulator. Could drugs help to enhance the training?

Benefits and risks

The use of drugs to enhance brain power has implications for individuals and for society. People need to think through the benefits and risks when making judgements about the rights and wrongs of using drugs in this way.

Individual benefits and risks

Our society is very competitive. Success in school and college is determined by results in tests and examination. Access to popular university courses depends on grades in A-level or equivalent examinations. Getting a good degree at a prestigious university can be a stepping stone to a well-paid and influential job. In these circumstances

72 Give examples, other than doing better in exams, to show how your life might be better if you were able to improve your:
a) memory
b) ability to reason
c) problem-solving skills.

73 Suggest reasons why people are willing to take drugs to enhance their cognitive abilities when little is known about how the drugs work and there is considerable uncertainty about the longer term side effects.

74 Individuals are free to take part in risky sports such as rock climbing. What are the grounds, if any, for stopping people from taking the risk of using drugs to improve their brain power?

75 Are there any circumstances in which it would be right to force people to take drugs to improve their cognitive abilities? If so, what are they?

76 Under what circumstances could drugs to enhance brain power give rise to:
a) a fairer and more equal society
b) a society that is less fair and more unequal?

77 Should drugs for cognitive enhancement only be available from doctors or should they be more widely available?

individuals have a strong incentive to use all available methods to improve their ability to concentrate on their studies, learn more and process information effectively.

Better brain power can not only give a person a competitive advantage, it also has the potential to make life more manageable, interesting and enjoyable. It is helpful to be able to think through the tricky financial, legal or political problems that people face in everyday life.

However, all drugs have side effects. With new drugs it is often years before all the side effects come to light, especially if they only affect a small proportion of the people involved. The long-term effects of chemicals that affect the brain on healthy people are not always known. Scientists do not know whether or not some people have a particular genetic disposition to suffer serious side effects from particular drugs.

Scientists also do not know always whether a treatment to improve one aspect of brain performance, such as memory, can have the desired effect without diminishing the brain's other abilities. Also, improving memory could have some unexpected consequences. We all have unpleasant experiences that we are happy to forget. It is possible to imagine the psychological harm that could arise if a drug to improve memory meant that people could not put various upsetting recollections out of their minds.

Social benefits and risks

Society benefits from the work of intelligent engineers, doctors, planners, managers and politicians. Employers argue that they want to recruit more skilled and intelligent people. We are all safer if pilots, bus drivers and those who run complex processes are alert and able to concentrate on the critical tasks they carry out. There is a case to be made that a society that raises its average intelligence has the potential to become more productive and wealthier.

Society would, however, suffer if it turned out that the use of drugs for cognitive enhancement had serious long-term effects on people's physical health or psychological wellbeing. This would lead to a substantial burden of expensive healthcare and sickness benefit.

Also, there is a danger in enhancing particular aspects of brain performance such as intelligence. Society not only needs people who are very bright; it also needs people who are enterprising, cooperative and caring.

Figure 1.33

The modern work environment demands a wide range of complex cognitive processes.

78 Give examples to show:
  a) why an understanding of the role of neurotransmitters in the brain is important
  b) how a drug to treat a brain disorder can work by affecting a neurotransmitter
  c) that a drug developed for one purpose may end up being used for another purpose
  d) why drugs that affect the brain have side effects.

79 a) Comment on the information on drug use in selected European countries shown in Figure 1.34.

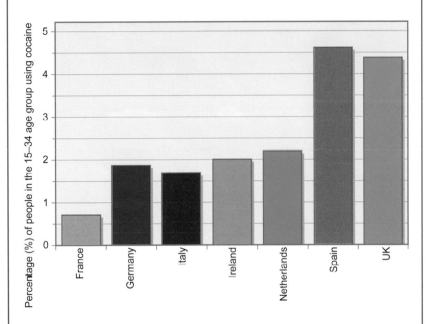

Figure 1.34

Cocaine use among age group 15–34 in selected European countries.

  b) Suggest reasons for the difference in the level of cocaine use in Spain and in the UK compared to the other countries.

80 a) Explain how depression differs from a general feeling of sadness.
  b) Some people would argue that the causes of depression are multifactorial. What is meant by this and are they right?

81 Diagnosis of mental illness can be controversial. A condition that is overdiagnosed in some places may be underdiagnosed in others.
  a) Why do difficulties arise in the diagnosis of mental disorders?
  b) What social factors can affect the extent to which a condition is diagnosed in particular circumstances?
  c) What are the potential consequences of overdiagnosis or underdiagnosis of a particular mental illness?

82 Our society has generally welcomed new technologies to make life easier and more rewarding. Are there particular reasons why new technologies to enhance brain power should, or should not, be similarly welcomed?

Chapter 2

Nature and nurture

- What makes us who we are? Are our genes responsible or is it our upbringing, or both of these?

- How does the environment influence early brain development?

- How has science changed our understanding of the role of our DNA in human behaviour?

- Is there a gene for antisocial behaviour?

- What are the implications of what we know about genes and behaviour for society and the family?

Figure 2.1

Do the answers to the origins of human behaviour lie in our DNA?

2.1 Society's ideas about nature and nurture

Most people are intrigued by possible explanations of the origins of human behaviour. This fascinating topic captures the imagination. It is something we can all relate to, and many of us have our own ideas that have been shaped by observations of relatives and friends. The terrible history of Nazi eugenics means that the idea that behaviour is genetically programmed became unpopular. Recent research provides evidence for how a person's experiences shape their personality, but people remain uneasy about intervening to change human genotypes.

The interpretation of nature and nurture by the media

The media are often a good source of information about science, but well-informed citizens need to be aware of the difference between news reporting and peer-reviewed scientific reports. Journalists wishing to be the first to report the outcome of an important scientific finding may not have time for exhaustive research. Tight deadlines mean they may only consult limited sources. Many will be tempted to report before findings have been peer-reviewed, particularly if the area is of great public interest.

Journalists hear about science from scientists, who in turn may have their own agenda. Much scientific research is funded by drug and biotechnology companies, and scientists announcing a new drug or treatment may have connections with these companies.

News embargoes

Peer-reviewed science research journals operate an embargo system. This involves sending midweek press releases about new research to journalists, provided they agree not to publish the stories until the journal is published.

Some journalists like the embargo system, because accurate and scientifically correct releases come to them directly from scientists. Others regard it as unwanted control over the flow of information between scientists and the public who fund them.

Sunday newspapers tend to be outside the embargo system, and have, in the past, published over-hyped and inaccurate science stories. These 'scoops' are excellent for selling newspapers, and tend to result from investigative work ahead of press releases. *The Sunday Times* infamously reported in 2006 that scientists were attempting to 'change the sexuality of gay sheep'. They later apologised that the science editor had been away, so the story had not been checked.

The embargo system acts as a marketing tool for the science journals; media publicity is maximised close to publication, allowing them to attract advertisers and therefore profits.

Sensationalising science

In 2007, researchers found that while 41% of research funding and published scientific papers on autism dealt with research on the brain and behaviour, only 11% of newspaper stories in the United States, United Kingdom and Canada dealt with those issues. Forty-eight per cent of the media coverage dealt with environmental causes of autism, emphasising a widely refuted study linking autism to the childhood MMR vaccine for measles, mumps and rubella.

Key terms

Eugenics is a philosophy which suggests that the human genome should be improved through various forms of intervention such as selective breeding.

Peer review is a process used for checking work carried out by scientists. Scientists working in the field, but from outside the immediate research team, assess the quality of the research. A peer-reviewed journal only publishes articles that have been checked by one or more independent experts in the field of the research.

Question

1 To what extent does the embargo system for scientific research mean that research that has been funded by the taxpayer is manipulated for the commercial interests of a private company?

Figure 2.2

Journalists tap into our interest in the influences that shape our personalities and behaviour. They sometimes publish news stories about new findings in genetics which give too much credence to unproven evidence and explanations. This type of journalism can encourage people to think that we are genetically programmed to behave in a certain way.

Questions

2 Do you think that it is the audience and readers or journalists who are mainly responsible for populist reporting of genetic stories?

3 Suggest why media reports about causes of autism focussed on a discredited link with the MMR vaccine rather than better substantiated reports.

4 Suggest reasons why the popular media are keen to report on the idea that a single gene controls particular aspects of human behaviour.

5 What are the implications of the fact that journalists do not write their own headlines – this job is given to specialist headline writers?

6 Why might media accounts of research overemphasise the potential for that research to lead to new drug therapies?

7 Not all human qualities are positive. To what extent do we all have negative qualities, such as a tendency to violence or anger?

8 Explain the difference between the shapes of graphs (c) and (d) in Figure 2.3.

Distinguishing between an argument that is backed up by good, scientific evidence and other weakly supported or minority views requires a critical approach. Newspapers may have an agenda, for example they may back the views of a particular political party. Their agenda may be obvious from the emphasis of their stories, or through the stories that they select.

Behaviour has a genetic predisposition, but is not pre-programmed. Environmental influences are usually just as important as genetic influences. Media interest in behavioural genetics has tended to focus on the possibility of finding 'a gene for x'. News stories about a gene for homosexuality, intelligence or criminality attract readers, partly because this idea that genes programme us to behave in a certain way threatens our concept of free will.

2.2 Genes and the human genome
Individual differences

Some people are good at organising, others hopelessly disorganised but have great ideas. Others are kind, resourceful, funny and creative to greater or lesser degrees. You probably would not want multiple versions of any one of your friends, but having a rich variety of human personalities allows us all to benefit and to contribute in an individual role.

If you lined up your class or group of friends between two points, one representing those students who are very good at organising their work, and the other for those who cannot organise their work at all, everyone in the class would be somewhere on that line. Most students would be somewhere in the middle. There would be one or two highly efficient and effective students at one end of the line, and one or two people with files that explode over the desk when touched at the other end.

If you made another line and had a point for 'male' and another for 'female', there would only be two groups of students. No-one would consider themselves somewhere between the two (or at least this is extremely rare). Gender is one of the human characteristics that are clearly either/or. Tongue rolling is another example: you either can roll your tongue or you cannot.

People are shaped by their genes and by factors in the environment that affect their growth and development since conception. In the case of diseases such as cystic fibrosis and Huntington's disease, and the either/or traits such as tongue rolling, the different versions of a single gene are responsible for the condition or characteristic.

Human height is determined by many genes, each with different versions, or alleles. In addition, environmental factors such as diet and exercise affect it. Continuously varying characteristics which are controlled by many genes plus environmental influences tend to produce a bell-shaped frequency distribution (see Figure 2.3). This is called a normal distribution. Most human characteristics cannot be attributed to a single gene. Human behavioural traits involve many genes with multiple alleles, and these interact with a range of complex environmental influences.

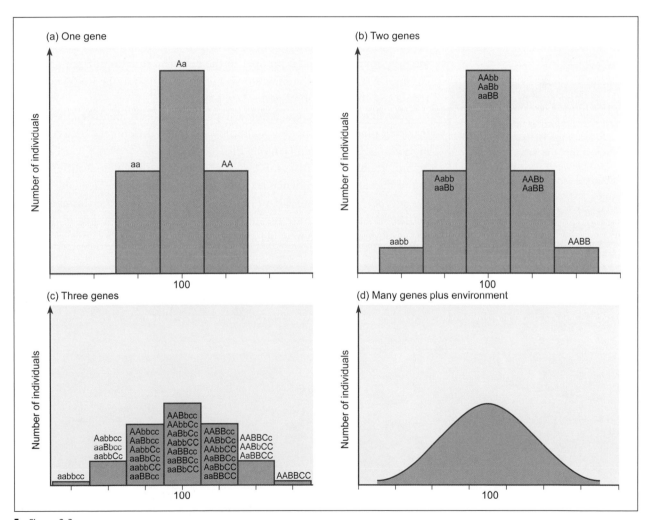

Figure 2.3

Graphs (a)–(d) show a hypothetical characteristic that depends upon the additive effect of alleles. These are particular kinds of alleles where each lower case allele subtracts five from the value of the characteristic being measured, each upper case allele adds five to the value. The characteristic has a mean value of 100 (imagine, for example length of a limb or mass). The y-axis shows the frequency, or number of people in the population with each value of the characteristic. Graph (a) shows the variation you expect to see if a single gene is responsible for all the variation: three phenotypes, AA, Aa and aa are seen. In this example, aa genotypes score 90, aA genotypes score 100, AA genotypes score 110. Graphs (b) and (c) show the variation possible if the trait being measured is determined by two and three genes. Graph (d) shows how, if random variation in the environment is added to the effect of several genes shown in (c), a bell-shaped curve is produced.

Questions

9 Why was it important to the success of the Human Genome Project that this work took place between several different countries and organisations?

10 What is the value of knowing the sequence of bases in all the DNA in human cells?

The Human Genome Project

The Human Genome Project was an international initiative to produce a complete map and sequence of the human genome. It began in 1990 and was expected to take 15 years to complete, but was actually finished by 2003, 50 years after the discovery of the structure of DNA. The resulting genome map and sequence is freely available, and has been published on the Internet.

The aim of the project was to sequence all 3 billion base pairs in the human genome. It was approached by breaking the genome into smaller, more manageable bits. Specialised technology was used to determine the sequence of bases in each piece of DNA. Computers then analysed the resulting sequence to find where these pieces of DNA overlapped (Figure 2.4). In this way the whole sequence was pieced together.

When complete, the whole genome sequence was found to contain about 20 500 genes, many fewer than expected. Much of the human genome is actually non-coding DNA, which does not contain the instructions for making a product in the cell. The function of non-coding DNA is not fully understood, but some of it may be involved in regulating the function of genes (see page 49).

Now that the complete genome sequence has been identified, research is taking place to define the commonly inherited differences between individuals. The Human Genome Project gave us an 'average' view of the human genome. Scientists now want to know how individual differences in the human DNA sequence account for individual differences in phenotype. Much of our DNA (99.8%) is identical with other humans – but the bits that differ are responsible for the genetic influence in diseases and complex traits such as behaviour.

Figure 2.4

Automated DNA sequencing machines at the Sanger Centre, Cambridge. The Human Genome Project could potentially lead to better drug design and greater understanding of genetic diseases.

Is it possible to tell if conditions are inherited?

We are all born with a genetic blueprint, our genotype, which influences our development before and after birth. How we develop depends partly on our genes and partly on the circumstances in which we grow up. The challenge is to determine the extent to which all our personal characteristics, our phenotype, is shaped by our genes or by our environment.

Scientists have looked for links between our DNA and our intelligence, mental illness, antisocial and criminal behaviour, eating disorders, addiction and even our personality traits such as shyness. This research has stimulated an abundance of media reports, but to date there is little evidence that any single gene makes a major contribution to a particular aspect of human behaviour.

For single gene disorders there is a one-to-one relationship between the gene and the disorder. If you inherit the faulty allele (or two alleles for a recessive condition) you will develop the disease regardless of your other genes and your environment. Single gene disorders have characteristic inheritance patterns in families that are easy for geneticists to recognise. For example, you only need one copy of the faulty allele for Huntington's disease, so each affected individual has at least one affected parent.

For more complex, multifactorial traits, including human behaviour, there is no one-to-one relationship between phenotype and genotype. Genes do contribute to the phenotype, but there may be many small effects from a range of genes plus environmental factors.

2.3 The relative contributions of nature and nurture

Nobody would dispute the involvement of genes in single gene disorders, but what about complex traits? Three main types of study can estimate to what extent individual differences for complex traits and behaviours can be accounted for by genetic differences amongst individuals. If a trait is genetically determined, then you would expect it to run in families, and this can be explored in family studies. However, families can also be alike because they share the same environment. Scientists can start to disentangle genetic and environmental sources of family resemblance using the experiment in nature (twins) and a common experiment of nurture (adoption).

Family studies

Experimental manipulation of human genes and breeding are obviously not possible for ethical reasons. Scientists are forced to explore naturally occurring genetic and environmental variations for clues to finding genes which have an influence on behaviour. Some characteristics 'run in families'. Cognitive ability and schizophrenia show increased similarities between individuals depending on how closely related they are. This gives a clue that there may be an inherited component. But, as families share a similar environment, similarities could still be due to either 'nature' or 'nurture'.

For more complex genetic conditions, twin studies and adoption studies are widely used to assess the relative contributions of genes and environment (Figure 2.5).

Adoption studies

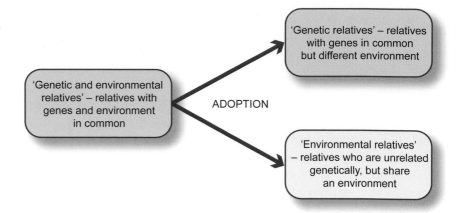

Figure 2.5

Adoption creates 'genetic relatives' who live in different environments (biological parents and their offspring adopted by others, and siblings adopted apart). It also creates 'environmental relatives' (adoptive parents and their adopted children; genetically unrelated children adopted into the same adoptive family). Research looking at the degree of similarity between these 'genetic' and 'environmental' relatives can be used to test the extent to which characteristics are due to either nature or nurture.

An adopted person with a particular disease or trait can be compared with other members of their adopted and biological families. If their condition has a genetic cause, researchers are more likely to find other affected people in the biological family than in the adopted family. This can be a powerful method of investigating some of the genetic and environmental elements contributing to a disorder. Adoption studies rely on access to information about the person's biological family.

Twin studies

It was Francis Galton, an eminent Victorian scientist, who first used twins to study the influences of nature and nurture. He commented that 'Twins have a special claim on our attention ... their history affords means of distinguishing between the effects of tendencies received at birth, and those that were imposed by special circumstances of their ... lives'.

Identical twins have exactly the same genetic make-up, as they develop from the same fertilised egg. If genetic factors are important for a trait, then identical twins are more similar than first-degree relatives (parents, siblings and offspring), who are on average only 50% genetically similar. Non-identical, or fraternal, twins develop from two separate fertilised eggs, and are on average only 50% genetically similar, just like other siblings.

Twin studies can be used to explore the contributions of nature and nurture (Figure 2.6). They assume that both identical and fraternal twins share the same environment, but differ in their genetic similarity. For scientists to conclude that a condition or trait is influenced by a person's genotype, identical twins must be found to be more similar for the trait than fraternal twins.

Genetic researchers use the twin design to estimate the relative contributions of genes and environment to variation of a particular trait in the population. Twin studies identify traits that have a big genetic component: geneticists can then set to work trying to find the variation in DNA that is responsible.

Twin and adoption studies can be combined in studies of identical twins reared apart. These twins are likely to have grown up in different environments, so any similarities are more likely to be genetic. These studies are rare, as only a small number of twins brought up separately are available to study.

Question

11 Describe the possible challenges and sensitivities of carrying out adoption studies.

Figure 2.6

Identical twins.

Questions

12 Suggest why same-sex fraternal twins are often used to compare with identical twins in twin studies.

13 Identical twins share the same alleles for each gene. What percentage of their alleles on average do non-identical twins share?

14 When children are adopted they are placed in families of a similar background to their biological family if possible. This is called selective placement. Is this policy helpful or unhelpful to scientists setting up studies looking at the causes of human behaviour?

A potentially very powerful way of studying environmental influences on development, health and behaviour is the study of identical twins, where only one twin shows the signs of a particular genetic trait. For example, one twin might have a disease whilst the other is healthy. As their genes are the same, any differences in their phenotype are likely to be due to some environmental trigger.

The Twins Early Development Study

Emma Meaburn is a scientist currently working as a molecular geneticist on a project called the Twins Early Development Study (TEDS) (Figure 2.7). She is part of a team led by Professor Robert Plomin, who is well known for his work studying twins. One of his current interests is to find out the extent to which intelligence is influenced by genes. From 1986 to 1994, Professor Plomin investigated the effects of genetics and the environment on ageing by studying pairs of elderly twins in America, some of whom were brought up together and some apart.

The TEDS team is following the development of twins born between 1994 and 1996 in England and Wales. In particular TEDS is comparing non-identical and identical twins (Figure 2.8). The aim is to investigate genetic and environmental influences on the early development of the three most common psychological problems in childhood. These are: communication disorders, mild mental impairment and behavioural problems. Professor Plomin stresses that the emphasis of the study is on the children themselves: "Although we use genetic techniques, our focus is on their behaviour and their behavioural problems. We start with the premise that genetic factors are important, but so is nurture and environment."

Figure 2.7

Emma Meaburn at the Institute of Psychiatry in London. Her first degree was in Human Biology. She followed this with an MSc in Genetics and then a PhD.

Figure 2.8

Twins involved in the TEDS study.

Emma is working in a team investigating the genetic factors involved in reading abilities. "My research focuses on the genetic component of reading abilities in early childhood. I want to identify the genetic variation that is responsible for the high heritability of early reading abilities. I do this by looking at how individual differences in DNA sequence (genetic variation) account for individual differences in reading abilities. It's really exciting working with an eminent scientist and it's such cutting edge research.

"The TEDS twins have been assessed longitudinally at 2, 3, 4, 7, 10, 12 and 14 years of age, on a range of cognitive, behavioural (for example, reading abilities) and environmental measures. More than 15000 pairs of twins have been enrolled in TEDS, and 5000 pairs have given us their DNA, which was extracted from cheek swabs.

"Two key findings have emerged from research into reading abilities using the TEDS sample. Firstly, reading abilities are substantially influenced by genes: 60% of the variation in early reading abilities is due to genetic factors. On the flip side, this also provides the best available evidence that the environment is very important (and is easier to modify).

"Secondly, what we call reading disability is simply the low end of a normal distribution of variation in reading abilities. The same genetic and environmental factors are responsible for all the variation in the population.

"In my own research I am looking at how differences in people's DNA may account for differences in reading ability. I look for single base changes in the DNA of the children and then look for associations between particular base changes and reading ability.

"One of the key findings is that the individual effects of each change in the DNA sequence that we find to be associated with reading abilities are so small that they are barely detectable. This makes identifying the DNA sequence changes associated with reading abilities technically very difficult. It also means that there are hundreds of sequence changes that each make a small contribution to reading abilities. Together, these small changes account for the large inherited component of reading abilities. There is definitely no single gene for reading ability."

Key term

Heritability is the proportion of phenotypic differences amongst individuals that can be attributed to genetic differences. It is a figure calculated for a particular population being studied at a particular moment in time. If heritability is less than 100% it means that factors other than genes must play a part.

DNA and the genetic code

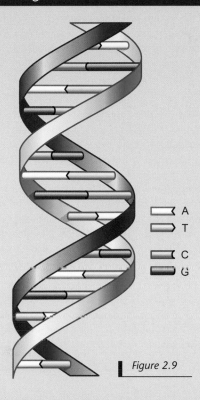

Figure 2.9

DNA in chromosomes is made up of two long chains twisted around each other. The two chains are joined by pairs of small molecules called bases. The sequence of the four bases (labelled A, T, C and G) is the code making up the genetic information in a cell (Figure 2.9).

The DNA in each human body cell contains all the genes. Each gene contains the recipe for making a product which is active in a cell, and controls the cell's activities. This product is usually a protein. The information in the DNA is a complete blueprint for making a human being (see Figure 2.17 on page 49).

Proteins are chains of amino acids. Changes to DNA, called mutations, often involve a change in the DNA code. This in turn affects the RNA produced from the DNA and the amino acids in any proteins produced from the RNA. Changes to DNA may have little or no effect, they may be beneficial, or may have a negative effect, such as causing a genetic disease. In the example in Figure 2.10, just one DNA base is altered. In this case, the change alters one amino acid in a protein chain.

The four bases making up the genetic code on a DNA strand are G, A, T and C. Each 'code word' of three bases determines the position of an amino acid in the protein being made. For example, GGT codes for one amino acid, and GTT for a different one.

A change as small as one single base being substituted for another may change the structure of a protein. This may in turn affect the way a protein works in a cell.

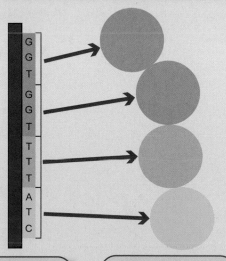

The genetic code sequence on DNA ...

... determines the proteins that are made in a cell.

Tiny changes to the genetic code ....

... may have large effects on a person's phenotype.

Figure 2.10

15 What do you understand by these terms or phrases in the account of Emma Meaburn's work:
   a) a team of scientists
   b) molecular geneticist
   c) communication disorders
   d) twins have been assessed longitudinally
   e) single changes in the base sequences of DNA
   f) there is definitely no single gene for reading abilities?

16 Suggest features of a child's environment that help to determine its reading ability.

17 Other than genetic factors, what might cause a condition to occur more often in a family than in the general population?

18 How might finding an association between a genetic marker and a certain condition help scientists to find the gene responsible for the condition?

The Human Genome Project has given molecular geneticists a new tool for exploring variation in the human genome. The most common type of genetic variation is SNPs. SNPs are like spelling differences in the genetic code, rather like the change of a single letter in a word. They account for up to 90% of the genetic variation amongst individuals, occurring about once every 100 to 300 bases along human DNA.

If scientists do not know where a gene for a trait might be located on the human genome, they look for evidence of the genes being close to areas of DNA that are easily located. These easily identifiable sequences of DNA are found spread throughout the genome, and are called 'markers'. Markers may be genes for a trait that can be easily observed or measured, or other small sections of DNA. Scientists try to find an association between a particular marker and a disease or trait. When a gene and a marker are close together on the same chromosome, they tend to be inherited together. The genetic marker closest to the disease allele shows the strongest correlation with the disease. Scientists can then study the nearby DNA to find the actual gene responsible for the condition. As their location on the human genome is known, SNPs have an important role as markers in genetic studies.

Scientists have invented a way to look at as many as one million SNPs distributed across the entire human genome, in a relatively short period of time. Already SNPs have revealed regions of the genome involved in high blood pressure, obesity, heart disease and a form of diabetes.

"It is important to remember that genetics is not destiny; even if you have the genetic sequence variations associated with poor reading ability, it does not necessarily mean that you will be a poor reader. The genetic variations act only as risk factors in a complex interplay with your environment. By identifying the genetic variants underlying reading disability we can better understand how it occurs, and hopefully develop personalised intervention programmes and treatments."

2.4 Genetic variation associated with complex traits

Medicalisation of behaviour

Modern studies of complex traits and behaviours assume that the differences between people are the result of the interaction of many genes and the environment (see Figure 2.3, page 35). The implication of this model is that some common complex disorders are just an extreme of the normal distribution seen in a population. If behavioural traits are continuously distributed throughout the population, then all of us lie somewhere on this continuous spectrum.

Diagnosis of a disorder can be interpreted in two ways. One model assumes that the genetic risk for a disorder is normally distributed, in the same way as any measurable trait such as height or weight. People show symptoms of the disorder once a certain threshold of genetic risk is reached. So, if you have a certain number of alleles associated with schizophrenia, you are likely to show the symptoms which define the disorder.

The second model also describes most behavioural traits (and some medical conditions) as continuous. Disorders such as schizophrenia, eating disorders, autism and learning difficulties are part of a continuous spectrum of human phenotypes. Diagnosis of a disorder is considered an artificial categorisation, providing a cut-off point in the continuous spectrum. Diagnosis is, effectively, a judgement that the disorder is causing such a degree of harm and suffering that it needs medical intervention.

Both models suggest that complex disorders are often highly heritable. They assume that a substantial proportion of phenotypic differences amongst individuals can be attributed to naturally occurring genetic variation.

Research which attempts to link genes with behaviour within and outside the normal range has social implications. It is clear that it is difficult to identify effects of genes for behaviour. Often behaviour is the result of small effects of many genes, genes may have more than one effect, and genes interact with other genes. The interaction between genes and environment is very complex, and the effect genes have may be different at different stages of our life. Also, behaviour is difficult to define and observe, and research on humans is often hard to replicate in a way that allows it to be taken seriously by the scientific community.

It could be argued that research into genetic variations associated with extremes of behaviour is only useful if it then leads to treatments which modify behaviour. Potentially, medicines could be targeted at individual genotypes with susceptibilities for certain diseases. Medical interventions might also include gene therapy, to change the genes which contribute to a trait.

The 2002 Nuffield Council on Bioethics report *Genetics and Human Behaviour* raises the concern that behavioural genetics research might encourage people to consider behaviour previously thought of as normal to be categorised as a disorder. The Nuffield report also suggests that any genetic tests for behavioural traits should be carefully regulated. Information could be sensitive for people personally, but could also be exploited by employers or society more widely to discriminate or stigmatise certain groups of people.

Researchers use family, twin and adoption studies to tease out possible environmental and genetic triggers for diseases such as schizophrenia. If a trait or disorder is shown to have high heritability, researchers can then go about identifying the genetic variation responsible. Studies suggesting an associated environmental factor lead to further studies which try to distinguish between the effects of the environment on people with different genotypes. For example, some scientists have reported that schizophrenia is associated with an increased use of cannabis.

Linkage studies

The goal of genetic research is to identify the genes that are responsible for the heritability of a trait or disorder. For single gene disorders, this is relatively straightforward due to the near perfect correlation between genotype and phenotype. By tracking affected families, the region of the DNA harbouring the disorder gene can be identified. Genes which occur close together on the same chromosome are known as 'linked' genes, and tend to be inherited together. Scientists try to identify known genes

Questions

19 Discuss how research into genes and behaviour could result in reduced tolerance of different behavioural traits, along with increased pressure to use medical interventions.

20 How does this 'medicalised' approach, where genetic testing could result in classifying certain genotypes as disorders, conflict with what we know about the interaction of genes and environment?

21 Produce one argument for and one against the view that employers should be allowed to use genetic tests which could identify people with susceptibility to particular types.

Figure 2.11

A family tree showing the distribution of four versions or alleles of a gene (numbered 1, 2, 3 and 4) amongst a family affected by an inherited disorder. Each person has two copies of any particular allele, one inherited from each parent. The alleles in black are the father's copies and the alleles in red the mother's copies. An allele which is co-inherited many times with a disorder may be causing the condition, or may be closely linked to the gene responsible. This type of analysis helps scientists track down genes that cause disease.

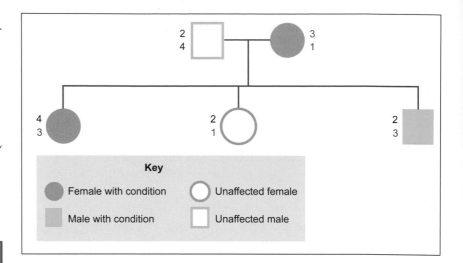

Key

● Female with condition   ○ Unaffected female

■ Male with condition   □ Unaffected male

Questions

22 Which allele (1–4) appears to be associated with the gene for the condition shown in the family tree in Figure 2.11?

23 What does this indicate about the possible relationship between this allele and the condition?

which are inherited along with the disorder being studied. This type of study is called linkage analysis.

Linkage studies look at markers which are spread throughout the genome. Scientists try to find an association between a particular marker and a disease or behaviour. In a family study, if only those members of the family with schizophrenia have a particular marker, this may indicate that the marker lies close to a gene responsible for schizophrenia (Figure 2.11). Scientists can then search the nearby DNA for the gene responsible for the condition.

In a family study, the easiest markers to look for are those which produce an observable characteristic. A task where patients have to move their eyes in the opposite direction to a moving visual target has been studied as a risk factor for schizophrenia. Low scores in carrying out this task are more common in patients diagnosed with schizophrenia and in their close relatives than in controls. The gene for poor eye tracking, which has been located on the human genome, has been associated with schizophrenia (Figure 2.12).

Studies which track DNA markers within families can give an indication of how much genes contribute to a condition. For complex traits such as behaviour, it is important to know how much genes contribute to differences between people, compared with any influence from the environment. The major challenge of genetic research is the identification of genes which have small effects but contribute to the heritability of common complex traits.

Genes or environment may show a consistent effect associated with a particular condition, and as a result, these effects show up as statistically significant in a large-scale study. For example, IQ and birth order are related: first-born children have IQs that are higher. This finding is statistically significant. But, the mean difference between first- and second-born siblings is less than two IQ points. This effect on IQ is extremely small; birth order accounts for just 1% of the difference in IQ between individuals.

For some complex traits, genes can account for as much as half or more of the differences in predisposition among individuals. For schizophrenia, if one of a pair of identical twins has the condition, there is a 48% chance on average (range 35–65) that their twin has also been diagnosed with the condition. This compares with a fraternal twin average of 17% (range 5–28). The comparison value for the general population is 1% (Figure 2.13).

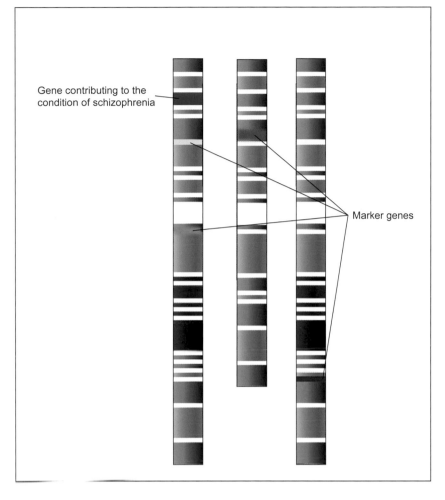

Gene contributing to the condition of schizophrenia

Marker genes

Figure 2.12

The diagram shows a representation of three single human chromosomes (you actually have 23 pairs of these). These are single molecules of DNA, which are duplicated to form the more familiar X-shape when a cell is about to divide. Each blue or white stripe represents a length of DNA that functions as a gene. Four marker genes and the gene for schizophrenia are in different colours to highlight them. The gene associated with schizophrenia is in red, on the chromosome on the left.

Questions

24 Which of the four marker genes shown in Figure 2.12 (yellow, green, pink and purple) are most likely to be the marker gene associated with poor eye tracking?

25 Referring to Figure 2.13, explain why having 'genes for schizophrenia' does not mean that a person will necessarily have schizophrenia.

26 A mutant allele of a gene called FTO has recently been associated with obesity. This gene normally switches off appetite, giving a feeling of fullness. The mutant allele stops this happening. Imagine you are a scientist interested in the potential commercial interest in a genetic test for the mutant allele. Explain why you will be interested in:
a) the heritability of this eating disorder in a particular culture associated with FTO
b) the size of the effect this genetic variant has on body mass.

Figure 2.13

Graph showing the percentage lifetime risk of different groups of relatives sharing a diagnosis of schizophrenia. The greater number of genes one person shares with a person with schizophrenia, the greater the likelihood of that person also being affected. Identical twins share 100% cent of genes but have an average 48% chance of developing schizophrenia if their twin is affected.

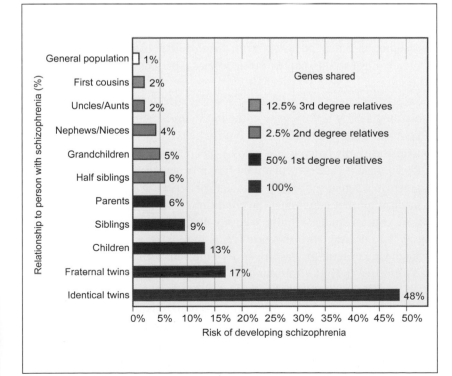

Genes shared

12.5% 3rd degree relatives

2.5% 2nd degree relatives

50% 1st degree relatives

100%

General population 1%
First cousins 2%
Uncles/Aunts 2%
Nephews/Nieces 4%
Grandchildren 5%
Half siblings 6%
Parents 6%
Siblings 9%
Children 13%
Fraternal twins 17%
Identical twins 48%

Relationship to person with schizophrenia (%)

Risk of developing schizophrenia

Science in Society **45**

Association studies

Scientists usually have to investigate many more people than can be obtained through family studies to locate a particular gene. They use other research designs to do this, such as case control studies. An alternative method used to identify the genes responsible for the heritability of complex traits is to identify any alleles associated with the trait. This works on the principle that if a genetic variation (for example, a SNP) contributes to an increased risk for a disease, then it should be found in a higher proportion of affected individuals than in unaffected controls. Association studies search for a correlation in the population between the genetic variation and the phenotype. Association studies can be case control or population based.

Case control studies

A case control study of a genetic disorder compares the frequency of genetic markers between cases and controls. Cases are people who have been diagnosed or classified as having the trait, and controls are unaffected individuals from the same population who have been matched for age, sex and other factors, including geographical location. Statistical analysis is used to identify any differences in frequency of alleles between the cases and the controls. The alleles that show a statistically significant difference between the two groups are then assumed to be either the genetic variation causing the disorder, or closely linked to the causative genetic variation.

For instance, scientists looking for genes that predispose people to Alzheimer's disease have used case control studies to investigate a gene which codes for a protein they call apolipoprotein E. This protein is found in the parts of the brain that are damaged in people with Alzheimer's disease. The scientists have found that some people with the disease have one allele of the gene, whilst those unaffected generally have a different allele. This suggests that a variation of the gene that codes for apolipoprotein E may be a risk factor for this form of dementia.

Case control studies can be prone to bias. The most common sources of bias are:
- Selection of cases: only the most severely affected cases, or those with a strong family history, may come to the investigators' attention.
- Poor selection of controls: the controls selected need to be matched to the cases if any comparison is to be meaningful.
- Recall bias: if case control studies are retrospective, they rely on a person's memory of any previous experience such as events or medication that may affect the condition.

Case control studies require accurate diagnosis of cases. One approach to dealing with this problem is to provide a standardised set of diagnostic criteria for each disorder. One source of such guidance is the World Health Organization's *International Statistical Classification of Diseases and Related Health Problems* (generally known by the initials ICD). For mental disorders, the alternative is the *Diagnostic and Statistical Manual of Mental Disorders* (DSMM) produced by the American Psychiatric Association.

Key terms

Case control studies are studies in which people who already have a certain condition (the cases) are compared with a control group of people who do not.

A **risk factor** is any genetic or environmental factor which increases a person's chance of developing a disease.

Questions

27 With reference to Figure 2.15, which genotype presents the greatest risk factor for developing schizophrenia among cannabis users?

28 If an association exists between cannabis smoking and schizophrenia, does this suggest that cannabis 'causes' schizophrenia?

29 In the light of these observations, health professionals could offer genotyping to identify those with the Val allele who are most at risk. Alternatively, they could recommend that nobody at risk of developing schizophrenia should use cannabis. Explain which approach is likely to be most effective at protecting people at risk.

Whole population association studies

An alternative approach to the case control design of association studies is to treat the phenotype being measured as a continuous trait. This approach assumes that the same genes are associated with variation throughout the entire population distribution. Rather than classifying individuals as 'affected' or 'unaffected', scientists look at everyone in the population, and look for an association between their genotype and scores which measure traits.

In contrast to linkage studies, association studies are powerful enough to detect genes which have only a small effect. For this reason, association studies are the method of choice when trying to identify the genetic variation underlying the heritability of traits.

However, in order for association studies to have the power to detect genes of small effect size, very large sample sizes are needed, of at least 1000 individuals. The studies also need to detect very large numbers of genetic markers (>500 000).

Longitudinal cohort studies

Random cohorts from the general population are studied over time to identify risk factors, either genetic or environmental, that predispose a person to a particular condition. Longitudinal study design allocates people to cohorts before they develop any symptoms. As a result, these studies are not as prone to the selection bias of case control studies.

An example of this type of study is the Avon Longitudinal Study of Parents and Children (ALSPAC). This study is based on 14 000 people born around Bristol between 1991 and 1992 and is also called 'Children of the Nineties'. The study was set up to investigate genetic and environmental factors that predispose people to develop disorders such as asthma, food allergies, autism, hyperactivity, dyslexia and eczema (Figure 2.14).

The gene which carries the code for an enzyme that breaks down dopamine in the brain has two alleles which differ by just one base. The name of the enzyme is abbreviated to COMT, so this gene is sometimes called the COMT gene. One prospective cohort study has shown that people with a particular variant of the COMT gene, and who also smoke cannabis, may have an increased risk of developing schizophrenia (see Figure 2.15).

Questions

30 Use the terms 'correlation' and 'cause' to explain why scientists who have found apolipoprotein E in the parts of the brain that are damaged in people with Alzheimer's disease cannot conclude that this protein causes the disease.

31 Explain why the 'cases' in a case control study are not selected randomly.

32 Suggest criteria for the selection of the control group for a case control study of Alzheimer's disease.

33 Suggest reasons why a diagnostic manual for mental disorders has to be updated and revised regularly.

34 The World Health Organization's ICD and the DSMM produced by the American Psychiatric Association have to define the boundaries between normality and disease. Suggest reasons why this guidance has proved controversial and open to criticism.

35 Half the scientists and doctors who worked on the latest classification of mental disorders have been shown to have had financial links with the pharmaceutical industry at some stage in their careers. Why might this have given rise to conflicts of interest?

Figure 2.14

ALSPAC, set up in 1991, is a study following the health of thousands of children around the Bristol area. Researchers have tracked the children from before birth and recorded information on the diet, lifestyle, socioeconomic status and family relationships of both the children and their parents. They have also collected blood, urine and DNA samples. The data and samples are a very important research resource and are made available to scientists all over the world.

Figure 2.15

The COMT gene has two alleles. Their protein product differs by just one amino acid. One allele codes for a methionine amino acid at a position where the other allele codes for valine. The alleles are referred to as either Met or Val. Error bars are shown to indicate the degree of uncertainty in the data.

Key term

Error bars on a graph or chart indicate the uncertainty or spread of values associated with a data point. Various measures of the spread of the data can be used to decide the length of error bars, but one form shows the size of one standard deviation about the mean value. If the error bars of two data points on a graph or chart overlap, it is likely that the difference between the two values is not statistically significant.

Questions

36 Identify three questions about human health or behaviour that you would hope that the ALSPAC study would be able to answer.

37 Suggest possible sources of bias in a longitudinal study.

38 Suggest reasons why a case control study is used rather than a population-based study when the condition being studied is only observed very infrequently.

39 A group of scientists claim to have found a link between a particular gene and alcoholism in a study of a remote community in Northern Canada.
a) Give a reason why this observation may not be relevant to the general population.
b) How might these scientists further test their hypothesis that this gene is a risk factor for alcoholism?

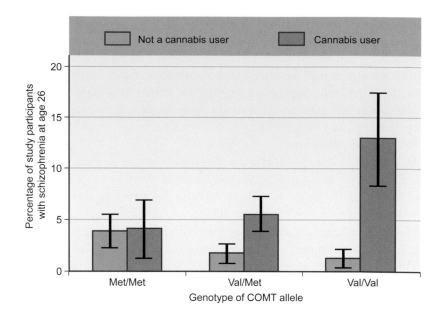

2.5 Brain development in childhood and adolescence

From conception, a human fetus develops rapidly in complexity. Cells in the early embryo are unspecialised and capable of developing into any cell type. Within days, particular cell types form, and within weeks organ systems emerge. Genes control this whole process. Thousands of genes are involved and different genes are expressed at different times during development. Different genes are also active in different cell types.

The effect of environment on brain development

At birth, a baby's brain contains almost all the neurones it will ever need. Before birth, connections start to link the neurones, but this process of wiring the brain accelerates rapidly after birth. During the first three years of a child's life the brain makes trillions of connections between neurones. Environmental stimuli are known to affect this process, before and after birth, and this plays a part in how people learn from experience (Figure 2.16).

Figure 2.16

These diagrams show that the neurones at birth are mostly unconnected to each other, but by the age of three years have formed dense connections.

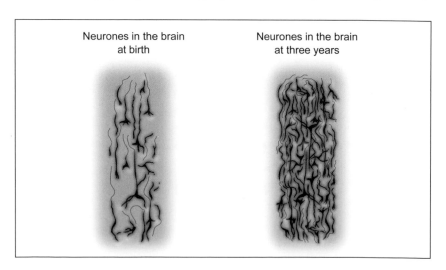

Gene expression

Gene expression is the process referred to when a sequence of DNA is transcribed to form RNA. The RNA molecule moves to the main part of the cell (the cytoplasm) where the code is translated into proteins (Figure 2.17).

The genes that are expressed in a particular cell will determine the type of cell and what functions it performs (e.g. muscle cell, neurone, etc.). Cells have a genetic plan for producing proteins. Proteins include enzymes, receptors, hormones, transport and storage proteins and signalling molecules. They are involved in almost all biological activities. Proteins play a vital role in determining the way that cells and organs grow and develop to give living things their unique characteristics.

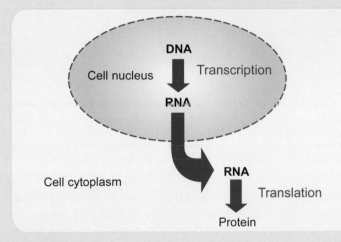

Figure 2.17

Every one of your body cells with a nucleus has the same set of genes, so how does a liver cell become different from a nerve cell? Not all genes are switched on in every cell all of the time. For instance, some genes are expressed in a developing fetus and are then switched off after birth. Control of gene expression plays an important part in the way cells differentiate to form skin, muscle, nerve and other types of cells.

Regulator genes are responsible for controlling the expression of other genes in a particular cell (Figure 2.18). Regulators may switch the gene on or off, or may enhance or depress the activity of a gene more subtly, rather like a volume control.

One way that the environment affects gene expression is by influencing the body processes that produce hormones. Hormones, which are transported in the bloodstream, stimulate cells to produce chemicals which in turn activate genes and protein production.

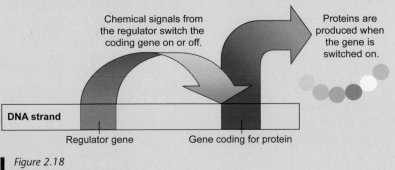

Figure 2.18

Key term

Gene expression is the series of processes in cells where DNA is transcribed to RNA, which may in turn be translated into protein molecules.

Question

40 Some scientists justify research on the expression of genes found to be associated with behaviour by claiming that once we know how the proteins they code for affect the brain, a better prediction of medical conditions and better treatment and prevention are potentially possible. How does the scientific community try to avoid claims which raise false hopes in affected individuals and families?

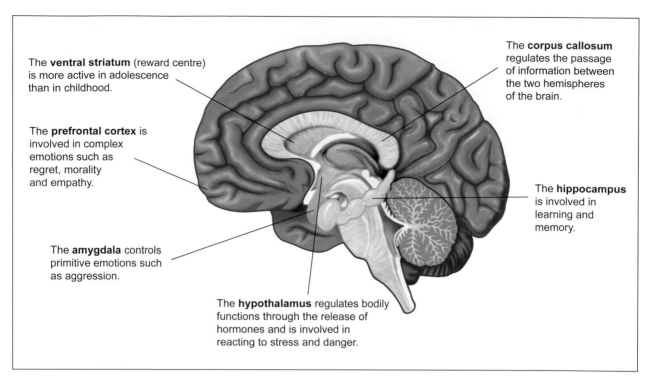

The **ventral striatum** (reward centre) is more active in adolescence than in childhood.

The **prefrontal cortex** is involved in complex emotions such as regret, morality and empathy.

The **amygdala** controls primitive emotions such as aggression.

The **hypothalamus** regulates bodily functions through the release of hormones and is involved in reacting to stress and danger.

The **corpus callosum** regulates the passage of information between the two hemispheres of the brain.

The **hippocampus** is involved in learning and memory.

Figure 2.19

Regions of the human brain thought to be associated with behaviour and the emotions.

Experiences can be beneficial or harmful: either way they are likely to have an effect on the brain's circuitry, particularly if they are a common part of a child's experience. During early brain development a baby's brain overproduces the connections between neurones. New connections that are used over and over again strengthen to form nerve pathways in the brain. Other pathways become redundant and may be removed if formed as a result of experiences that are not repeated. This process of forming nerve pathways is associated with learning and memory. It is particularly active in infancy but connections continue to be made throughout our lives in response to experience. Every time you learn something new, new connections are made between neurones in your brain.

Animal studies have indicated that stress, lack of stimulation and maternal neglect can lead to both changes in the brain and abnormal emotional responses. Scientists have also found evidence which suggests that life experiences can directly affect human brain development. Certain areas of the brain appear to be particularly vulnerable, including structures involved in some emotional responses, eating and sexual behaviour.

Another area of the brain that is affected by trauma is the bundle of nerves that joins the two hemispheres of the brain and allows information to pass from one side of the brain to the other. This is the corpus callosum. One research study examined the brains of children admitted to hospital as a result of neglect or abuse. Brain scans revealed that the corpus callosum was up to 40% smaller in this group of children compared to normal.

Questions

41 Parts of the region of the brain called the hippocampus (see Figure 2.19) handle spatial memory and spatial navigation. These parts are larger in the brains of London taxi drivers. Why might this be so?

42 Give an example of a finding connected with the effect of the environment on brain development, where child psychologists must have worked together with neuroscientists.

Parenting and education

Studies on children's early development emphasise the importance of a happy, stable home environment for the social, emotional and future academic achievement of young people.

Windows of development

It is an accepted fact that our environment can have an effect on our attitudes and behaviour. Scientists think that there are periods during a child's life when brain development is particularly sensitive to environmental input. These sensitive periods may be especially important in speech and emotional development. This theory has led to the production of a wealth of tools and advice for parents wishing to boost their children's intellectual and emotional development. These include videos and TV programmes for babies that are designed to stimulate brain development.

Neuroscientists advise that there is little evidence that learning tools such as these can enhance a baby's intellectual ability but there is evidence that everyday experiences do promote healthy development (Figure 2.20).

Human emotional control and social attachment develop most rapidly from 10–18 months. Children need to make attachments to a primary carer during this period, whether this is in the family or good quality day-care. A UK government study published in 2007, led by Kathy Sylva and Sandra Mathers of Oxford University, examined 810 children in 100 neighbourhood nurseries. They identified that children who spent 30 hours or more per week in a nursery showed signs of being more antisocial. Children who attended for 35 hours or more displayed more worried and upset behaviour.

Figure 2.20

Connections in the brain of a baby develop in response to their experiences.

Questions

43 What questions should a peer reviewer ask about the children sampled in the Oxford study of day-care when considering whether the report's conclusions are valid?

44 What other questions should parents ask in relation to the Oxford day-care study when considering the appropriateness of day-care for their own child?

45 What issues does the Oxford day-care study raise for government and policy-makers?

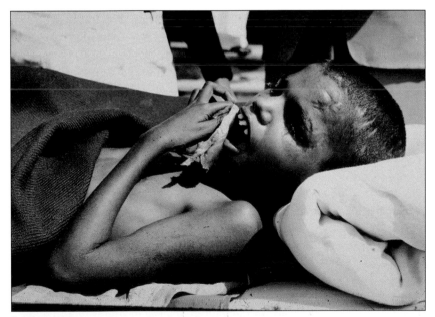

Figure 2.21

In 1954, seven year old Ramu was discovered in Lucknow, India. It is believed he was brought up by wolves having been snatched by a wolf from his mother's lap as a baby. Ramu lapped milk from a glass, tore his food apart and would gnaw on bones for hours. Despite being reunited with his family after they recognised him during a chance visit to Balrampur Hospital, Ramu was never able to return to society and spent the next 14 years in Lucknow Hospital until his death in 1968.

Figure 2.22

Most parents want to provide a good upbringing for their children. The advice given to parents is affected by scientific insights as well as traditional views in society about child rearing.

Questions

46 What are the implications of windows of opportunity for the education system?

47 Should TV be banned for young children?

48 Do the results of the 2007 study of TV viewing and ADHD suggest that TV viewing is a direct cause of ADHD?

49 Explain how good state nursery schools can help to reduce the divide in academic success between richer and poorer groups in society.

The rare studies of children who have been separated from other human beings at an early age suggests that socialisation and language development cannot be learned after the critical windows of opportunity have passed (Figure 2.21).

'Windows of opportunity' are times when learning can take place, involving changes to connections between neurones in the brain. Once the window is passed, it becomes much more difficult to learn. For many skills, missing the window does not mean that the skill cannot be learned. It just means it will take more effort and practice. It is much easier to learn a new language or a musical instrument before the age of 10, but many people succeed with these in adulthood.

Most parents consider their children's education as a partnership between school and home. Schools encourage parents to talk to their children, and to take part in activities such as reading and constructive play. This type of activity takes time and effort on the part of parents and carers, but these years, particularly the pre-school years, have a lasting influence.

A 2007 study reported in the *Journal of Pediatric Psychology* recruited 170 pre-school children as part of a longitudinal study. The mean number of hours spent watching TV was 2.35 hours per day. Results indicated that an elevated level of TV viewing was associated with higher levels of attention deficit hyperactivity disorder (ADHD).

A second study, published in the journal *Science* in August 2008, said the benefits of supportive parental behaviour (reading to children, playing with numbers and shapes, nursery rhymes and visits to the library) were detectable. Parents' wealth and level of education and good quality pre-school education also affected children's achievement in maths tests at age 10. Without these benefits an average child from a poor background would be in the bottom 20% at school. With all three advantages (supportive parents, parental wealth and education and good pre-school education) the child would, on average, move into the top 20%. The study followed nearly 3000 children at more than 800 primary schools from age three onwards.

Educational psychology and research into how children learn and develop has influenced practice in schools for many years. The UK National Curriculum is based on studies designed to shed light on the ways in which children's understanding of concepts develops as they mature. UK schools are required to have behavioural policies which consistently reward good behaviour and provide sanctions for antisocial behaviour. Educational psychologists are employed to work with teachers to identify children with specific learning or behavioural disorders, so these children can be offered additional support.

The genetics of learning and intelligence also has implications for our education system. Identifying children with particular abilities, or at risk for particular conditions, could be helpful. However, teachers are not genetics experts, and there may be a temptation to overestimate the importance of those genes. It could also lead to discrimination, with certain students denied educational opportunities, or the unhelpful labelling of some students leading to a self-fulfilling prophesy, where students do not see the point in trying to learn.

Adolescence, a time of change

Selective destruction, or 'pruning', of neurones in the brain continues from birth until adulthood. Grey matter in the brain increases in early childhood, but from puberty it begins to thin (Figure 2.23).

The changes to grey matter in adolescence correspond with increasing cognitive ability. However, other parts of the brain are also reorganised at this time. The prefrontal cortex, involved in planning and reasoning, is not fully developed until the early twenties. The reward centre (ventral striatum) is more active in adolescence than in adulthood, leaving teenagers more susceptible to the rewards of high risk behaviour (see Figure 2.19). With immature connections between the cognitive and emotional centres of the brain, teenagers are more vulnerable to psychological disorders.

Questions

50 A study investigating the interplay between child abuse and IQ has shown that the IQ of children from abusive backgrounds can improve if they are adopted into other families. Should this be a consideration when social services are considering removing children into foster care?

51 Argue from both sides about the desirability of screening pre-school children for genes associated with reading difficulties.

Key terms

White matter describes parts of the central nervous system made up of axons only.

Grey matter describes parts of the central nervous system made up of cell bodies and synapses.

Figure 2.23

Brain scans show the thinning of grey matter during adolescence. This is thought to correspond with pruning of redundant connections between neurones, and an increase in the fatty sheath surrounding the neurones.

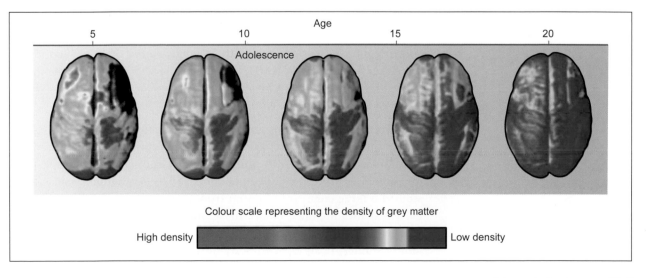

Colour scale representing the density of grey matter

High density — Low density

One study found evidence that schizophrenia may be caused by faults in the brain's wiring that occur during fetal brain development. The resulting abnormalities lie dormant until a person approaches adulthood. Brain scans show that differences exist in the pattern of thinning of the grey matter of adolescents who go on to develop schizophrenia, bipolar disorder and other conditions. One aim of this research is to inform development of drug therapies which aim to prevent the severe grey matter loss in schizophrenia, and prevent the reorganisation of neurones that leads to bipolar disorder.

2.6 Antisocial behaviour and criminality

Finding effective ways to deal with antisocial behaviour is a pressing issue for society. As a result, its origins are the subject of much research. Social scientists have found that risk factors for behaviour of this kind can include aggression at home, family breakdown, poverty, weak parenting, criminality in the family and even having a large number of siblings. Geneticists are interested in exploring the extent to which a person's genotype can lead to antisocial behaviour. In popular terms this leads to questions such as: 'Is there an ASBO gene?'.

The antisocial behaviour of a Dutch family

In June 1993, *Science* published a paper by Professor H. Brunner on a study of criminal behaviour in a Dutch family. A significant number of the men from this family had learning difficulties and displayed impulsive, aggressive behaviour. They were well known to the authorities and had been charged with a range of criminal offences including attempted rape and arson.

Studies of this family revealed that the affected men had abnormally low levels of the brain chemical monoamine oxidase A (MAOA). This chemical is an enzyme that breaks down neurotransmitters such as dopamine and serotonin. Low levels of MAOA could lead to a build up of neurotransmitters which, in turn, could adversely affect behaviour, possibly causing the aggression seen in these men (see Chapter 1).

The researchers noted that the women of the family appeared to be unaffected. This implied that the condition was sex linked and the gene responsible lay on the X chromosome. Scientists have since confirmed that the gene for MAOA is on the X chromosome. The researchers studying the affected men in the Dutch family found that they had a mutation of the gene for MAOA, limiting how much of the enzyme their bodies could produce. This added support to the theory that MAOA was involved in antisocial behaviour in this family.

The interaction between genes and environment

A study published in 2002 describes the interplay between the gene for the enzyme MAOA and childhood experience. A team of psychologists at King's College London, led by Avshalom Caspi, studied a large cohort of children from Dunedin, New Zealand. Earlier studies included laboratory experiments which linked genetic deficiencies in MAOA production to extreme aggression in mice, and family studies of the Dutch family described above. The Dunedin

Questions

52 Using your knowledge of dopamine and serotonin from Chapter 1, suggest how MAOA inhibitors act as antidepressants.

53 Explain why family studies such as the Dutch MAOA study need to be replicated in the general population for their conclusions to be verified.

cohort was set up using children born between 1972 and 1973. Detailed information has been collected ever since, and the study is on-going. Scientists collected details of how the children were treated by their parents, and records on any evidence of the children taking part in criminal or serious antisocial behaviour.

Previous evidence about the origins of antisocial behaviour has indicated that child abuse is a significant factor. Abused children are 50% more likely to become criminals in adulthood than other children. This finding also means that a very large number of abused children grow up to be responsible, law-abiding adults.

The team at King's College wanted to find out whether or not it is the level of MAOA in the brain that determines the extent to which abused children show antisocial or criminal behaviours. The scientists focused their investigation on 499 male members of the Dunedin cohort for whom blood or saliva samples for DNA analysis were available. These men came from a wide variety of backgrounds, although those of native Maori descent were not included.

What was interesting was the link between the three factors; low levels of MAOA in the brain, a history of child abuse and criminality as adults (Figure 2.24). The men with all three factors present only accounted for 12% of the group studied but they were responsible for 44% of the violent crime committed by that group. In direct contrast, those men who had also been maltreated as children but who had high levels of MAOA in their brains were not more likely to be involved in criminal or antisocial behaviour. The high levels of MAOA appeared to protect their developing brains from this effect of abuse.

Questions

54 Why are only men studied in the Dunedin cohort?

55 Suggest why the Dunedin study excluded men of Maori descent.

56 What are the implications of the Dunedin study for children's social services?

57 Which two columns in Figure 2.24 provide the best evidence that maltreatment is associated with violent behaviour?

58 Which two columns best illustrate that levels of MAOA are important?

59 How does publication of findings in scientific journals help to influence accepted scientific theories?

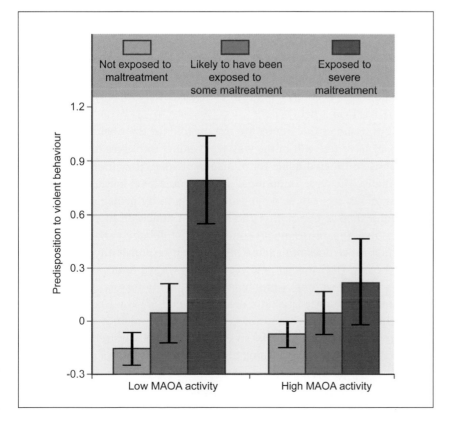

Figure 2.24

The graph shows the association between childhood maltreatment and a predisposition to violent behaviour when correlated with the activity of the MAOA enzyme. Those men who had inherited the less active form of the MAOA gene and suffered severe maltreatment were the most likely to be violent. Error bars are shown to indicate the degree of uncertainty in the data.

Question

60 The Dunedin study helped to change scientists' approach to the study of nature and nurture. Nature/nurture studies traditionally compared variations in phenotypes due to the action of genes with variations due to environmental influences. Explain how new knowledge about the MAOA gene changes this approach.

Standard deviation
Figure 2.25

Standard deviation is a measure of the spread of data. Data which spread far from the mean have a large standard deviation. A small standard deviation indicates that data points are clustered closely around the mean.

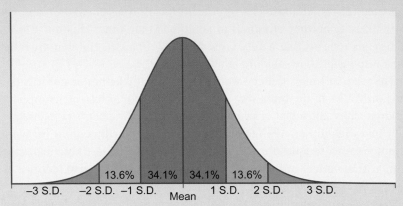

A set of data showing a normal distribution (see Figure 2.26). In a normal distribution, 68% of the data points lie within one standard deviation (S.D.) of the mean and 95% lie within two S.D. of the mean.

The Dunedin study is investigating a possible genetic explanation for some types of human behaviour. The findings suggest that genes and the environment might together affect behaviour. What the results imply is that although our genes do not predetermine our characters, they do have an effect that can be neutralised or enhanced by our experiences.

Genetics and the legal system

Some people have concerns that the idea that genes determine our behaviour could lead us to take less personal responsibility. For instance, our response to breaking the law could be "My genes made me do it" or we could say "There's no point in eating healthily, it's my genes that make me fat, I can't help it".

The law assumes that adults are responsible for their behaviour, and that we all have free will in the way we conduct ourselves in society. A person is considered liable for punishment when they break the law intentionally. The term 'intentional' is important here, because automatic or unconscious acts can be defended, as can acts by people judged insane or of diminished responsibility. The Nuffield Council on Bioethics report *Genetics and Human Behaviour* concludes that genetic variance within the normal range does not excuse people from responsibility to behave within the law. Over the last few years in the United States, some of those on trial for serious crimes have used a family history of violent behaviour as a defence against a death sentence. If people could excuse their behaviour on the grounds of genes or environment, it would, in effect, remove the need to make an effort to behave within the law. This idea also affects the way we think about free will. It affects our attitude to whether we can influence our own lives and the lives of our children, or whether we are at the mercy of our genes.

Questions

61 List some potential concerns with associating a particular combination of genes with lack of legal responsibility.

62 Genetic forensic profiling could be used to predict whether a person is likely to commit a crime before they actually do. How does this affect the legal concept of 'innocent until proven guilty'?

2.7 Intelligence and 'g'

The search for the biological origins of intelligence has been pursued for a long time and has provoked arguments inside and outside the scientific world. The most well known and commonly used measure is the IQ test. An IQ or 'intelligence quotient' test measures a person's ability with diverse cognitive tests such as vocabulary, spatial visualisation, memory and the speed with which they can process information. Modern IQ tests rank a person's score according to where they lie in a normal distribution for their age group. An IQ score of less than 70 indicates that an individual has a score in the lowest 2% of the distribution, which often involves some learning problems (Figure 2.26).

In an attempt to define a measurable form of intelligence, scientists around a century ago proposed the concept of general cognitive ability or 'g'. This was in response to the observation that if you measure a person's ability in various different types of test, such as those testing reasoning ability, memory or ability with language, their scores tend to be very similar regardless of what is being tested. In theory, a general score could be given, which is a measure of their intellectual ability. IQ has a defined scale, because its calculation is based on a standard set of tests. The concept g describes a hypothetical quality that contributes to ability in any tests measuring cognitive ability. IQ can be thought of as the results of g (general intelligence) plus a mixture of specific cognitive skills which are measured in IQ tests.

The heritability of g is high: genes contribute around 60% of the effects that result in intelligence differences between individuals. This idea has been adopted by those trying to find evidence for differences in intelligence between men, women and those of different races and social classes. An infamous book, *Bell Curve: Intelligence and Class Structure in American Life*, published in 1994 by academics Richard Hernstein and Charles Murray, attempted to legitimise racial inequalities and warned against those of low IQ breeding more rapidly than those of high IQ in the elite. Such arguments had some parallels with the ideas of Francis Galton and other twentieth century eugenicists and very quickly provoked a storm of debate about the meaning of intelligence.

Questions

These questions relate to Figure 2.26.

63 What are the values of the mean, median and modal IQ in this population?

64 What is the standard deviation of IQ in this population?

65 A normal distribution can be divided into quartiles, each representing 25% of the data. The interquartile range describes the spread of data from the lowest 25% to the highest 25%. In other words it is the spread of values of the middle 50%. If the range of measurable IQ lies between 55 and 145, what is the interquartile range?

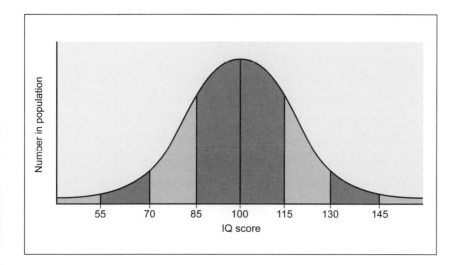

Figure 2.26

A bell curve or normal distribution showing the distribution of IQ in the UK population; 68% of people have scores between 85 and 115, 96% between 70 and 130. In a normal distribution, the mean value is the same as the median (midvalue) and the mode (most frequent value). These three different measures of the centre of the data are not the same value when the data do not form a perfect bell shape.

Number in population

IQ score

In the debate about IQ in the 1990s, some people argued from a political point of view rather than scientific evidence. Research findings were judged by their implications for society, and people found it difficult to make their own judgements on the basis of unbiased information. In November 1994, the American Psychological Association (APA) concluded that there was urgent need for an authoritative report that could be used as the basis for discussions about intelligence. The APA set up a task force with members chosen by an extended consultative process, with the aim of representing a broad range of expertise and opinion. The report was drafted, circulated and revised several times, and controversial sections were agreed through wide discussions.

The APA report concluded that there is evidence of a genetic contribution to intelligence, but that the mechanism by which genes affect intelligence is still unknown. The report acknowledged that a person's environment also has a large influence on intelligence; again the report admits that the mechanism of how environment has an influence is not known. A steady rise in mean intelligence scores was reported in the years leading up to the report. There was a more controversial conclusion that there is little direct evidence that genes are responsible for the differences in IQ observed due to caste and culture.

The standardised tests used measured particular forms of intelligence, but not creativity, wisdom, practical sense and social sensitivity. Despite their importance, these qualities remain difficult to measure, or to relate to more traditional tests of intelligence.

Many questions raised by the report remain unresolved, and the complex nature of questions about the origin of intelligence will continue to be explored by scientists and social scientists.

Genes for g

Despite its unfortunate association with eugenic ideas, scientists find g a useful measure in the search for variations in genes that show an association with intelligence. However, this view is qualified by the

Questions

66 Why was it important that scientists and non-scientists from a range of backgrounds were part of the task force involved in the APA report on the genetic influences on intelligence?

67 What are the social implications of an attempt to link genes with IQ?

68 Which two bars in Figure 2.27 suggest that genes are responsible for a large part of the variation in IQ in humans?

69 The correlation between 'g' and a person's educational attainment and occupational level in adulthood is around +0.50. Explain why you would describe this as 'moderate' correlation.

Figure 2.27

The graph shows how intelligence correlates with both shared environment and how closely related two people are. The x-axis gives the correlation of IQ with degree of relatedness or shared environment. Correlation scores can be from −1.0 to +1.0, but in this graph the lowest value is 0.0. A score of 0.0 indicates that there is no correlation. Unrelated people reared apart show no correlation, but those who are biologically related and/or are reared together shows some degree of positive correlation for IQ.

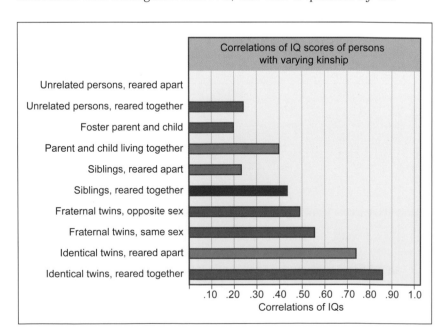

understanding that there is always going to be more to intelligence than simply some factor called 'g', and that it is likely to involve many genes, each with a very small effect.

Studies have indicated that g is a highly heritable trait. Research to date supports the idea that possibly thousands of genes influence g, each having only a small effect. Studies also indicate that each gene's effect may be additive, leading to a stronger overall genetic effect on intelligence, but one that cannot be pinpointed to one simple genetic origin. Some weak associations between certain genes and intelligence have been reported in the scientific literature, such as the CHRM2 gene which is associated with communication between neurones and the SSADH gene, which is involved in a rare form of learning disability.

A recent study investigating a group of 7000 seven year olds used a two stage approach to find the genotype variations that are associated with intelligence. The children underwent verbal and non-verbal reasoning tests and gave DNA samples. The researchers then looked for differences in the DNA of the children being studied by analysing SNPs, the single letter changes that are common in people's genomes. They first examined a staggering 500000 SNPs looking for those regions of DNA that differed between children with high and low intelligence scores. This generated 47 SNPs that demonstrated a correlation with intelligence and warranted further investigation.

The second stage of the study investigated these 47 SNPs in children whose test scores covered the whole intelligence range. Comparing the genotypes of these SNPs with the test scores of the children revealed six regions of DNA that appeared to be associated with intelligence. In other words certain SNP genotypes were more common in children of high intelligence. The data for one SNP are shown in Figure 2.28.

The effect of each SNP allele was found to be very small. The DNA region that gave the largest effect only accounted for about 0.4% of the variation in test scores between individuals in the study. Interestingly, the effects of each DNA region appeared to be additive: added together, six of the SNPs accounted for about four IQ points (see Figure 2.29).

Questions

70 Explain why further research into the precise mechanism of genes such as CHRM2 and SSADH is likely to strengthen the hypothesis that there is a link between these genes and intelligence.

71 Which genotype does Figure 2.28 suggest is associated with higher intelligence?

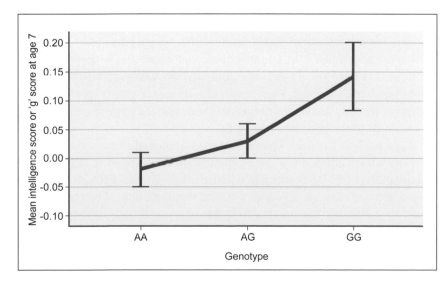

Figure 2.28

The alleles for this SNP are either A or G. The subjects can have both alleles the same, (AA or GG) or have one of each allele (AG). The mean intelligence score 'g' is given on the y-axis; the higher the figure the greater the intelligence score. Error bars show the spread of the measurements. The value 'g' has a mean value of 0. 0.12 on the y axis equates to an increase of around 2 IQ points.

Figure 2.29

This graph shows the relationship between the number of high intelligence alleles and g score. The x-axis indicates how many SNPs associated with high intelligence the children had. Error bars are shown.

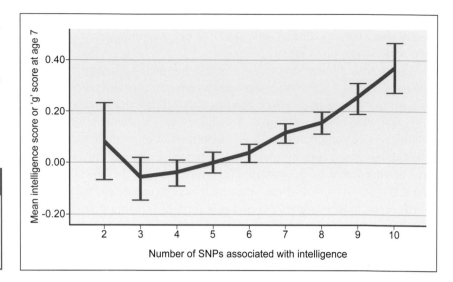

Question

72 In Figure 2.29, what appears to be the relationship between g score and the number of high intelligence SNPs?

This study examined a huge number of genotypes in thousands of people. Although it did indicate a few regions of the genome that could affect intelligence, the size of the effect seen was very small. This may be because the genotypes tested were not those that play a major role in the brain development relevant to intelligence. An alternative explanation is that no gene of major effect exists. This type of study that looks at the whole genome is very new, and more powerful and efficient methods may yet be developed that allow scientists to pin down the most crucial genes.

There is strong evidence for the existence of important environmental influences on g. As mentioned in the APA report, it has been found that IQ scores are rising, possibly due to improvements in education and lifestyle factors such as better nutrition.

2.8 Epigenetics, and how experience is inherited

There are many strands to the research being carried out to explore the way that genes and environment influence personality and behaviour. An important line of research is investigating the way that the environment affects gene expression not by altering the DNA sequence, but by influencing other molecules that bind to DNA. These epigenetic changes determine how much RNA is transcribed, and where and when it is made.

Scientists have known for some time that DNA is associated with other molecules within the cell. These molecules influence gene expression by affecting the way molecules needed to transcribe the genetic code into RNA attach to the gene (see page 49).

For a while it has been known that environmental influences such as diet and illness affect the way epigenetic molecules attach to DNA during an organism's life. Until recently scientists thought that DNA strands are wiped clean of all these molecules during the formation of egg and sperm cells. Now evidence is emerging that these molecular tags can sometimes be passed on to offspring, as DNA replicates during cell division to form eggs and sperm. The implication of these animal experiments is that a child's development may not only be influenced by its own

Key term

Epigenetics is the study of the control of gene activity. Epigenetic theory is based on the idea that there is a control system of 'switches' that can turn genes on or off. The theory suggests that factors in people's experience, such as nutrition and stress, can control the switches and lead to changes in human phenotypes that can persist without there being any alteration in the DNA base sequence in their cells.

Figure 2.30

Epigenetic theory can help to account for some rare genetic conditions. An example is Prader Willi syndrome. This boy has the syndrome. One of the symptoms is poor regulation of the appetite. This condition is much more common than is accounted for by straight genetic inheritance. The normal gene that goes wrong in Prader Willi syndrome is only active when inherited from the father. The mutation causing the syndrome 'silences' this gene inherited from the father. As the copy of the gene from the mother is normally kept silent, this mutation results in no activity at all from this gene in Prader Willi.

environment, but also by the environment its parents and even its grandparents were exposed to long before it was conceived.

This epigenetic inheritance theory helps to explain observations that have long puzzled scientists. For instance, Dutch women who survived near starvation during the Second World War gave birth to underweight babies. This was no surprise. What was surprising was that their children also went on to have small babies themselves, even though they grew up with enough food. This suggests a mechanism of inheritance that does not involve changes to the code in DNA molecules.

There is some evidence to suggest that epigenetic changes are involved in the development of cancer. Some scientists are also suggesting that they could be implicated in the rise of cases of conditions such as asthma and even behavioural conditions such as autism.

Question

73 Why does epigenetic theory represent a big shift in thinking for people educated in the explanation that it is the genetic code in DNA molecules that transfers all the genetic information from one generation to the next?

Epigenetics and transgenerational influences

"The length of DNA that makes up the human genome is like a piano with the different keys representing different genes. Epigenetics is about the music, the pattern in which the keys are played." So says Professor Marcus Pembrey, an eminent geneticist who has come up with some radical new ideas on how the environment can cause genes to express themselves (Figure 2.31).

More amazing still, just as music can be recorded and played again, Professor Pembrey has evidence that the pattern of gene activity triggered by the environment can be passed down through generations. This is likely to involve epigenetics, where genes are marked or tagged by experience, although the DNA sequence is not changed.

To understand how this works we have to think about how genes work in the body. "Every cell in the body contains a copy of the genome, but not all the genes are expressed. Something must be switching genes on and off. Just imagine if all the genes were expressed and skin cells expressed the same genes as blood cells and produced haemoglobin, we'd all look like rotten tomatoes."

Figure 2.31

Professor Marcus Pembrey.

Professor Pembrey explains that there are two ways genes can be switched on by your interaction with your environment. There can be a temporary response, or genes can be reprogrammed for life. When you eat a meal, the cells in your stomach, liver and pancreas immediately switch on the genes that code for digestive enzymes so you can digest your food.

Another kind of genetic switching that controls gene expression happens in the unborn child. Different genes are switched on at different stages of fetal development as and when they are needed. This cascade of genes switching on and off is tightly controlled but can be influenced by external factors.

"This is 'developmental programming'," explains Professor Pembrey, "Say a mother has an experience that makes her anxious or depressed at a critical time in her pregnancy. This could affect the developmental programming of the fetus and even subtle changes could lead the child to develop behavioural problems later."

This hypothesis is based on a real correlation his colleagues found in the ALSPAC project (see page 47). This study has revealed some interesting results. For example, eating oily fish in pregnancy can improve children's eyesight; and there is a link between anxiety levels in pregnancy and higher levels of cortisol in children. Cortisol is a chemical the brain produces in response to stress and may lead children to be more susceptible to stress themselves.

"The question we're interested in is whether children with problems have simply inherited it from their mother through certain genes, or whether something has happened during the pregnancy to switch genes on or off." Here, Professor Pembrey suggests an answer to his own question. Animal experiments show there are epigenetic molecules that sit on the DNA and can alter the gene action. "Epigenetics is the molecular mediator of nurture. It is a cellular memory, so the health of an individual in middle life is influenced by what happened to them as a fetus, or at critical times in their childhood."

A study in Canada has found experimental evidence for epigenetic molecules: "You can get two strains of rats, one of which has terrible maternal instincts and gives birth to nervy disturbed pups," explains Professor Pembrey. "The other strain are good mothers, and lick their pups after they are born, and care for them properly. These pups are not nervy."

"If you take the pups from the bad mothers and foster them with the good mothers, they get licked, and grow up normally." Then comes the really interesting bit: "Epigenetic chemical tags have been found on the DNA of cells in the hippocampus in the brain of these adopted rats. If these epigenetic chemicals are removed from the DNA the pups become nervy again." So the mother's behaviour appears to be responsible for creating epigenetic changes in the pups.

Not only can external factors that happen in a critical period change the expression of DNA in an individual, but those changes can also pass down the generations – this is the stunning result of Professor Pembrey's research both on the 'Children of the Nineties' and on a collaborative project with a Swedish public health doctor, Olov Bygren.

Looking at parish records showing harvests as well as births and deaths, Bygren and Pembrey were able to show a correlation between a man's life expectancy, the occurrence of heart disease and shortages of food at critical times in the lives of that man's grandparents. The 'memory' of food shortages is actually carried in the father's sperm. "There is a real transgenerational effect on mortality based on the food supply of the paternal grandparents." So you are, in part, what your grandparents ate!

Why should this be? How does this fit in with everything we understand from Darwin to the double helix in terms of inheritance and mutations? Marcus Pembrey has a hypothesis based on environmental pressures such as food shortages: "When the chips are down, the organism switches into survival mode, as if saying 'as soon as we're born we must eat as much as we can' – and epigenetic chemicals act to switch the right genes to make this happen. So, it could be that humans can be switched into a kind of survival mode at times of pressure."

Professor Pembrey adds that there are enormous implications for public health arising from what is being discovered about epigenetics and transgenerational responses. Currently in Britain there is a problem of over-eating and obesity, and if this is influenced by epigenetics, it could take many generations to sort out, rather than a quick fix by Jamie Oliver changing school dinners.

2.9 Who decides what research takes place?

Epigenetics is at the cutting edge of research. It relies on large scale studies such as ALSPAC to provide longitudinal population data, and expertise and facilities in other scientific disciplines. Scientific research only takes place if it is funded. Most research funding in Europe comes from the research and development departments of corporations and government, with relatively small amounts of funding by charities.

The factors which drive the direction of scientific research are complex. This partly depends on what is technically possible, any priorities dictated by the source of funding, the underlying objectives of the research, and access to the resources needed (scientists and specialist facilities). Scientific research is increasingly expected to bring economic benefits. Scientists in universities and public institutions often have industrial partners, as they have to consider how their research could be used commercially. Research directed in this way helps society by generating both employment and income, in addition to any direct benefits such as medicines or new technologies. However, commercial interests may limit the focus of research, which becomes driven by narrow priorities.

The creation of the European Research Council (ERC) in 2005 represented an important landmark for science policy. Decisions about research funding are decided by the Scientific Council, consisting of 22 distinguished scientists from a broad range of fields. Scientists can compete for support, with scientific excellence as the main criterion for funding, recognising the importance of 'blue-skies' research.

Questions

74 What are the implications of Professor Pembrey's research for:
a) parenting
b) an individual's responsibility towards their own lifestyle?

75 Why is it important that several independent research groups around the world have found evidence to suggest that there is more to inheritance than just the genes?

76 How could epigenetics be used to justify the idea that:
a) 'genes have a memory'
b) 'you are, in part, what your grandparents ate'?

77 Rewrite these statements in simpler language:
a) Epigenetics is the molecular mediator of nurture.
b) There is a transgenerational effect on mortality based on the food supply of the paternal grandparents.

78 Why might scientists and commercial funders have different research priorities?

79 Suggest how the general population might influence research priorities.

Blue-skies research does not have external constraints. Many important scientific discoveries have been made as a result of research, which, at its start, did not seem be of direct use to society. The discovery of the structure of DNA is typical of blue-skies research. In 2005, Mark Walport, the director of the Wellcome Trust, announced that the charity was committed to long-term basic research. "There is usually a long interval between important scientific discoveries and impact on human health. The trust has built its reputation by supporting first class, long-term biomedical research that ultimately has the potential to improve health for all."

Dr Walport made a press statement saying that scientists felt under pressure to fit their work in with government priorities. His view is that research that will improve our understanding of health and disease does not necessarily come about through short-term targets.

The idea that human behavioural traits are passed from generation to generation is not new, but the current era of behavioural genetics research promises considerable benefits for society. Public understanding of the implications of this research is vital, as is the continued education of future scientists in the ethical and social issues surrounding this research.

Review Questions

80 Use examples to illustrate the extent to which the following ideas can help you to explain issues related to nature and nurture:
  a) Many factors can influence which genes are expressed at any point of time, including stage of development, where the cell is in the body, and the action of other genes.
  b) Genes can be switched as a result of environmental factors in ways that can be passed on to later generations without altering the DNA code.

81 a) Outline the procedure for a case control study.
  b) Discuss the strengths and weaknesses of this type of study in establishing whether or not there is a correlation between a factor and an outcome.
  c) Suggest an example of a circumstance in which a case control study is the only feasible method to use for this kind of research.

82 a) Outline the procedure for a longitudinal population-based study.
  b) Discuss the advantages and disadvantages of this type of study for testing a hypothesis that a particular factor causes a given outcome.
  c) Explain why it is difficult, in complex situations, to obtain convincing evidence that a factor does not cause an effect.

83 Give examples to illustrate the following statements in the context of the scientific study of nature and nurture:
  a) The topics which scientists choose to investigate are strongly influenced by previous work and the publications of other scientists.
  b) Scientists value findings that are subject to peer review, published and replicable.
  c) Behavioural genetics research is highly collaborative, involving researchers from many disciplines from all over the world.

84 With the help of examples from the study of nature and nurture, discuss the extent to which the popular media play a part in providing accurate information, stimulating debate, influencing public opinion, and setting the agenda for future research.

85 Write a short paragraph to a journalist, explaining why their headline 'A gene for intelligence' is wrong.

Chapter 3

Watching the brain working

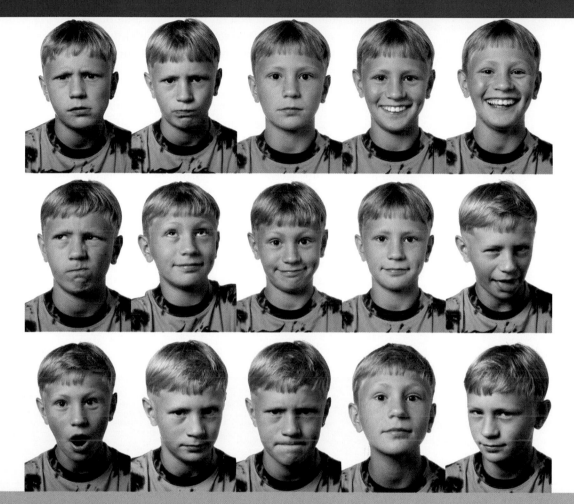

- What can you tell about what your friends are feeling, or thinking, just by looking at their faces?

- How do scientists find out about how our brains work and what have they discovered?

- Is there any truth in popular ideas about the brain such as the difference between left- and right-brained people, or the idea that the brain behaves like a computer?

- How can brain scans help doctors, and others, decide how to look after people in a coma or babies born early with damaged brains?

- What ethical issues arise when studying normal and damaged brains?

Figure 3.1

Can you suggest an emotion being shown by each of these faces?

3.1 Finding out about the cerebral cortex

In many ancient cultures across the world it was thought that feelings came from the heart. This tradition lives on in expressions such as 'heart-warming', 'heart-felt' and in all the symbolism of romance and the heart. Yet our hearts cannot feel anything. We may feel our heart beating strongly, but it is the brain which is doing the feeling. Even a pain in a toe when you drop something on your foot would not be painful without the work your brain does to experience it as painful. The nerve impulses coming from the toe tell the brain where the pain is, and how bad it is. The brain then creates conscious sensation, but the way this happens is far from understood.

When we look at a dead human brain it does not seem a very promising organ for all the thinking that it does (Figure 3.2). It has the consistency of cold custard with lots of bulges and grooves on the surface. Early psychologists got quite excited about all the bulges and thought that they were a clue to personality. They made a pseudoscience out of 'phrenology' – the study of the shape of the skull.

Phrenology was very popular in the nineteenth century and continued to have a following in the early twentieth century despite being rejected by mainstream science. Phrenologists thought that a bulge on the skull meant that the part of the brain beneath was well developed. They devised specialised methods for measuring and mapping the bumps of people's skulls. Each part of the skull was assigned a particular function (Figure 3.3). Although this was all pure invention or pseudoscience, the phrenologists were the first to propose the largely correct idea that different brain areas have different jobs.

Question

1 Suggest observations and reasons that might have led to the ancient tradition that the heart is the seat of the emotions and the intellect.

Key term

A **pseudoscience** is based on ideas which pretend to have a scientific basis, but for which there is no evidence.

Figure 3.2

A human brain removed from the skull, showing the highly folded cerebrum.

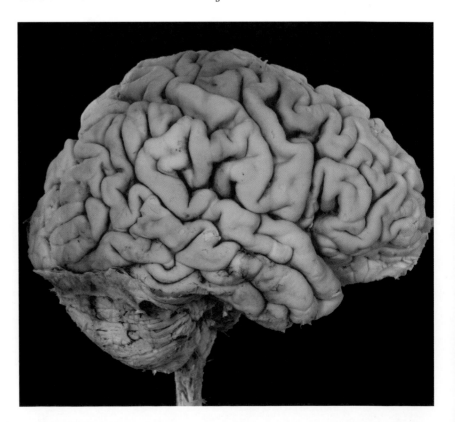

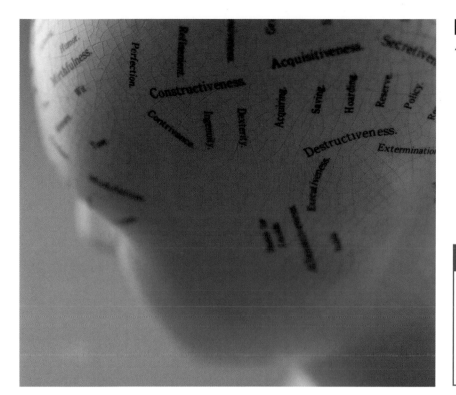

Figure 3.3

A phrenologist's model of the head.

Evidence from brain injuries

Some early evidence that different parts of the brain have different functions came from head injuries. Poor Phineas Gage, for example, is famous for the unfortunate accident that happened to him, at the age of 26, while working on the Canadian railways in the 1840s. He was a foreman responsible for checking the explosives in the holes drilled into the rock when clearing the route of a new railway track. He had to use a long metal spike to push the dynamite down to the bottom of the hole. One day the spike caused a spark which ignited the dynamite. The metal spike flew up like a missile, striking Phineas just below his left eye (Figure 3.4). It passed right through his eye socket, emerging from the top of his skull, and landed 100 metres away. The spike was more than a metre long and weighed over 6 kg.

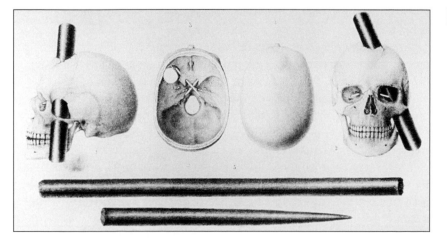

Figure 3.4

Drawings showing details of Phineas Gage's accident.

Despite these terrible injuries, Phineas Gage survived and after a few weeks he was able to walk, hear, see and speak almost normally and his memory was good. However, he was no longer the capable and likeable foreman that his colleagues remembered: he became antisocial and boastful and could not hold down a job. His reasoning and decision making were greatly impaired. After his death, Gage's body was exhumed and his skull and the metal spike remain on display in Harvard Medical School.

Computer reconstructions show that the spike had passed through the part of Gage's brain just behind his forehead. This region is known as the prefrontal cortex, and has overall control of everything we do: it defines our personality and makes us individuals. With so much damage to this part of his brain, Gage could not reason properly or make sensible decisions, and he never recovered these mental faculties, though he lived for another 12 years.

Case studies

The example of Phineas Gage is a case study: a one-off example. Psychologists can learn a great deal about how the brain works from such unique people. However, in an ideal world, experimental methods, using large samples, should be used. Phineas Gage may not have been typical and scientists need to be sure that they do not place too much weight on evidence from just one person's brain.

Animal models

The best animal model for the human brain is the chimpanzee, as the chimp brain is very like ours in structure, though it is only one-third of the size and has a much smaller cortex. In 1935, scientists at Yale University used chimpanzees to investigate the function of the prefrontal cortex. They wanted to investigate the idea that the prefrontal cortex is the decision-making centre of the brain. They cut some of the nerve connections in this region and noticed that the chimps became much less excitable and less easily frustrated.

In the same year, the process was adapted for humans by Antonio Egaz Moniz of the University of Lisbon Medical School. He developed a technique in which he drilled a small hole on each side of the forehead, inserted a special surgical knife and cut nerve fibres connecting the prefrontal lobe, or section of cortex, to other parts of the brain. The name given to this procedure is 'lobotomy' based on Greek words meaning 'lobe' and 'cut'.

After a lobotomy, some patients with severe mental disorders were quieter and easier to control. The procedure became popular for a time. Between 1936 and 1978, doctors in the USA carried out about 35 000 lobotomies. Gradually, however, it became clear that the benefits of the treatment to patients were questionable and the side effects could be severe. After a lobotomy many patients became changed characters. They were less responsive to emotions and unable to think ahead.

Moniz was awarded the Nobel Prize for his work on lobotomy in 1949. He advised extreme caution in using lobotomy, and felt it should only be used in cases where everything else had been tried. He retired early after a former patient paralysed him by shooting him in the back.

Questions

3 Suggest reasons why early studies of the way the brain works had to focus on case studies of people with damaged brains.

4 Suggest advantages and disadvantages in neuroscience of:
- detailed studies of single cases
- large scale clinical trials.

Question

5 Why might the benefits and side effects of a lobotomy be assessed differently by:
a) the doctor who carried out the operation
b) the patient
c) people caring for the patient?

Figure 3.5

A robotic arm controlled by electrodes placed in the brain of a rhesus monkey. This allows the monkey to feed itself marshmallows and chunks of fruit while its own arms are restrained. In some ways, a monkey's brain can be a good model for the human brain.

Animals offer an alternative to experimenting with people. So far as we know, nerve cells behave in the same way in all mammal brains but this does not mean that the brains do. Monkeys and apes (primates) have been used extensively to study brain structure and function as well as for testing medical techniques and drugs. They are our nearest living relatives, but this means that they are also highly intelligent and capable of much suffering (Figure 3.5).

Scientists argue that without primate experiments our medical knowledge would be much less advanced. Even so, any research with primates in the UK is strictly regulated by the Animals (Scientific Procedures) Act of 1986. While scientists have to justify their use of any animals in research, primates have special status under the law and the justification for their use must be especially strong. No experiments are allowed on any of the great apes, including chimpanzees, gorillas and orang-utans.

The cerebral cortex

The cerebral cortex covers the surface of the two cerebral hemispheres of the brain, but it is only about 3 mm thick. Within the cortex there are millions of neurones, each with thousands of synapses joining the cells to each other.

During human evolution, the forebrain has greatly expanded and folded back over the top of the rest of the brain. The contorted brain surface (Figure 3.2) allows a very large area of cortex to be packed inside the protective skull. The cortex provides the thinking or computing power of the brain. It is made up of the bodies of nerve cells and is known as grey matter. Inside the cortex are thousands of axons linking together neurones in different regions of the brain as well as bringing in sensory information from the rest of the body and sending out commands to the muscles. The axons are coated with a layer of fatty insulation called myelin, which is white. The axons with their myelin make up the white matter.

Questions

6 a) What do you understand by the term 'animal model' in scientific research?
   b) Rats and mice are widely used in medical research but they are not suitable models for many aspects of brain research. Suggest reasons why.

7 Why do scientists have to be very cautious about generalising from their findings with animal brains to human brains?

8 a) Suggest reasons why research with chimpanzees is no longer allowed in the UK.
   b) Suggest arguments that would persuade an ethics committee to approve pure or applied research with primates into any one of these areas: Parkinson's disease, thinking and reasoning, vision, stroke.

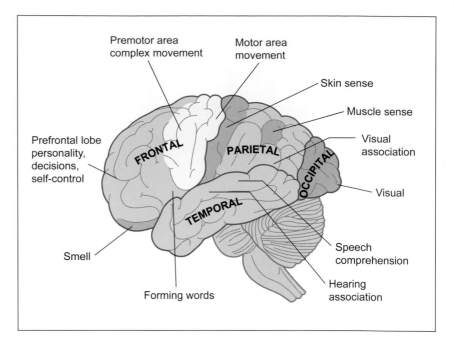

Figure 3.6

The four lobes of the cerebral cortex: frontal, parietal, occipital and temporal, showing the approximate distribution of sensory (purple), association (green) and motor (yellow) areas.

The functions of the different areas of the cerebral cortex have been roughly mapped out using evidence from injuries, stimulation with electrodes during brain operations and modern scanning methods (Figure 3.6). The cortex has three main functions:

- Sensory areas receive and process nerve impulses from sensory receptors in the eyes, ears, nose, tongue or skin.
- Association areas are regions, such as parts of the temporal and prefrontal lobes, which receive information from the sense areas and organise a response via the motor areas. These areas integrate incoming sensory information with stored memories to make decisions. Parts of the association areas are probably responsible for conscious thought.
- Motor areas send out nerve impulses to the muscles and glands, causing them to take action.

The cortex maps the body and the world in a rather surprising way – upside down and back to front. The left side of the brain controls movement in the right side of the body and vice versa. Also, the motor areas are arranged with the toes near the top of the brain and the head near the bottom: the motor area controlling the tongue, lips and voice box is close to the ears. The cortex's touch sensory areas are also on the opposite side of the brain to the parts of the skin from which the signals are coming.

The more sensitive areas of the skin, such as on the hands and lips, are served by a bigger area of cortex than less sensitive parts of the body, such as the back. A similar story applies to the motor areas. Parts of the body with many different muscles, such as the tongue, face and hands, have more cortex controlling them than, for example, the forehead or abdomen (Figure 3.7).

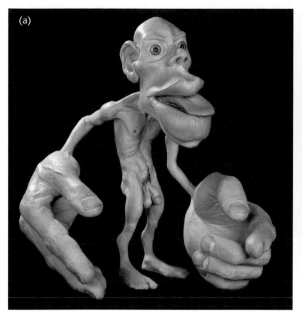

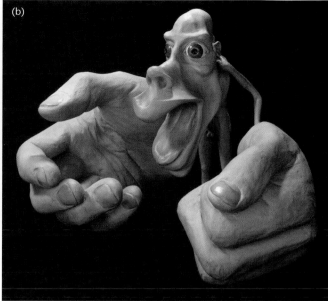

Figure 3.7

These distorted figures have body shapes which are in proportion to the area of (a) touch sensory cortex and (b) motor cortex which controls each body region. Scientists call them the sensory homunculus and the motor homunculus. An homunculus is a 'little man'.

It is important to note that there is no inflexible link between particular functions and particular parts of the brain. The brain can show a remarkable ability to adapt to damage. People can recover significantly from strokes (when the blood flow to parts of the brain is cut off) because other parts of the brain take over from the damaged regions. People with hydrocephalus can think surprisingly well while having very little cortex. These are examples of the plasticity of the brain.

3.2 Language and the brain

What is language?

Vervet monkeys in Africa use a different alarm call in response to a snake, a leopard or an eagle (Figure 3.8). The three calls can be compared with using words: the monkeys use simple sounds, each with a different meaning. On hearing an alarm call, the monkeys take suitable evasive action, such as running down from the trees if they hear an eagle alarm, or climbing up into the trees if there is a snake on the ground.

Questions

9 According to Figure 3.7, which parts of the body have relatively large areas of the cortex involved in controlling their movements? Suggest why this is so.

10 What are the implications for our understanding of the brain, of the fact that people can recover to a remarkable extent from brain damage that has affected movement, speech or memory?

Key terms

A **stroke** is caused by damage to a blood vessel serving a region of the brain. The blood vessel can become blocked by a blood clot, or it can rupture, causing leakage of blood into the brain.

Brain **plasticity** describes the way that other parts of the brain can sometimes take over the job of a part of the brain that has been damaged.

Figure 3.8

Vervet monkey in the Masai Mara reserve, Kenya. Vervet monkeys run up trees when there is a ground predator such as a snake or leopard, and run down trees when there is an aerial predator such as an eagle. Look-out monkeys have different alarm calls for each predator.

Figure 3.9

Bonobos have been taught to communicate with humans using sign language or symbols. Here the bonobo, Kanzi, is communicating with a scientist by selecting symbols to make three- or four-word sentences. Kanzi is able to use over 200 symbols.

Questions

11 When recording the ability of a chimpanzee to learn to use signs, what types of observation would convince you that the observed behaviour was the result of learning and not just happening by chance?

12 Suggest reasons why humans have evolved big brains as a result of evolution by natural selection.

Scientists have studied the extent to which bonobos and chimpanzees can learn to communicate. The studies use sign language, or symbols, because these animals are not good at making the sounds of words (Figure 3.9).

Human learning and language far outstrips what any other primates can achieve. Now that you are studying A2 you probably know between 15 000 and 20 000 words. You also know that the order in which you use the words conveys meaning. You understand that 'the dog bit the postman' does not mean the same as 'the postman bit the dog'. This is the real key to language; we can be creative by using words in an order that no-one has used before, yet we are usually understood immediately. Language is flexible and creative, but follows rules of word order and syntax which make it comprehensible.

Speaking and understanding

Scientists can learn a lot about the brain and language by looking at what happens when things go wrong. Some people are unable to speak, write or understand language. This condition is called aphasia. In 1861, Paul Broca described a patient with aphasia who could only say a few words such as 'tan'. He named the patient Tan. When he dissected Tan's brain after death, he found damage, caused by disease, to a region that became known as Broca's area, in the left frontal cortex. Further evidence of the importance of Broca's area comes from people who have had strokes. Brain scans show that when the stroke is in Broca's area, the patient has impaired ability to speak, though they may still be able to understand what people are saying.

There is a different brain area which controls the understanding of language, known as Wernicke's area, in the temporal lobe nearer to the back of the head on the left side of the brain. People with damage to Wernicke's area cannot understand language. They can speak clearly but the words make no sense (Figures 3.10 and 3.11).

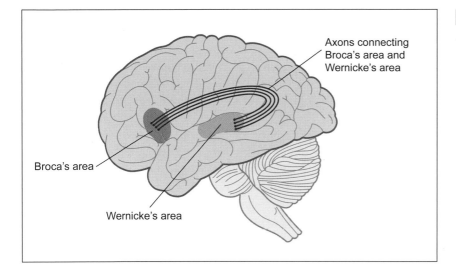

Figure 3.10

Some of the brain areas used in language.

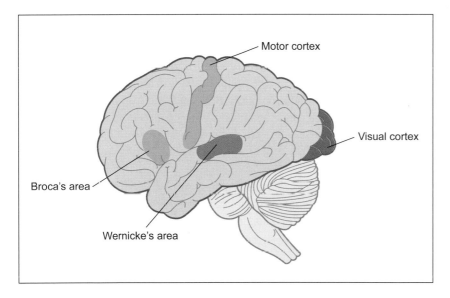

Figure 3.11

Regions of the cerebral cortex used when reading aloud. The visual cortex analyses information arriving from the eyes, then sends nerve impulses to Wernicke's area which interprets the meaning of the words. Nerve impulses then pass to Broca's area which forms the words and instructs the motor area to move the larynx and tongue in the correct way to speak them.

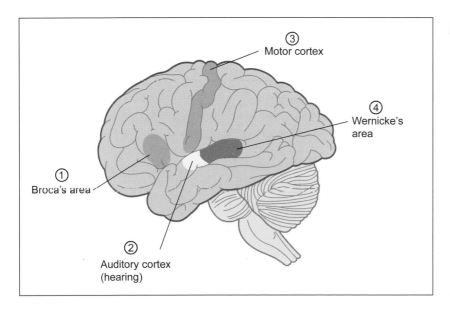

Figure 3.12

Regions of the cortex used when replying to a spoken question.

Questions

13 a) With reference to Figure 3.12, give the numbers, in the correct sequence, for the four brain areas used when replying to a spoken question.
b) Explain the reasons for the sequence you have given in part a.

14 Suggest why it is difficult to learn how the brain works by studying just one particular region of the brain at a time.

All the areas of the brain which control language are on the left side of the cerebral cortex. This is true of most people, even if they are left-handed. However, damage to the equivalent regions of the right hemisphere can affect a person's emotional response to language and the understanding of any non-literal use of words, such as puns and figures of speech. Such differences in the functions of the two sides of the cortex are one of the features that distinguish human and animal brains. Scientists describe the differences between the left and right hemispheres as lateralisation of the brain.

No two brains are the same, however, so the maps of the cerebral cortex in text books are a summary of what is generally true for most people. About a third of left-handed people have speech control in the right hemisphere, but textbooks show the more common situation.

Individual differences in brain structure and function can help scientists to learn more about mental illnesses, personality or changes within an individual over time. All these are active areas of research by neuroscientists.

3.3 Investigating learning

Humans and animals can respond to stimuli in a simple, automatic way, known as a reflex action. For example, if we touch something hot with a finger, we quickly and automatically pull our hand away. These reflexes help us to avoid danger. The behaviour is controlled by a simple nerve pathway from the sensory receptors, up to the brain and back again to the muscles. Much of this behaviour is inborn and no conscious thought is required.

However, many of the impulses reaching our brains from the sense organs cause no immediate response. Perhaps your teacher has been talking for a few minutes and you have not said or written a word. However – assuming you were listening – you will have remembered quite a lot of what was said. Scientists suggest that when we learn something, new synapses are made in our brains and this changes our responses to future stimuli.

Psychologists are very interested in our attitudes, prejudices and decision-making processes, and in what happens to the brain if we suffer injury or mental illness. The way we learn and change our behaviour during our lifetime is the subject of many exciting areas of research using new brain imaging techniques.

We sometimes think of memories as being like photographs of past events, but in fact we have many kinds of memories. Some types of learning involve moving our muscles in a skilled way, for example riding a bicycle, typing or playing the piano. This type of motor learning involves the cerebellum. We do not have conscious memories about all the muscle movements needed to ride a bicycle: once learnt we just remember how to do it subconsciously.

Memories and learning from our experiences can affect our future behaviour. Changes in the brain in response to past experience help to shape our individual personalities and make us all different. One estimate is that our brains make an average of one million new synaptic connections every second of our lives. Parents, teachers, coaches and advertisers all spend their time trying to direct these learning processes in young people.

Deception and lie detectors

Some people want to hide what they remember to avoid getting into trouble. For the police, the legal system and security services, it is very important to find out whether or not suspects and witnesses are telling the truth. It takes a lot of mental effort to tell a consistently false story. When the police interview a witness or suspect, they may use techniques such as asking the person to tell the story backwards, or from the point of view of a bystander. These techniques can help a witness recall more details about an event, but they also put an extra cognitive load on a suspect and can cause them to be inconsistent and make mistakes.

One type of instrument for detecting lies is based on the effects of the stress involved in lying. When suspects lie they typically secrete more of the hormone adrenaline, which makes them sweaty, causes their hearts to beat faster and their rate of breathing to increase. The polygraph is an instrument designed to detect these changes, so the polygraph has been used as a lie detector (Figure 3.13).

Figure 3.13

Using a polygraph detector.

17 Distinguish between a false
positive result and a false
negative result in the context of
using a polygraph to detect lies.

18 The polygraph is based on the
principles that lying makes
people anxious and that their
anxiety can be detected and
measured. What is it about these
principles that makes the use of
the polygraph very controversial?

Some criminals are very skilful at lying. They can be superficially charming and believable, yet be cold-blooded killers. Such people may show few emotions and so avoid detection by a polygraph. Also, many innocent people are naturally nervous when interviewed by the police, and this may be picked up by the polygraph. As a result, the use of polygraphs is highly controversial.

In recent years there has been increasing interest in the possibility of using brain imaging as an alternative method of lie detection. Functional magnetic resonance imaging (fMRI) has been available to researchers for about 10 years, and may already be in use by security services as a lie detector in some countries. fMRI shows the areas of the brain which are most active when doing a particular task, and has the potential to show an increase in the use of brain areas used in deception.

MRI and fMRI scanning

Magnetic resonance imaging (MRI) depends on the magnetic properties of nuclei of hydrogen atoms in water molecules. The subject is placed in a tunnel inside a very powerful electromagnet with a strength about 50 000 times that of the Earth's magnetic field (Figure 3.14). The tunnel is very noisy so the subject is given ear plugs.

As the instrument carries out a scan, a beam of radio waves picks up a series of signals from the nuclei of the hydrogen atoms as they resonate with the magnetic field. The signals vary with the type of tissue surrounding the water molecules.

The signals are fed to a computer which creates an image of the soft tissues of the body. Images of the brain clearly show the boundaries between white matter and grey matter, the ventricles and differences in the density of neurones. Signals can be detected from different 'slices' of the brain, producing images which look like a cross-section through the head (Figure 3.15). The images produced by MRI scanners are very useful for investigating brain injury, brain tumours and degenerative brain changes.

Key term

Ventricles are spaces inside the brain that contain fluid.

Figure 3.14

Using an MRI scanner.

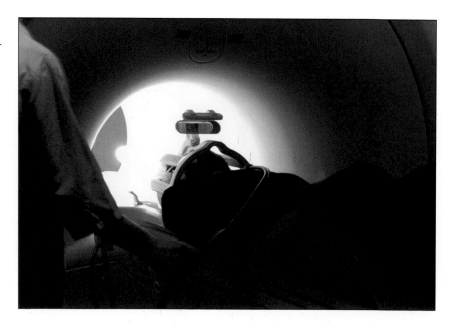

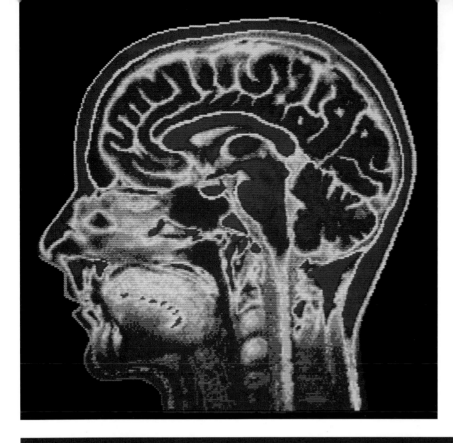

Question

19 Name the parts of the brain that you can clearly identify in Figure 3.15.

Figure 3.15

MRI scan of the head, showing brain structure.

The electromagnetic spectrum
Figure 3.16

Electromagnetic waves are named according to their wavelength. Waves with short wavelengths include gamma rays and X-rays. These merge into ultraviolet, followed by the visible spectrum, the colours we see. Beyond the visible spectrum are the longer wavelengths of infrared, microwaves and radio waves. Ionising radiation is radiation with enough energy to break up molecules and turn them into electrically charged atoms (ions).

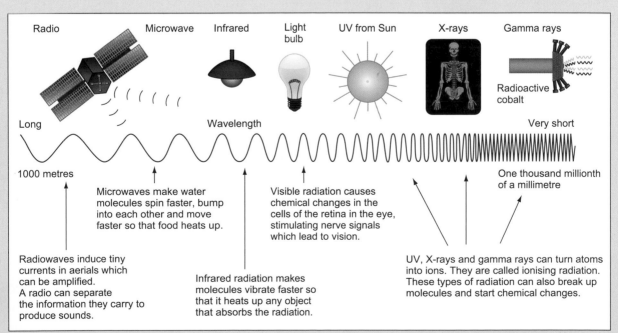

Radio   Microwave   Infrared   Light bulb   UV from Sun   X-rays   Gamma rays

Radioactive cobalt

Long   Wavelength   Very short

1000 metres

One thousand millionth of a millimetre

Microwaves make water molecules spin faster, bump into each other and move faster so that food heats up.

Visible radiation causes chemical changes in the cells of the retina in the eye, stimulating nerve signals which lead to vision.

Radiowaves induce tiny currents in aerials which can be amplified. A radio can separate the information they carry to produce sounds.

Infrared radiation makes molecules vibrate faster so that it heats up any object that absorbs the radiation.

UV, X-rays and gamma rays can turn atoms into ions. They are called ionising radiation. These types of radiation can also break up molecules and start chemical changes.

In the last 10 years, MRI technology has been extended to allow scientists to compare the activity of different areas of the brain. The technique is called functional magnetic resonance imaging (fMRI). fMRI shows which areas of the brain are actually working as we carry out different mental processes. This has opened up many kinds of exciting areas for research such as investigating language, pain and emotion as well as offering new diagnoses of diseases and the possibility of commercial applications.

The fMRI technique works by detecting changes in blood flow in the brain. When a particular area of the brain becomes active, the neurones send out more electrical impulses and start to use more oxygen for respiration. When neurones take up more oxygen, chemical signals cause nearby blood vessels to dilate, so more blood is sent to the active brain area (Figure 3.17). Oxygenated blood has less magnetic effect than deoxygenated blood, so when a part of the brain becomes active, its magnetic resonance signals change. An fMRI scanner is able to track activity in the brain very shortly after it happens, using the brief changes in blood flow in different brain areas as they begin and cease activity. The results of a scan are usually shown in false colours on a brain image to make them easier to see.

The slight delay between an increase in brain activity and its detection by the fMRI scanner is a consequence of the way the blood flow responds to the change. Immediately after neural activity increases, there is a momentary decrease in the extent to which the blood in the area is oxygenated as the neurones take up extra oxygen for respiration. This is followed by a period where the blood flow increases, more than compensating for the increased oxygen demand. The blood oxygen level of the brain region now rises above normal and is detected by fMRI. The blood flow peaks after around 6 seconds and then falls back to below the typical level before returning to normal.

Figure 3.17

Changes in blood flow when a region of the brain becomes active. The blood vessels dilate, allowing more oxygenated blood into the brain region. The blue arrows show oxygen diffusing from the blood vessels into the neurones.

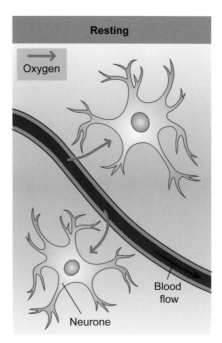

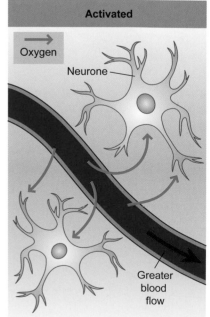

Systematic errors

Systematic errors affect all measurements in the same way, making them higher or lower than the true value. Systematic errors can arise when there are flaws:

- in the measuring equipment, or
- in the way that the measurements are carried out.

Identifying and eliminating systematic errors is important for increasing the accuracy of data. Some systematic errors can be corrected by checking the readings with another instrument. If both agree, this increases confidence that the readings are correct. It is still possible that something in the measurement procedure makes all the measurements consistently high or low.

Can fMRI be used to detect lies?

Many agencies connected with insurance, the legal profession and the security services are urgently seeking a reliable lie detection service. They can be tempted to use anything on offer which looks better than the discredited polygraph. Some US companies are already offering commercial fMRI lie detection services. For example, they offer scans to those suspected by insurance companies of making a false claim.

In order to tell a lie, the prefrontal cortex must, in theory, work harder to suppress the truth and construct a lie. So a lie can, in principle, be detected, since more brain regions are involved than when telling the truth. However, lie detection is faced with the problem that well-practised lies may look more like truth telling, especially when compared with innocent, but nervous people.

In lie detector trials, volunteers are asked to press a 'yes' or 'no' button as questions are presented on a screen inside the fMRI scanner. The questions might relate to recent activities, or to information given to the subject. The volunteer may be told to lie about one item and tell the truth about another. The technique has a reported lie detection rate of over 90% in some laboratory trials.

In order to try the technique in more realistic situations, Professor Sean Spence of Sheffield University recently tested subjects for a television documentary. The subjects included a woman convicted of assaulting her child, ex-detainees from Guantanamo Bay and a woman who claimed sexual abuse from her father. The results indicated that at least some of those tested were telling the truth, though of course it could not prove their innocence (Figure 3.18, page 80).

Professor Spence thinks that much more research is needed before fMRI can be used reliably for criminal cases. fMRI also has many practical disadvantages:

- It takes many hours to analyse the results of a scan.
- The apparatus is bulky and claustrophobic and requires the cooperation of the subject.
- fMRI measures blood flow to different parts of the brain. This is an indirect measurement of brain activity and may not be a real reflection of the neurological functioning of the brain.

Key terms

Errors of measurement are unavoidable differences between measured values and true values. Often the true value is not known, so scientists have to assess the degree of **measurement uncertainty** in their results.

Random errors cause repeat measurements to vary and scatter about a mean value.

Systematic errors affect all measurements in the same way, making them all either higher or lower than the true value.

Questions

20 Give an example of a systematic error of measurement arising from a flaw:
a) in a measuring instrument
b) in the procedure used to make the measurement.

21 Explain why systematic errors do not average out whereas the effect of random errors can be reduced by averaging.

22 Explain how mistiming when recording an fMRI brain image could lead to systematic errors in the results.

23 Suggest reasons why detecting lies experimentally in a laboratory is not a fair test of fMRI's ability to detect lies during an interrogation by the police.

24 Professor Spence points out that, ideally, baseline trials should be done before a lie detector test, using questions unrelated to any criminal charges. How could baseline trials improve the validity of a lie detector test?

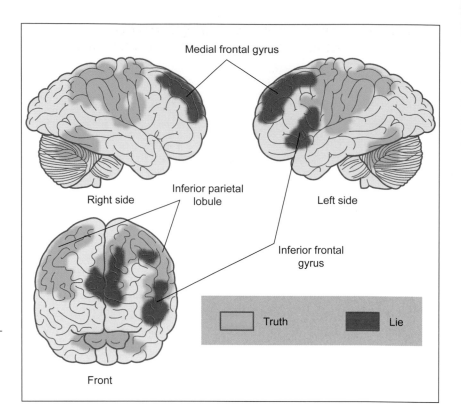

Figure 3.18

Differences in average fMRI image when a subject is lying or telling the truth. The differences in brain activity when a person is telling the truth compared with a lie are shown by the blue and red areas.

Labels in figure: Medial frontal gyrus, Inferior parietal lobule, Inferior frontal gyrus, Right side, Left side, Front, Truth, Lie

Questions

25 a) What are the features of Figure 3.18 that suggest that fMRI scanning could be used to detect lies?

b) Why is great caution needed when interpreting an image such as Figure 3.18?

26 Even if a lie detection test is devised which is safe and trustworthy, should it be used? Neuroethicists have called for full public discussion on the potential uses of brain scanners before they are made more widely available. Make a list of questions you would put to a public review body looking into the non-medical uses of brain scanners.

27 Suggest ways in which the technique of fMRI scanning might be abused by people in positions of power or authority.

- There is a time lag between the start of mental activity and changes in blood flow, and the changes in blood flow are complex.
- The images from the scans are subject to many different interpretations. Who is to know whether a part of the brain becoming active really indicates a lie? There is no specific lie-telling centre in the brain: the prefrontal cortex can become active for all kinds of reasons.
- The uncertainties surrounding the significance of a scan could lead to deliberate misinterpretations in an attempt to obtain convictions.

What the security services really need is something portable, instantaneous and reliable. A possible answer comes in a device being developed by Professor Britton Chance at the University of Pennsylvania, using infrared (IR) light that is close to the red end of the visible spectrum. This type of laser spectroscopy shines invisible infrared light through the skull and reflects it off the brain to reveal brain activity. The scans are claimed to be able to detect transient changes in the prefrontal cortex when a subject lies, and could be used, for example, at security gates in airports. As with fMRI, the scanner detects changes in blood flow when a brain region becomes active, but shows much less detail. Although potentially simple and quick, the system is still in the experimental stage and its reliability needs to be established. When the changes in many individuals are summed together, there are clear differences in IR scans between telling a lie and telling the truth. To be useful, however, average responses are no help: the system must be reliable at detecting a lie in any individual.

Any technique can potentially be misused. However, current scanning technology is a long way from mind reading, and so it is important not to exaggerate its capabilities. Its benefits may outweigh its possible misuse, and we may one day become as confident about using lie detectors as many are about DNA fingerprinting.

Neuromarketing

Do you prefer Coke® or Pepsi®? These two soda drinks have a very similar composition, yet people often express a clear preference for one of them. If the two drinks taste very similar, then any preference must be due to differences in people's perception of the two brands. The Coke–Pepsi test has recently been the subject of an fMRI study at Baylor College of Medicine, Texas, which was published in the journal *Neuron* in 2004. This research helped to set in motion a new commercial strategy called neuromarketing.

When tasting each drink, the reward centres of the volunteers' brains became active. This is a normal response to a sugary taste. In each subject there was more brain activity for the drink with the taste they had preferred during blind tasting.

In a second series of tests, the students were either shown an image of a Coke can just before the drink was delivered, or, as a control they were shown a simple coloured disc before getting their drink of Coke. When the students knew for sure that they were drinking Coke, there was a much greater brain response than when the drink was anonymous, whatever their declared preference in the taste tests.

But in parallel tests, knowing a drink was Pepsi did not enhance the brain response. Clearly, something about the brand image of Coke caused the students to have a strong surge in brain activity, which was not caused by a Pepsi image. Moreover, the Coke brand activated brain regions beyond those associated with reward, including parts of the prefrontal cortex connected with emotional responses as well as a part of the brain involved in memory called the hippocampus. It seems that the Coke brand caused the students to have a learned emotional reaction. This might help to explain the much greater market share of Coke compared with Pepsi, despite the similarity of the two drinks, the lack of any preference for Coke in blind tasting tests and the fact that equal numbers of students preferred Coke and Pepsi in blind tasting.

Experiments of this kind encouraged the commercial world to take a closer look at the potential benefits of fMRI in developing more effective marketing and advertising techniques (Figure 3.19). In the Coke–Pepsi example, further tests might be able to show which features of Coke lead to the emotional response associated with the brand. This could include features such as the shape of the bottle, the colour of the packaging, the sound of the name or some other feature. Such information is of great commercial value, and may reveal information unavailable from conventional psychological tests. For example, the Coke–Pepsi research showed that there was no correlation between a person's stated preference for a drink and their behavioural and brain responses to the two brands. So, brain images can reveal responses to a brand about which the participant may be unaware, or is deliberately hiding.

Figure 3.19

Neuromarketers seek to use the findings of neuroscience to enhance the marketing techniques they use to promote brands.

28 a) The researchers chose only right-handed people for the study of car logos. Suggest a reason for this aspect of the experimental design.

b) At one stage in the study, three participants stated that they did not like any of the fourteen car brands presented. Their results were omitted from the analysis. Explain whether you think omitting these results was justified.

c) Why could it be considered unethical to use students to test reactions to products such as soft drinks and cars?

29 The organisation called Commercial Alert seeks to put ethical constraints on commercial activity. Their director has commented that: "People are subjected to an epidemic of marketing-related illnesses – obesity, diabetes, alcoholism – and millions of children will eventually die from the marketing of tobacco. Neuromarketing is the corruption of medical research to induce disease and human suffering." In the light of these comments, discuss whether neuromarketing should be banned by law.

Figure 3.20

Changes in MRI images of Alzheimer's patients over 18 months from initial diagnosis. The images are colour coded to show the areas of greatest change in cortex thickness, ranging from red (most loss) to blue (no change).

Related studies at the University of Magdeburg in Germany looked at how different car logos affect the brain's activity, again using fMRI. Fourteen different car logos were presented, each bearing the name of the car brand, and fourteen student volunteers were asked to imagine driving a car of the brand shown. After the scan, the students completed questionnaires to classify the cars as 'favourite brand', 'sports and luxury' or 'good value'. It was found that 'sports and luxury' logos activated brain areas related to high self-esteem – but 'good value' logos did not. Also, logos of favourite car brands caused reduced activation of areas of the prefrontal cortex concerned with strategic-based reasoning. These results suggest that the brain may respond in an emotional, less rational way in response to brands associated with iconic cultural symbols.

Multinationals are increasingly looking to neuromarketing to help in advertising and product development. Not everyone is happy about this. A group called Commercial Alert seeks to keep the American commercial sector within ethical bounds. They worry that businesses may gain the power to control our perceptions and behaviour in ways we will be unable to detect, and that neuromarketing may tip the balance of power from the buyer to the seller.

Brain imaging and mental illness

Brain imaging can compare healthy brains with the brains of people suffering from a mental illness, such as Alzheimer's disease, Huntington's disease or schizophrenia. Alzheimer's disease is a very common cause of dementia in older people. The disease is characterised by the build-up of abnormal proteins, known as plaques and tangles, in brain tissue. There is also a gradual loss of brain volume. The causes of these changes are still largely unknown.

At the University of California, Los Angeles, sophisticated techniques have been developed by Professor Paul Thompson for analysing MRI scans showing the structure of the brains of patients suffering from Alzheimer's and other brain diseases. Each of the many 'slices' of the brain from a patient's MRI scan is mapped on a grid. The shape of the brain on the grid is then 'flexed', using tailor-made software, to make it conform to the shape of the typical healthy brain. The extent of the modification needed for different brain regions to make them 'normal' gives a measure of the deterioration caused by the disease. The results of many people's scans are combined to show the typical development of the disease. The changes can be displayed on a colour coded brain image (Figure 3.20), or even converted into moving images.

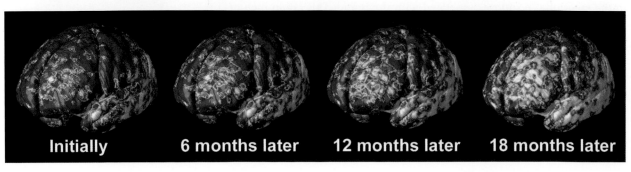

Initially   **6 months later**   **12 months later**   **18 months later**

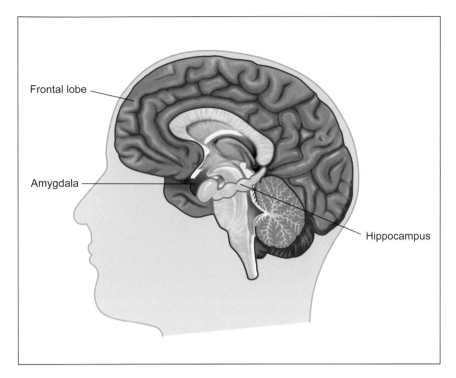

Figure 3.21

The hippocampus and amygdala are parts of the forebrain.

Frontal lobe

Amygdala

Hippocampus

Combined scans of many Alzheimer's patients show that the first changes typically happen in the hippocampus, which is the part of the brain that controls memory (Figure 3.21). This reflects the usual early symptom of Alzheimer's, which is memory loss, for example forgetting words. After 18 months the brain deterioration spreads to other parts of the brain such as the amygdala, where emotions are controlled, and to the frontal lobes. Again this conforms to the devastating changes seen in Alzheimer's patients, who can have rapid mood swings, loss of self-control and personality changes. The overall loss of brain tissue in Alzheimer's patients is about 5% a year, which is more than ten times as rapid as in a control group matched for age, sex and handedness.

The California neuroimaging group has a constantly expanding database of MRI brain images of people suffering from Alzheimer's and other mental diseases. Such databases can greatly improve studies of the effectiveness of new drug treatments, diets or other interventions. The progression of disease in a patient can be compared with the average progression for a person of their sex and age to assess the effectiveness of a treatment in slowing brain deterioration.

Distinguishing Alzheimer's from other forms of dementia is very difficult, and previously relied on post-mortem examinations of brain tissue for confirmation. Recent work at University College London indicates that MRI can accurately identify people suffering from Alzheimer's disease. A computer program is used to distinguish scans of Alzheimer's brains from those with other conditions. Early and accurate diagnosis, as with all diseases, is essential for treatments that can alleviate the symptoms or delay the progress of the disease.

Current research is looking at the possibility of identifying brain changes before the onset of symptoms in Alzheimer's and Huntington's diseases, offering the possibility of therapy before the disease shows

Questions

30 In drug trials for Alzheimer's disease, using brain imaging, discuss whether it would be necessary to have a control group taking a placebo.

31 What ethical issues arise when involving Alzheimer's patients in trials of new drug treatments?

any obvious outward signs. There are currently around 700 000 people with dementia in the UK and over 20 million worldwide (mostly with Alzheimer's) and the numbers are likely to double in 20 years due to the ageing population. There is therefore a great urgency for better diagnosis and treatment.

Figure 3.22

Professor Sophie Scott at the Institute of Cognitive Neuroscience in London.

Brain imaging, language and hearing

Professor Sophie Scott is a psychologist working at the Institute of Cognitive Neuroscience, which is part of University College London (Figure 3.22). She uses scanning techniques such as fMRI and PET to research how our brains control speech production and speech perception. One interesting finding is that as we listen to someone talking it is not just the parts of the brain associated with hearing that light up, but also parts that we use in speaking. Similarly when we speak, parts of the brain associated with hearing also light up.

PET scans

PET stands for positron emission tomography. Radioactive fluorine-18 atoms, attached to glucose molecules, are used as a tracer in the bloodstream. If the tracer is injected into arteries serving the brain, the radioactive atoms collect in the most active areas of the brain, where the blood flow is greatest. The radioactive fluorine atoms have a short half-life of about 110 minutes. They decay emitting positrons.

When positrons and electrons collide they destroy each other and release gamma rays. The gamma rays are detected by a scintillator surrounding the patient. The PET scan is usually combined with a three dimensional X-ray of the brain called a CAT scan, and this provides a clear picture of the brain with the most active areas highlighted. As with fMRI, the patient can carry out mental tasks while in the scanner, enabling the localisation of brain function to be studied.

Key term

A **positron** has the same mass as an electron but a positive charge. It is the antiparticle of the electron.

Sounds and emotions

As Sophie explains: "One particular interest of mine is how we process the expression of emotion in voices we hear. There are two parts to speech, the words themselves and the melody of speech – how the words are delivered and the emotion behind that. The technical word for this is prosody.

"We have found that hearing someone make an emotional noise activates the parts of the brain we would use to make that sound oneself. We discovered this by putting people in the scanner and playing firstly sounds linked to negative emotions like a noise of disgust or screaming, and then positive noises like people cheering or laughing.

"We found the effect of laughter to be much greater than other noises, even though people did not actually move their faces or make a noise in the scanner. When you hear someone laugh, your brain gets ready to join in. This is probably the reason laughter tracks are added to TV programmes – the sound of people laughing strongly activates the brain to laugh, or at least smile."

It is indeed very difficult not to laugh when you hear someone else start laughing. There have been several instances of pairs of TV presenters breaking down into helpless giggles, even when the content of the programme is inappropriate. "People like to try to get into groups and situations where we are going to be overcome with infectious laughter" says Sophie. "It could even be that laughter was an earlier form of communication than language in human evolution."

Restoring speech

The fMRI scanner that Sophie uses is in a building a few streets away from her office. It is temperature controlled and so feels quite cold. The screens in the control room show a series of slices through the subject's brain, but the bright colours do not show up until the results are processed. "It is important to remember that fMRI is four dimensional – you are comparing images of the brain taken a few seconds apart, and it is only when those images are compared and the differences enhanced that you see the colours."

This work is not of purely academic interest. Sophie Scott is also using PET scans to study how people with cochlear implants process speech. Cochlear implants are becoming a more frequent way of restoring hearing in both young and old people: in those born deaf and those who have lost their hearing later in life. But the sound the implants provide is very different from sound we usually hear through our ears (Figure 3.23). The deaf former MP Lord Jack Ashley described it as "like a croaking Dalek with laryngitis".

"If you lose your hearing and have a cochlear implant you have to learn to listen all over again. It is then very hard to appreciate the melody and emotion of speech and it is hard to hear music. Using scanners enables us to see how the brain copes with the new sounds.

Question

32 In the context of MRI scanning, what does Professor Scott mean when she says that:
a) "parts of the brain … light up"
b) "fMRI is four dimensional"?

Figure 3.23

A cochlear implant stimulates the hearing nerve (auditory nerve) directly. The nerve carries the information to the brain, where it is interpreted as sound.

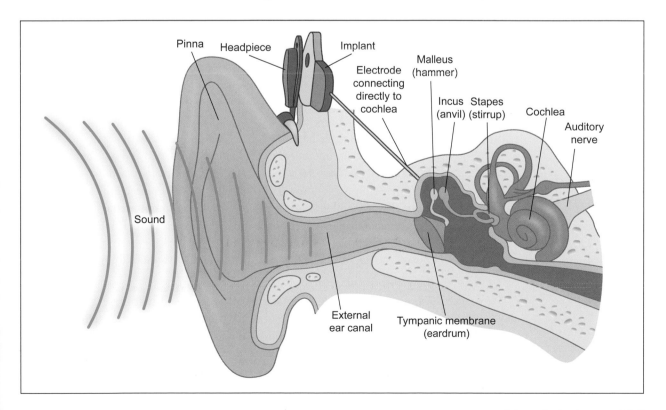

33 Suggest reasons why a child born deaf can learn to enjoy music with the help of a cochlear implant but an adult that goes deaf, and receives identical treatment, is much less likely to be able to do so.

We are looking at plasticity in the brain – if a child is born deaf and has a cochlear implant, the chances are their brain will learn to hear well, including enjoying music. If an adult who has enjoyed music all their lives suddenly goes deaf and has a cochlear implant, they are not likely to be able to process music, even though they can learn to interpret speech."

Rewards from research

Sophie herself is a musician in her spare time, and a deep feeling for people losing their hearing flows into her face as clearly as one of the processed images from the scanner. "Yes, that is a motivation in my work. If you can restore someone's hearing you are bringing the world back to them. Similarly with stroke victims, if you can restore speech, they can engage with people around them again. It is wonderful to be able to do that."

3.4 True or false? Popular ideas about the brain

The two cerebral hemispheres of the human brain look like mirror images of each other. However, scientists have found that, for most people, the left side of the brain has the greater role in language (see Section 3.2). There is a popular view that the left side of the brain is the logical, verbal and dominant side while the right side is imaginative, emotional and better at spatial tasks. Creative and artistic people are sometimes said to be right-brained, whereas logical and systematic people are considered left-brained. Scientists have explored ideas of this kind in search of evidence that the two halves of the brain have different functions and that there may be differences between the brains of males and females.

Right brain or left brain?

The two hemispheres of the brain communicate using a band of nerve fibres called the corpus callosum which carries nerve impulses backwards and forwards between the two sides of the brain using about 250 million nerve axons. A drastic way to investigate differences between the right and left hemisphere's functions is to cut these connections between the two halves and see what each half could do on its own.

Amazingly, an operation of this kind was carried out on about a dozen people in the 1960s in a last-ditch attempt to control severe and life-threatening epileptic fits. When most of the connections were cut surgically, the epileptic patients showed a great improvement in their symptoms, and most were apparently unaffected in their mental abilities. Cutting the corpus callosum prevented the excessive brain activity which caused the epileptic fits, by confining the disturbances to one hemisphere.

Split brain patients and what they see

The American psychologist Roger Sperry realised that these 'split brain' patients offered a golden opportunity to investigate lateralisation in the human brain. He wanted to know whether the separated cerebral hemispheres would behave like two brains in one head, with their own streams of consciousness, and to what extent the two hemispheres would show different abilities.

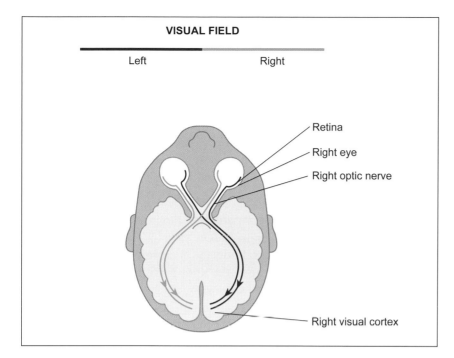

VISUAL FIELD

Left   Right

Retina

Right eye

Right optic nerve

Right visual cortex

Figure 3.24

When a participant looked straight ahead, light from the left visual field (red) fell on the right side of the retina of each eye, which sends nerve impulses to the right visual cortex. Light from the right visual field (green) fell on the left side of the two retinas, which sent nerve impulses to the left visual cortex.

In all people, the axons in the optic nerves running from the eyes to the brain connect to the visual cortex in such a way that images from the left half of the screen (left visual field) go to the right hemisphere and images from the right half of the screen (right visual field) go to the left hemisphere (Figure 3.24).

Sperry and his student Michael Gazzaniga devised some ingenious tests which showed up the different abilities of the two hemispheres. In one test the group of male participants in the study were asked to stare at the centre point of a screen. An image was flashed up, for one-tenth of a second, in either the right or the left half of the screen. This was long enough for the image of the object to be detected, but too brief for the eyes to move. Next the participant had to find the same object by touch, using either the right or the left hand.

When a person with a split brain was shown an object in the right visual field he could name it, because his language ability was controlled by his left hemisphere. But when an object was shown in the left visual field, the subject said that no object was shown. However, he could pick out the object by feeling with his left hand, from a selection of objects offered behind the screen. When different objects were shown to each hemisphere simultaneously, the two hands each searched for different objects. The left hand ignored the object the right hand was searching for and vice versa.

Further experiments of this kind showed that the left hemisphere is usually the more able at language and detailed analysis. The right hemisphere is better at tasks which cannot easily be put into words or symbols, such as recognising faces, music or copying a picture. The right hemisphere does have some language abilities too, and is better than the left at making sense of figures of speech such as 'turning over a new leaf'. Sperry was awarded the Nobel Prize in Medicine in 1981. It is largely from his studies that our ideas about the 'analytical' left brain and the 'synthetic' right brain arise.

Questions

34 Explain why a person with a split brain was able to select the object displayed as an image in his left visual field with his left hand.

35 Suggest a major limitation in the validity of drawing general conclusions from the studies of these split brain patients.

Question

36 What criteria would you use to decide whether or not to pay serious attention to a website offering to help you discover your brain type and improve your learning?

Some popular mental training courses offer to improve the 'weaker' side of your brain, that is the less dominant side. It is also sometimes claimed that current school systems overemphasise the three Rs, and hence the education of the left hemisphere at the expense of the right. However, almost all mental activities use both hemispheres to some extent, so distinguishing between right- and left-brained people is probably too simplistic to be of serious value in devising teaching methods. Nevertheless, you can find websites offering to test whether you are right- or left-brain dominant and offering all kinds of analyses of your own brain. Some of this is intriguing, but much of it is rubbish. The challenge is to tease out the sense from the psychobabble.

Split brain patients and false memories

Gazzaniga's studies on a split brain patient have led to some interesting discoveries about false memories. In one of his investigations, he showed a picture of a snow scene to the right hemisphere and a picture of a chicken's foot to the left hemisphere (Figure 3.25). He then asked the participant to point with each hand to one of four smaller pictures picking the ones best related to the original pictures. The left hand pointed to a shovel (appropriate for shovelling snow) and the right hand chose a chicken (to go with the chicken's foot).

The left hand is controlled by the right hemisphere, which is unable to speak. So, Gazzaniga asked the patient why he had pointed to a shovel with his left hand. It might have been that the patient could not answer on the grounds that the left hemisphere, which controls speech, did not know why the right hand had pointed to a shovel, because of the cut corpus callosum. But instead of saying he did not know, the patient gave an invented answer, which was that the shovel was used for cleaning out the chicken shed. This answer is interesting because it makes sense.

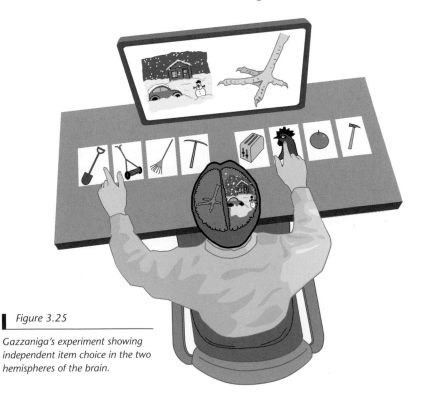

Figure 3.25

Gazzaniga's experiment showing independent item choice in the two hemispheres of the brain.

It is thought that the left hemisphere is responsible for seeking the meaning of events, looking for order and reason, often on limited evidence. It can easily make mistakes as it tends to overgeneralise, constructing a logical past as opposed to a true one, even in intact brains. We all have false memories, and psychologists believe that we commonly reconstruct our memories after an event by adding untrue details which are consistent with our general understanding of the meaning of an experience. Adding extra details to improve a story is called confabulation. It seems that our left hemisphere is very adept at confabulation, and that we may be unaware of the extent to which we are doing it. Research also shows that the wording of questions can influence our recall of past events.

Male brain, female brain

Simon Baron-Cohen directs the Autism Research Centre at Cambridge University. He claims that there are big differences between the typical female brain (empathiser) and the typical male brain (systemiser). He argues that most, but not all, female brains are predominantly hard-wired for empathy and most, but again not all, male brains are predominantly hard-wired for systemising.

Empathisers are sensitive to other people's emotions and thoughts. They respond to these with an appropriate emotion. This means that empathisers intuitively figure out how people are feeling, and how to treat people with care and sensitivity. Systemisers have a drive to analyse and explore systems. They try to figure out how things work.

According to Baron-Cohen's empathising–systemising (E–S) theory, we all have a brain type somewhere on the spectrum from extreme empathising to extreme systemising, with most of us having a good share of both qualities. But females, in general, tend towards the empathiser end of the spectrum and males, in general, towards the systemiser end. This theory suggests that males are more likely to be autistic than females. Baron-Cohen regards autistic people as being very good at systemising and very bad at empathising.

Baron-Cohen quotes, as evidence of his theory, examples from our everyday experience of differences in the typical interests of boys and girls, men and women. As shown in Chapter 2, this raises the question of whether or not these different interests arise from cultural influences, or are inborn. There is increasing evidence that some differences are present from the earliest weeks of life. Psychologists often assess babies' likes and dislikes by measuring how long they look at pictures of objects.

Studies at Durham and Loughborough Universities have recently shown that 9 month old baby boys looked for longer at pictures of toys which included a steering wheel and a car, whereas girls, at the same age, spent more time looking at toys which included a doll and a pram. Boys also looked longer at more active film scenes.

The babies tested did not show any preference for looking at pictures of babies of one sex or another. Babies do not show self-recognition until at least 18 months of age (Figure 3.26, page 90), and the ability to classify pictures of people as male or female does not appear until about two and a half years of age. So it seems that, very early in life, there are differences in what boy and girl babies choose to look at. These early preferences are likely to be reinforced and modified through later experience.

Questions

37 Explain the connection between Gazzaniga's experiment illustrated in Figure 3.25 and the idea that the left brain is good at confabulation.

38 Why does evidence about confabulation cast doubt on the validity of lie detecting techniques?

Questions

39 Suggest some types of behaviour you might observe when watching a group of children at play that might lead you to characterise a particular child:
a) as an empathiser
b) as a systemiser.

40 Suggest examples of the typical interests of men and women that could be quoted in support of Baron-Cohen's theory.

41 a) Comment on the validity of drawing conclusions about gender preferences of babies by measuring differences in their attention to pictures.
b) Explain whether the evidence shows that babies under a year old have a concept of being a girl or a boy.

Figure 3.26

The rouge test of self-recognition. The baby touches its face when it sees the rouge on its face in the mirror. This is a standard test of self-recognition.

Questions

42 When a man has a stroke, language abilities are likely to be more impaired than when a woman has a stroke. Explain how this observation is related to the hypothesis that lateralisation of language functions is greater in men than in women.

43 Comment on the validity of selecting only those brain areas known to be associated with language interpretation in the study reported in *Nature* in 1995.

44 You are in an A2 Science in Society class containing five boys and five girls. State whether each of the following statements is true, giving reasons.
a) All the girls are better at empathising than any of the boys in the class.
b) On average the girls in the class are better at empathising than the boys.

Lateralisation in male and female brains

Many people suffer damage to their brain function through having a stroke. Strokes that occur in Broca's or Wernicke's areas can seriously affect a person's language abilities. It has been found that women tend to have less language impairment than men after strokes, and this has been explained by the hypothesis that language functions are more lateralised in men's brains.

In a study reported in *Nature* in 1995, American scientists used fMRI to compare brain activity in 19 males and 19 females as they carried out four language tasks. The tasks involved identifying patterns of lines, lower and upper case letters, rhymes and word meanings. The two main areas of the cortex known to be involved in language interpretation were scanned. It was found that both males and females used both hemispheres to some extent. However, males were highly lateralised for the rhyming task whereas females used both hemispheres almost equally for this. These findings show that sex differences in language lateralisation depend on which aspect of language processing is involved. Where sex differences in the brain exist, they are likely to be complex.

3.5 Life, death and consciousness

Neuroscience has an important role in helping us to understand who and what we are. Learning more about how our brains work can also give us a more realistic perspective on our place in the natural world. Seeking biological answers to key questions about life and consciousness can help us to be better prepared to make difficult judgements about the treatment and care of brain-damaged infants and adults.

Scientists have put forward theories to account for the experience of human consciousness. There is no one accepted explanation and most of the ideas are controversial. Some scientists have attempted to locate consciousness in a particular part of the brain but there is no agreement about which part it should be. Many scientists, however, think that trying to identify a seat of consciousness is misconceived and based on erroneous views about how the brain works.

Modern science is essentially materialist. The views of Francis Crick (of DNA fame) are typical of this perspective. He believed that all the brain's properties could be explored by scientific methods. In his book, *The Astonishing Hypothesis*, which was published in 1994, he wrote that "You, your joys and your sorrows, your memories and your ambitions, your sense of personal identity and free will, are in fact no more than the behavior of a vast assembly of nerve cells and their associated molecules."

Despite views of this kind, neuroscientists are still far from being able to explain the mystery of human consciousness. In her book *The Human Brain: A Guided Tour*, published in 1997, the neuroscientist Susan Greenfield described the subjective experience of consciousness as the ultimate puzzle. She concluded by writing that neuroscientists have made exciting and fundamental discoveries; discoveries that are slowly allowing scientists to see the types of questions they need to ask and the types of answers they might expect. In her view science has made astounding progress towards understanding the brain in the last 20 years or so, but nevertheless this is an adventure that is just beginning.

States of consciousness

Brain injury

In 2005 a 23 year old woman received a severe brain injury in a road accident. Five months later she was sometimes awake, but still did not respond to anything around her, and was diagnosed as being in a vegetative state (Figure 3.27).

Clinical state	Wakefulness	Awareness
Normal consciousness	High	High
Coma	None	None
Vegetative state	High	None
Minimally conscious	High	Slight/variable

This patient was the subject of a study by the Impaired Consciousness Research Group at Cambridge. The technique of fMRI was used to measure her brain's responses when words were spoken to her. To begin with she was scanned while a meaningful sentence was spoken, and this

> ## Key term
>
> People show signs of **consciousness** if they are aware of their environment and their own relationship to it.

> ## Question
>
> **45** a) How do you know that you are conscious?
> b) Think of your behaviour since you woke up this morning. Can you remember times when you felt more conscious or less conscious?

> ## Key term
>
> Patients in a **vegetative state** as a result of severe brain damage are in a state of wakefulness without awareness. People in this state cannot speak, follow simple commands or respond to stimuli in any meaningful way.

Figure 3.27

Differences between comatose, vegetative and minimally conscious states.

Questions

46 Why is it so hard to make sense of the sentence with ambiguous words?

47 Suggest an experiment that the scientists could do to confirm that the patient was able to cooperate with the study and that she was not showing automatic, non-conscious responses.

48 With reference to Figure 3.27, discuss the state of consciousness of the 23 year old woman studied by the Impaired Consciousness Research Group.

was compared to a series of meaningless sounds chosen to correspond to the words in the sentence. The meaningful sentence activated the language centres in her brain but the meaningless noise did not.

She was then read sentences containing ambiguous words, such as those in italics in the sentence: 'The *creak* came from a *beam* in the *ceiling*'. The three words in italics all sound like other words with different meanings. Such words make extra demands on Wernicke's area of the brain to make sense of spoken language. Ambiguous sentences caused a significant additional response in the patient's brain, just as in a healthy brain.

To test conscious awareness in the patient, further tests were done in which she was asked to imagine playing tennis and visiting all the rooms in her house. Her fMRI responses were found to be statistically indistinguishable from those of twelve healthy volunteers.

The scientists took this to mean that the patient was able to cooperate with the scientists by imagining particular situations when asked to do so. The authors of the report on the study say that this confirmed beyond any doubt that she was consciously aware of herself and her surroundings. However, she was unable to make any movements or to talk, meaning that she was unable to demonstrate her consciousness.

Brain scans are extremely complicated. Neuroscientists and clinicians do not always agree about how they should be interpreted. They do not yet know how to distinguish a conscious brain from an unconscious brain from brain scan evidence alone. However, identifying evidence of some brain activity in vegetative patients is likely to refine drug treatment and rehabilitation. Studies at China's Zhejiang University showed that a familiar voice calling their name led to significant activity in the temporal lobe in some severely brain-damaged patients. Such knowledge is likely to be very reassuring to family and friends and motivate them to help with long-term care.

Figure 3.28

A headset for thought-controlled computer games.

Helping people with brain injury

Cambridge's Impaired Consciousness Research Group was established in 1998 to bring together the skills of health professionals and academics in the care of brain-damaged people. They have developed a technique for testing whether someone has any degree of awareness of their environment, with the help of pattern recognition software to interpret brain images.

They are also hoping to develop a brain–computer interface tailored to individual patients. A prototype brain–computer interface already makes it possible to control a computer game just by thinking, using a wireless headset to pick up electrical signals from the brain's surface (Figure 3.28). It can be used, for example, to control avatars in games played in a virtual world. Just by thinking the appropriate thoughts, a person can cause the avatar to move right or left, or even adopt a particular facial expression, such as smiling.

This type of technology has the potential to help people with brain injury. Some unfortunate patients, for example, are fully conscious but unable to speak or move in any way, apart from sometimes retaining vertical eye movements. This condition, called locked-in syndrome, is the result of injury to parts of the brain stem or cerebellum. With the help of an interface that picks up electrical signals from their brains, such patients may be able to control the cursor on a computer screen linked to a voice synthesiser.

Brain stem death

In most cases it is fairly straightforward to determine when someone is dead: the heart stops beating, breathing ceases and soon all other organs die, including the brain.

The development of life-support machines has made decisions about death more difficult in some cases. A new definition of death was needed after the 1950s, once new technology made it possible to ventilate the lungs, maintain blood circulation and eliminate waste products from the body (Figure 3.29). Although the functions of the lungs, heart and kidneys can be taken over by machines, those of the brain cannot.

Keeping the heart beating is essential so that the brain continues to be supplied with oxygen. If the brain stem is damaged so severely that it dies then there is little point in stimulating the heart to keep it beating. This is because the brain stem controls essential internal reflexes which keep the body alive, including breathing and control of the heart beat.

After a brain injury, the cerebral hemispheres may become virtually inactive as shown by electroencephalography (EEG – see page 94), yet they may sometimes regain their functions, so long as the brain stem remains active. This means that doctors in intensive care units need tests to help them distinguish between those patients who might recover and those who have no chance of regaining consciousness and whose heart will stop beating in a short while once artificial support is removed.

The tests used to determine whether or not the brain stem is dead are only carried out once doctors are sure that the patient has suffered irreversible brain damage.

First, the doctors check that the patients are not affected by factors which might affect the tests – such

Question

49 Suggest in simple terms how it is possible to use brain activity to control a cursor on a computer.

Figure 3.29

A nurse adjusting controls on a ventilator attached to an unconscious patient. The ventilator helps the patient to breathe.

50 Someone has had a hard bump on the head. Suggest what sort of tests a paramedic might do to see if there are any signs of brain injury.

51 Why is an accurate diagnosis of brain stem death important when there is a possibility of organ transplants?

52 Suggest reasons why the code of practice for diagnosing brain stem death states that:
a) diagnosis should be carried out independently by the doctor in charge of the patient and by a second doctor
b) neither doctor should be a member of a transplant team.

as drugs or an extremely low body temperature. Then they carry out a series of tests to see if the normal reflexes that involve the brain stem are working. In one test they shine a torch into both eyes to see if the pupils react to the light. In another test they put a tube down the patient's throat to see if it causes gagging or coughing. The final test is to remove the patient from the ventilator for a short time to see if they show any sign of attempting to breathe on their own. Patients who do not react in any way to any of the tests are brain stem dead.

Electroencephalography

Electroencephalography (EEG) is a technique for picking up the minute electrical signals on the surface of the scalp. It is similar to recording the electrical activity of the heart from electrodes placed on the skin of the chest (this gives an electrocardiogram, ECG).

The combined effects of the activity of all the neurones in the brain produce wave-like changes in electrical potential. These waves become amplified or change their shape when a brain region becomes active. They also change during the various phases of sleep or when someone has an epileptic fit. EEG is much simpler to use than MRI or PET and can help to diagnose brain abnormalities in babies or children as well as adults.

EEG is widely used in brain research. The instruments are portable and non-invasive. The technique can show changes over short time intervals more accurately than fMRI, although it is not so good at detecting fine details between different areas.

The brains of premature babies

Babies born prematurely face a range of health problems. Babies sometimes survive from as early as 23 weeks of gestation, but some brain damage is quite common, often caused by internal bleeding. Doctors need ways to assess any brain damage in such tiny and vulnerable infants so that they can give them the best possible treatment.

Doctors can use ultrasound to obtain an image of the brain but this technique cannot reveal detailed internal structures. An EEG can be used to look at the general quality of brain activity. MRI gives a much better image but requires the patient to be still, and may stress the baby, increasing its blood pressure and triggering possible further bleeding. Until recently, babies had to be sedated while being scanned by MRI. To get round this problem, specially adapted incubators have been designed which continue to monitor the baby's condition while it is placed in an fMRI scanner. The baby's head is gently strapped down and it is monitored on screen while in the incubator inside the machine.

Imperial College London's Department of Paediatrics has recently used fMRI to scan over 100 babies born before 30 weeks gestation. The babies' brains showed problems such as bleeding into the spaces in the brain, and over-activity in the white matter. These symptoms could be linked to the development of conditions that affect movement and are classified as cerebral palsy. Other minor brain injuries seemed not

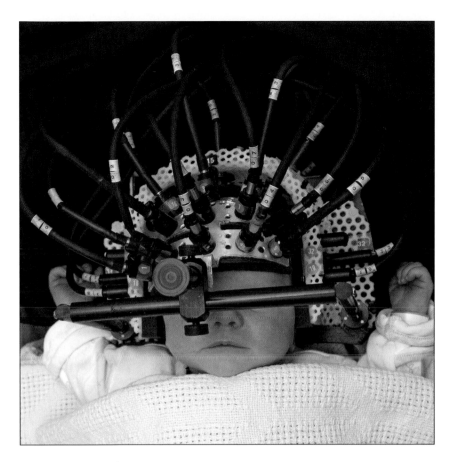

Figure 3.30

Scanning the brain of a baby using optical tomography.

to lead to any difficulties. In order to make the link between the brain scans and later symptoms, mental and physical development were assessed when the babies were between 18 and 36 months of age. The assessments were carried out by trained paediatricians, who had not been shown the MRI results.

MRI is time consuming and carries some risk in newborn babies. A more recent technique is to use optical tomography, which scans the brain surface using flashes of infrared light (Figure 3.30). The scan shows whether any brain areas are becoming deoxygenated, allowing doctors to give immediate treatment, if needed.

The use of brain imaging in babies is still under trial, and it is very difficult to make predictions about a baby's future outcome from early scans. This is because there is still insufficient knowledge about how different brain structures relate to their functions. Also, all babies are different: similar looking brain damage in two infants can lead to very different outcomes.

A further uncertainty is the degree of brain plasticity in young brains. This is illustrated by the effects of an operation which either removes large parts of a damaged hemisphere from the brains of young children suffering from extreme epilepsy or disconnects that part of the cortex from the rest of the brain. Children who have had this surgery gradually learn to adapt. The parts of the brain that remain are able to compensate to the extent that some of these children can lead quite normal lives.

Questions

53 Why was it important for the paediatricians not to know the results of MRI scans when assessing the babies' development?

54 a) Why is it valuable to be able to detect any damage in the brains of premature babies and estimate the possible effects on future development?

b) A doctor's predictions about the future development of a brain-damaged baby are likely to be very uncertain. Comment on how this uncertainty might affect decisions about the baby's treatment.

The decision to withdraw treatment

When babies are born with severe handicap the question arises as to whether life-saving treatment should be given. Similar issues apply to adults in a permanent vegetative state (PVS – sometimes called a persistent vegetative state).

Tony Bland, 22, suffered severe brain damage when he and hundreds of other football supporters were crushed in an overcrowded stand at Hillsborough stadium in April 1989. In 1992 a judge at the high court ruled that doctors could disconnect the feeding tubes keeping him alive. It was thought that there was no reasonable possibility that he would emerge from his permanent vegetative state. His life-support machine was switched off on 22nd February 1993 and he died on 3rd March. The high court has since sanctioned withdrawal of feeding from many more PVS patients, and several described as in 'near-PVS'. Doctors, families and the official solicitor all agreed that death was in the patients' best interests. However, questions continue to be raised about the possibility of emerging from a permanent vegetative state.

In 1996 a 24 year old South African cyclist, Louis Viljoen, was hit by a vehicle, sustaining brain damage, and was diagnosed as being in a permanent vegetative state. In 1999 his mother, who was caring for him, was prescribed the sleeping pill zolpidem. Because her son was restless, the doctor suggested giving one of her pills to him. Half an hour later he began to say a few words, and after regular treatment with the pill he recognised his family and friends and could remember some of his past.

This drug's dramatic effects, discovered by chance, appear to be a result of the reactivation of dormant parts of the brain. It seems that zolpidem binds to certain inhibitory synaptic receptors, known as GABA receptors. The drug may work by reducing excessive inhibition at GABA receptors in dormant brain areas. Neurologists disagree about whether people benefiting from this drug were in true permanent vegetative state, and further trials of the drug are currently being carried out. In the British Medical Association's (BMA) view, recoveries from PVS indicate that the original diagnosis was wrong.

Drugs are unlikely to help all people with severe brain damage, and for many unfortunate victims, the diagnosis of PVS means that they will never recover. Such patients often lack the swallowing reflex, so they die if no longer fed though a tube.

Withdrawing treatment is different from euthanasia, which means assisting someone to die. A person in a permanent vegetative state is, by definition, unable to give consent for treatment or its withdrawal, and this poses a moral dilemma for carers, though occasionally a person's views may have been expressed before an accident. The BMA says that no decisions about withdrawing treatment should be made for at least 12 months after a brain injury with PVS diagnosis. This means that a pregnant woman in a permanent vegetative state would have the possibility of having her baby saved.

Questions

56 Outline why it is helpful to have a legal decision about withdrawing medical treatment, rather than leaving the decision to family and doctors alone.

57 Brain-damaged patients who die after treatment is withdrawn may be considered as organ donors if they or their family have given consent. Comment on the moral issues raised by this.

58 Sometimes a decision is made to withdraw treatment from a baby born with abnormalities or from a brain-injured person.
a) List the people whose interests should be taken into account when such a decision is made.
b) Suggest, with reasons, which person on your list should make the final decision.

Problems with words

A person who is awake but has no awareness of their surroundings following a brain injury may initially be diagnosed as in a 'continuing vegetative state'. This can be upgraded to 'permanent vegetative state' at a later stage (normally 6 months after a stroke or heart attack and 12 months after an accident). The word 'permanent' implies that there is no hope of recovery, so the term 'persistent vegetative state' (also shortened to PVS) is sometimes used instead. This confusing terminology places extra demands on healthcare workers when explaining the possible outcomes to friends and family, and also causes possible confusion when cases come under legal consideration for withdrawing treatment.

Brain injury can place an almost intolerable burden on family and friends, especially when there seems to be no possibility of improvement. Any decision about withdrawing treatment must balance the rights of the patient with those of the family. Brains are flexible and adaptable, especially in young people, and there is always the hope, however faint, that scientists may be on the threshold of great medical advances in diagnosis and treatment which could make the outlook for brain-damaged people much better.

Question

58 Explain why the two meanings of the 'P' in PVS can create difficulties for healthcare workers and families.

Review Questions

59 Neuroscientists use a variety of methods to study the brain. Discuss the following statements about how neuroscientists work, illustrating your answers with examples from this chapter and from your own reading.
   a) Scientific measurements are always subject to a degree of uncertainty.
   b) Data are more reliable if systematic methods are used for sampling, observing and measuring.
   c) It may be possible to interpret data from complex equipment in more than one way, in which case interpretations need to be checked and discussed with others doing related research.
   d) Scientists may reach different, competing, conclusions from the same set of data. When this happens the explanation may lie in the financial interests of the scientists involved or their loyalty to the organisations they work for.

60 Give examples to illustrate the following statements:
   a) Some new areas of scientific research raise ethical issues.
   b) Scientists have a responsibility to ensure that their practice is in line with
      i) national and international ethical regulations and
      ii) decisions made by ethics committees.
   c) Some decisions involve balancing the rights of certain individuals and groups against those of others.

Responding to global climate change

The second largest source of greenhouse gases in the UK is agriculture. This includes the methane produced by cows fermenting grass in their stomachs. The cows belch the methane into the air.

■ How does the Earth's climate system work?

■ How do we know that the climate has changed naturally over the past million years?

■ How and why have atmospheric greenhouse gas concentrations changed in the past and how has human activity contributed to these changes?

■ How can climate models help us project future changes in climate?

■ What are the likely impacts of future climate change on our world and how should we respond to its threats?

Figure 4.2

A large petrochemical plant in Grangemouth, Scotland. Industry in general, and the energy industry in particular, is the main source of carbon dioxide emissions into the atmosphere in the UK. Most greenhouse gas emissions are invisible, unlike the condensing clouds of steam in this picture.

4.1 The climate system

Key parts of the climate system

The Sun provides the energy to drive our climate. However, the Sun's radiation is distributed unevenly over our planet and varies with the seasons. This distribution arises because of the elliptical shape of the Earth's orbit round the Sun and the tilt of its axis relative to the plane of its orbit (Figure 4.3).

The uneven heating stirs up the atmosphere, creating vast currents of air. These air flows are modified by a variety of factors, which include the rotation of the Earth, contrasts in temperature between land and sea, and major features of the land surface such as mountain ranges and large ice sheets.

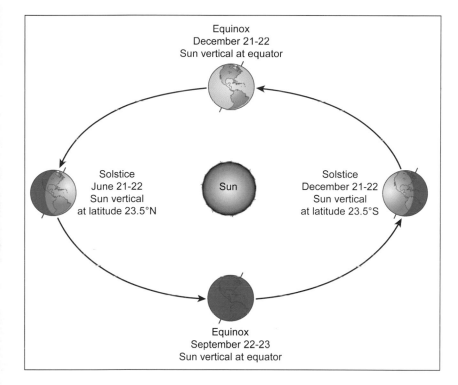

Figure 4.3

The nature of the Earth's orbit around the Sun.

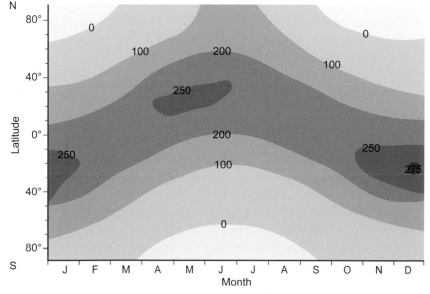

Figure 4.4

The seasonal and geographical variations in solar radiation received at the top of the atmosphere. The units are watts per square metre (W/m²).

Questions

1 The latitude of the UK mainland is from 50° to 59° North. How does the weather experienced in the UK relate to the pattern of seasonal radiation shown in Figure 4.3?

2 Show how Figure 4.3 can account for the worldwide pattern of seasonal radiation from the Sun plotted in Figure 4.4.

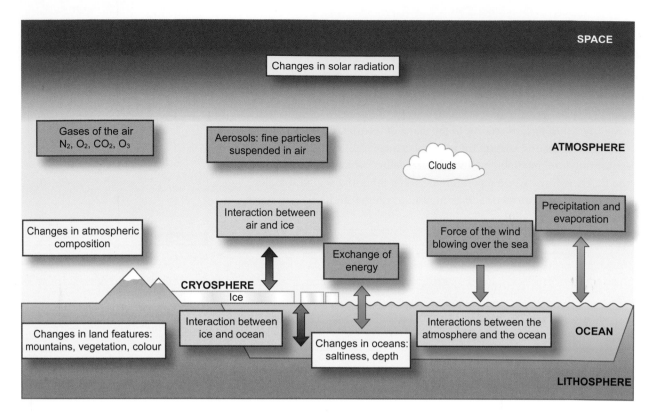

The following labels appear within Figure 4.5:

SPACE

Changes in solar radiation

Gases of the air N$_2$, O$_2$, CO$_2$, O$_3$

Aerosols: fine particles suspended in air

ATMOSPHERE

Clouds

Interaction between air and ice

Precipitation and evaporation

Changes in atmospheric composition

Force of the wind blowing over the sea

Exchange of energy

CRYOSPHERE
Ice

Interaction between ice and ocean

Interactions between the atmosphere and the ocean

OCEAN

Changes in land features: mountains, vegetation, colour

Changes in oceans: saltiness, depth

LITHOSPHERE

Figure 4.5

The main parts of the global climate system, the links between them and the key changes that affect the climate.

Although we tend to think of weather and climate as occurring within the atmosphere, the Earth's climate system involves much more than this. There are, in all, five main parts to the climate system (Figure 4.5).

- The atmosphere, which contains not only nitrogen and oxygen but also water vapour, and trace gases, such as the greenhouse gases. Suspended in the air are tiny particles of matter, forming aerosols. Some of the particles in these aerosols come from natural processes such as volcanic eruptions and others from human activity such as industrial processes.

- The oceans, which cover 70% of the Earth's surface and contain 95% of the water on the planet. Ocean currents transfer the energy of the Sun around the globe. They transfer as much energy as the atmosphere. The oceans heat the land and air during the winter and cool them during the summer.

- The cryosphere, which is made up of the large polar ice sheets, smaller ice sheets, glaciers and sea ice. These are stores of freshwater. They are nearly white, so they reflect much of the radiation from the Sun that falls on them back to space. Scientists say that they have a high albedo.

- The lithosphere, where chemical weathering of rocks plays a part in the natural cycling of elements, such as carbon, in the environment. Soil moisture is an important store of water.

- The biosphere, which includes land plants and marine plankton. Plants and plankton play an important part in moving the chemical elements between the Earth's spheres, through processes such as photosynthesis and respiration. Microorganisms in soil release gases into the air as they break down the organic matter from dead and decaying plants.

The greenhouse effect

Radiation from the Sun

The greenhouse effect is a natural part of our climate system: indeed without it, the mean global temperature would be around 33 °C colder than it is now. This would be far too cold for life to exist, as we know it. Scientists explain the greenhouse effect by showing what happens to the radiation from the Sun when it falls on the Earth.

The Sun is a hot body surface with a surface temperature of around 6000 °C. It emits short-wave radiation with most of the energy in the visible and ultraviolet (UV) regions of the spectrum. When this radiation hits the top of the Earth's atmosphere, about one-third of it is reflected back into space. The rest of the radiation passes into the atmosphere, which it warms. About half the energy of the radiation is absorbed by the Earth's surface.

The warm surface of the Earth also emits radiation. However, the Earth is much cooler than the Sun, and this means that the re-emitted radiation has a much longer wavelength and lies in the infrared part of the spectrum. Whereas the Earth's atmosphere is relatively transparent to incoming UV radiation, a large proportion of the outgoing infrared radiation is absorbed by the atmosphere. The energy from the radiation warms the lower atmosphere (the troposphere) and especially the Earth's surface.

Questions

5   There is no life on the Earth's two neighbouring planets, Venus (surface temperature +450 °C) and Mars (surface temperature −45 °C). What are the particular conditions that make the Earth suitable for life as we know it?

6   Give examples to illustrate the general law that the hotter an object the shorter the wavelength at which it emits most radiation.

7   Describe two possible effects that are observed when radiation is absorbed by a material.

Figure 4.6

Diagram showing how the greenhouse effect works. For a stable climate there has to be a balance between the incoming energy from the Sun and the energy radiated back into space by the Earth.

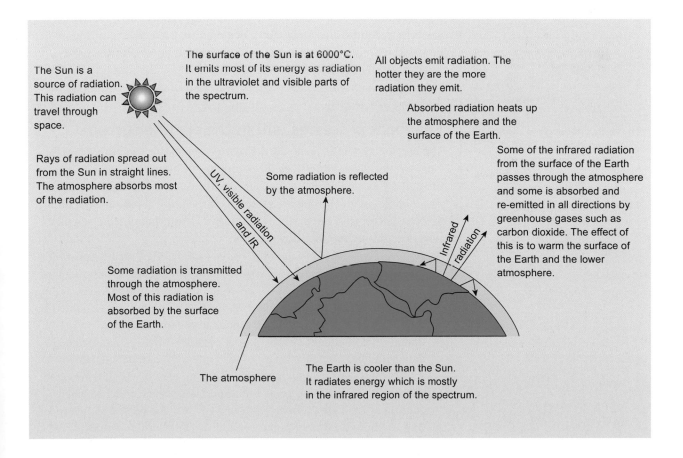

The Sun is a source of radiation. This radiation can travel through space.

The surface of the Sun is at 6000°C. It emits most of its energy as radiation in the ultraviolet and visible parts of the spectrum.

All objects emit radiation. The hotter they are the more radiation they emit.

Absorbed radiation heats up the atmosphere and the surface of the Earth.

Rays of radiation spread out from the Sun in straight lines. The atmosphere absorbs most of the radiation.

UV, visible radiation and IR

Some radiation is reflected by the atmosphere.

Some of the infrared radiation from the surface of the Earth passes through the atmosphere and some is absorbed and re-emitted in all directions by greenhouse gases such as carbon dioxide. The effect of this is to warm the surface of the Earth and the lower atmosphere.

Infrared radiation

Some radiation is transmitted through the atmosphere. Most of this radiation is absorbed by the surface of the Earth.

The atmosphere

The Earth is cooler than the Sun. It radiates energy which is mostly in the infrared region of the spectrum.

Gases in the air

The gases in the air that absorb infrared radiation are called greenhouse gases. Nitrogen and oxygen make up almost all of the air, but they are not greenhouse gases. People are familiar with the idea that carbon dioxide is a greenhouse gas but it can come as a surprise to learn that the most important greenhouse gas is water vapour. It is present in highly variable quantities in the atmosphere, ranging from about 2% in the tropics down to almost 0% above the polar regions and above deserts. The percentage of water vapour in the air is largely determined by the temperature and, globally, is not affected to a significant extent by human activities.

The greenhouse gases that are added to the air as a direct result of human activities are carbon dioxide (CO_2), methane (CH_4), nitrous oxide (N_2O), halocarbons (including CFCs) and low-level ozone (O_3). All the halocarbons in the atmosphere come from human activities but the other greenhouse gases, present in trace amounts, are controlled both by natural and anthropogenic processes. Increases in the main greenhouse gases since the industrial revolution, starting in the 1780s, have mainly been the result of human activity and it is these increases that have enhanced the greenhouse effect. The effect is to upset the energy balance of the Earth. More energy is retained and less radiated into space, so that the Earth gets warmer.

It is only recently that worries about the enhanced greenhouse effect have become a major concern. However, scientific knowledge of the greenhouse effect, and the possibility that human activity might contribute to it, goes back some way. As long ago as 1826, a Swedish scientist called Svante Arrhenius calculated that a doubling of the concentration of carbon dioxide in the atmosphere might warm the atmosphere by about 6 °C on average. However, it was not until the 1980s that the possibility of anthropogenic warming of climate became clearly apparent to scientists.

Feedback processes within the climate system

The climate system is made all the more complex by feedback processes. Negative feedback diminishes, or dampens, an input that tends to change the system. Positive feedback reinforces, or amplifies, an input. The complexity of the climate system is largely the result of the many feedback processes. Important feedback processes that climate scientists have to consider are as follows:

* Temperature and water vapour. Water vapour is the most important greenhouse gas. Where the Earth is warmer the level of water vapour in the air is larger. The consequence is that the warming effect arising from an increase in carbon dioxide in the air is more than doubled by the resulting increase in water vapour in the atmosphere.
* Radiation and clouds. Clouds play a complex role in climate and the detailed effect of clouds on climate is not well understood. However, we do know that clouds have two opposing effects. On the one hand, clouds reflect incoming solar radiation back to space and so cause cooling at the Earth's surface (Figure 4.7). On the other hand, clouds trap re-emitted infrared radiation and so contribute to warming, much like water vapour. Different types of clouds have different effects.

Questions

8 Explain why the percentage of water vapour in the atmosphere is much higher in the tropics than it is at the poles.

9 How does motor traffic give rise to ozone in the lower atmosphere?

10 Which of these gases absorb infrared radiation: carbon dioxide, CFCs, methane, nitrogen, nitrous oxide, oxygen, ozone and water vapour?

11 Why does enhancing the greenhouse effect make the Earth warmer?

Figure 4.7

Clouds reflect light from the Sun. They also help to keep the Earth warm by absorbing radiation. The effects of clouds on climate are complex and not fully understood.

- Ocean circulation. Warm and cold currents in the oceans play a major role in climate by distributing heat energy around the planet. They also contribute moisture through evaporation. There are strong links between the oceans and climate. Small changes in ocean circulation can therefore have profound effects on climate.
- Ice. Glaciers and ice sheets reflect solar radiation back into space. Ice is a good reflector of radiation. It has a high albedo. Increased surface warming causes a reduction in the amount of ice cover leading to a lowering of albedo and hence further surface warming.

Triggers for climate change

As well as the enhanced greenhouse effect, there are other trigger factors that can lead to climate change. Scientists refer to these factors as 'climate forcing variables'. They operate on a range of timescales from as long as millions of years down to tens of years or less. Often a very small change can be amplified to produce large-scale changes in climate.

Movement of tectonic plates is one of the processes that leads to climate change on timescales in the range of tens of thousands to millions of years. One reason for this is that ocean currents alter as the continents move and land bridges between them open and close. This affects the way that heat energy is carried round the globe. Another reason is that mountain building alters the circulating air currents in the atmosphere. Also water flowing down mountains weathers rocks and transports chemical elements from the land to the seas.

A second trigger factor arises from the slight changes in the way the Earth orbits the Sun. These affect the amount and distribution of the radiation reaching the atmosphere. Scientists have been able to show that the orbital variations are responsible for the ice ages over cycles of about 100 000 years.

Questions

12 Give **two** examples of positive feedback in the climate system.

13 Give **one** example of negative feedback in the climate system.

Key term

In the context of the Earth's climate system, the term **climate forcing** refers to any factor that leads to a change in the overall balance of radiation entering or leaving the lower atmosphere. Positive forcing tends to warm the atmosphere. Negative forcing tends to cool the atmosphere.

Figure 4.8

A giant mushroom cloud of steam and ash exploding out of the Mount Pinatubo volcano in the Philippines during its eruption on 12th June 1991. Volcanoes give out some carbon dioxide but less than a hundredth of the carbon dioxide from human activities. Measurements of carbon dioxide in the air over the last 50 years do not show any significant rises after eruptions.

Question

14 How do scientists account for the changes in the Earth's climate:
a) in the short term
b) in the long term?

Changes in the energy of solar radiation at different wavelengths also affect the input of energy to the Earth's atmosphere. Scientists have recorded a number of different solar cycles. Of these, the best known is the 11-year sunspot cycle, which is linked to changes in solar output.

A fourth factor is the effect of large volcanic eruptions. These inject dust particles into the atmosphere, which scatter the Sun's radiation back into space. This cools the Earth's surface. The particles can also increase the amount of rainfall by helping clouds to form. The effects of eruptions, although quite significant, are short-lived. The eruption of Mount Pinatubo in 1991 (Figure 4.8) injected large amounts of aerosols into the stratosphere – more than any eruption since that of Krakatoa in 1883. Over the following months, the aerosols reduced global temperatures by about 0.5 °C.

4.2 The origins and effects of greenhouse gases

The most important greenhouse gases have natural as well as anthropogenic sources. Moreover, emissions of greenhouse gases from human activities do not simply enter the atmosphere and remain there;

rather, they enter into cycles of chemicals in the climate system. At any point, the contribution of a greenhouse gas to the overall greenhouse effect depends on two things: first, the concentration of the gas in the atmosphere; and second, the effectiveness of the gas at trapping radiation.

The carbon cycle and carbon dioxide

Carbon flows between the different reservoirs in the carbon cycle (Figure 4.9). Scientists have to consider each of the reservoirs and the rate of flow of chemicals between them if they are to explain the effects of emissions of carbon dioxide from human activities. Some transfers between reservoirs are too slow to be of significance in the timescales that concern us. Rocks, for example, are a major store of carbon but natural transfers into and out of this reservoir are too slow to be of great relevance here.

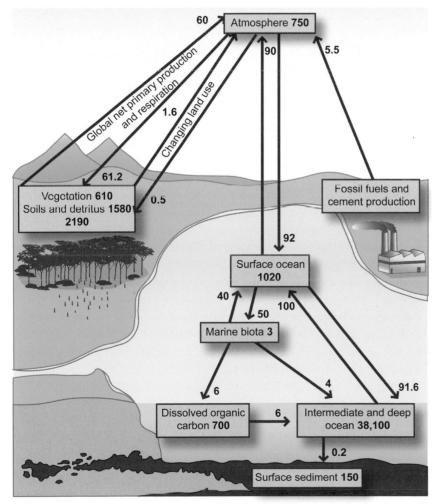

Figure 4.9

A simplified model of the global carbon cycle. The boxes are reservoirs of the element in different combinations with other elements. The numbers in the boxes are estimates of the total mass of carbon worldwide in each reservoir. The units are gigatonnes. (1 gigatonne, Gt = 1000 million tonnes) The numbers by the arrows are flows showing the rate of movement of carbon from one reservoir to another in gigatonnes per year.

Questions

15 Refer to Figure 4.9.
 a) Give an example of a chemical compound in vegetation that contains carbon.
 b) Give an example to explain the term 'marine biota'.
 c) Give an example of a change in land use that adds carbon dioxide to the atmosphere.
 d) Explain how burning fossil fuels adds carbon to the atmosphere.
 e) Give an example of a manufacturing process based on rocks that adds carbon dioxide to the atmosphere on a large scale.

16 Refer to Figure 4.9.
 a) What is the total mass of carbon passing into the atmosphere each year?
 b) What is the net change in the mass of carbon in the atmosphere each year?
 c) Do the figures in the diagram suggest that human activities are having a significant impact on the global carbon cycle?
 d) What happens to most of the carbon dioxide from human activities that enters the atmosphere?

17 What is the value of thinking of what happens to carbon in the climate system in terms of a cycle?

18 The values in Figure 4.9 are estimates.
 a) Explain why there is considerable uncertainty in the numbers.
 b) Which of the values do you think is most difficult to estimate and why?
 c) Which of the values might be estimated fairly reliably?

Figure 4.10

Past variations in atmospheric carbon dioxide concentration from Mauna Loa Observatory (green) and three different Antarctic ice cores (red, blue and purple).

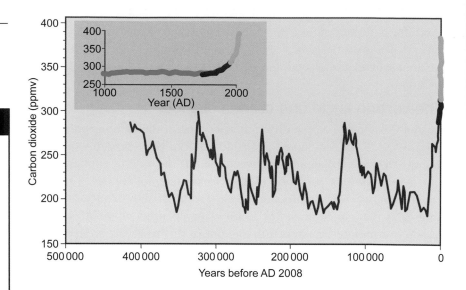

Key term

Concentrations of trace gases in the air are often measured in parts per million by volume (ppmv). The proportion of carbon dioxide in dry air is 0.0387% by volume which is 387 ppmv. Lower concentrations are measured in parts per billion by volume (ppbv). The concentration of methane in the atmosphere is currently around 1750 ppbv.

Questions

19 Why is Mauna Loa a good place for making accurate measurements of the concentration of carbon dioxide in the Earth's atmosphere over a period of years?

20 Refer to Figure 4.10.
a) Explain why the concentration of carbon dioxide in the air follows the pattern of the ice ages and identify a past period that was glacial.
b) What can you conclude about the concentration of carbon dioxide in the air from about 2000 years before the present to 1750?
c) What accounts for the sharp upturn in values after 1750?

21 Which components of the global carbon cycle are most likely to affect atmospheric carbon dioxide concentrations on timescales of up to a century?

Scientists need good data to add numbers to the carbon cycle. They have excellent records of carbon dioxide in the atmosphere from direct measurements. The record from instruments at the Mauna Loa observatory in Hawaii extends back to 1958. Mauna Loa is the highest mountain in Hawaii and the observatory is 3400 metres above sea level. Air samples are collected through air intakes that are several metres above the ground in the midst of a barren area of volcanic rock.

The measurements at Mauna Loa are complemented by the results from the analysis of Antarctic ice cores (see Section 4.3). The results extend the atmospheric carbon dioxide record back several hundred thousand years (Figure 4.10).

The large variations in the carbon dioxide concentration in the air over the longer timescales reflect the pattern of the ice ages. All the available evidence suggests that the carbon dioxide levels have not been as high as present values for around 25 million years.

Because of important feedback processes within the carbon cycle, there is no simple relationship between emissions of carbon dioxide and the concentration of the gas in the air. Scientists therefore have to use theoretical models of the carbon cycle, which take into account the feedbacks, to predict future atmospheric concentrations.

Other greenhouse gases

Methane

Methane (CH_4) is around eight times more potent as a greenhouse gas, per molecule, than carbon dioxide. So, although its concentration in the atmosphere is much lower than that of carbon dioxide, it makes a significant contribution to the enhanced greenhouse effect. Like carbon dioxide, the concentration of methane in the atmosphere started to rise after the industrial revolution from a fairly stable level in the preceding millennia. Wetlands are the main natural source of methane. Anthropogenic sources are from fossil fuel production, agriculture, waste treatment, landfill sites and biomass burning.

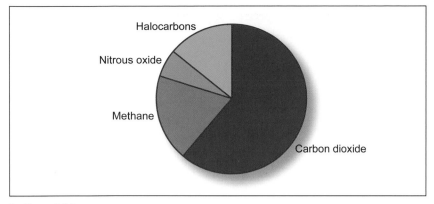

Figure 4.11

Contribution of gases that are evenly mixed in the atmosphere to enhance the greenhouse effect. Ozone is excluded because it is not evenly distributed in the lower atmosphere. Halocarbons include CFCs and related compounds.

Nitrous oxide

The concentration of nitrous oxide (N_2O) in the atmosphere is about 0.3 ppmv. This is around 16% higher than in pre-industrial times. A large proportion of natural emissions come from ecosystems, especially from microorganisms in soils. The major anthropogenic emissions are from fertiliser use, biomass burning and the chemical industry.

Ozone in the lower atmosphere

Ozone has a vital role in protecting life on Earth from the destructive effects of the Sun's UV radiation. This ozone occurs in the upper atmosphere (the stratosphere). Ozone in the lower atmosphere (the troposphere), on the other hand, is a greenhouse gas and a by-product of various industrial processes and the exhaust fumes from motor vehicles. Although it is poorly mixed within the atmosphere, and its concentration highly variable, the contribution of ozone to the enhanced greenhouse effect is significant. It probably ranks third behind carbon dioxide and methane.

Halocarbons

Halocarbons include a wide range of compounds that are exclusively anthropogenic. One of their main uses is in refrigerators but they can also be used to fight fires and kill pests. Most damaging to the ozone layer in the stratosphere are the CFCs (chlorinated fluorocarbons) and these gases are also potent greenhouse gases. As a result they are being phased out and replaced by chemicals that are less harmful. The replacements include other halocarbons, which, while being less damaging to stratospheric ozone, still contribute to the greenhouse effect.

Global warming potential

The contribution of a greenhouse gas to the enhanced greenhouse effect depends on its concentration in the atmosphere and the extent to which the gas absorbs infrared radiation. Also important is the lifetime of that gas within the atmosphere. Some gases remain in the atmosphere much longer than others. A gas that survives for a hundred years in the atmosphere has more time to enhance the greenhouse effect than one that is absorbed or destroyed in days or hours (Figure 4.12).

Questions

22 State and explain whether the following changes give rise to positive or negative feedback within the carbon cycle.
a) Plankton living in the upper parts of the oceans take up less carbon dioxide when the water temperature rises.
b) Plants grow faster when the carbon dioxide concentration in the atmosphere rises.
c) Many organisms, including microorganisms, respire more when the temperature rises.
d) Trees in forests suffer from stress that harms their growth when the temperature rises.

23 Explain why the following activities add methane to the atmosphere:
a) extracting fossil fuels
b) agriculture
c) waste treatment.

Key term

The **global warming potential** of a greenhouse gas measures the extent to which it absorbs infrared radiation and warms the atmosphere over a specified length of time compared with the effect of emitting the same amount of carbon dioxide.

Gas	Pre-industrial concentration (pre-1750)	Global mean concentration in the troposphere (2004)	Units	Lifetime in atmosphere (years)	Global warming potential		
					20 years	100 years	500 years
Carbon dioxide	260	377	ppmv	variable	1	1	1
Methane	730–688	1847–1730	ppbv	12	62	23	7
Nitrous oxide	270	319–318	ppbv	114	275	296	156
Ozone in the lower atmosphere	25	34	ppbv	hours to days	n/a	n/a	n/a
CFC11 and CFC12	0	250–545	pptv	45–100	6300–10 200	4600–10 600	1600–5200

Figure 4.12

Past and present concentrations of selected greenhouse gases and their global warming potentials compared to carbon dioxide over different periods of years. The unit 'pptv' stands for parts per trillion by volume. 1 pptv is equivalent to 0.000 001 ppmv.

Questions

24 Why does methane contribute about a third as much to the greenhouse effect as carbon dioxide despite its atmospheric concentration being over 200 times lower?

25 a) Why are the global warming potentials of CFCs so large when their concentrations in the atmosphere are so low?
b) Why does the global warming potential of methane get smaller as the time frame gets larger?

26 Which country emits the most carbon dioxide per head of population?

27 Give one example each to show how these sectors, shown in Figure 4.13, add greenhouse gases to the atmosphere:

a) buildings
b) waste
c) agriculture
d) land use other than agriculture.

Worldwide contributions to the enhanced greenhouse effect

Figure 4.13 shows that a few countries are responsible for most of the enhanced greenhouse effect. Although China has now overtaken the USA as the biggest single emitter of carbon dioxide, its much larger population means that it ranks well down the list of per capita emissions.

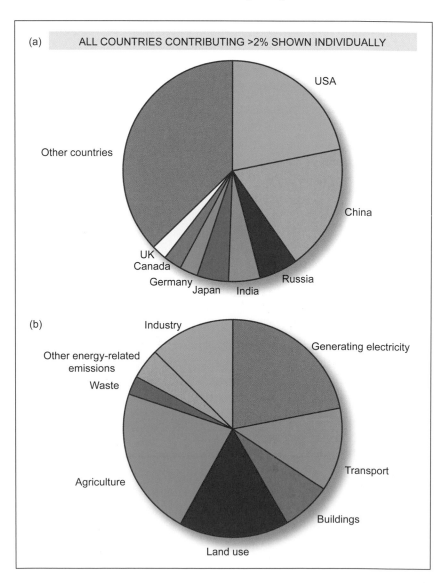

Figure 4.13

(a) Carbon dioxide emissions by country, or country group, for 2004 and (b) total emissions of all greenhouse gases by sector as measured by the quantity of carbon dioxide that would have the same global warming effect.

4.3 How do scientists find out about climate in the past?

Instrumental records

Weather records, collected by meteorologists, provide us with the best information about our climate in recent years. However, if we are interested in finding out about climate change over longer periods of time, meteorological data can be much less useful. The main reason for this is that meteorological stations have generally only been collecting data since about the mid-1800s. Many stations started recording much later than that. Even so, meteorological data are still very useful.

In the 1970s, the British climatologist Gordon Manley published a record of changing temperatures for Central England extending back to 1659 based on a compilation of data, painstakingly researched over several decades. This data series, which is the longest available instrumental record of temperature in the world, is regularly updated by the Hadley Centre, which is the research centre studying climate change in the UK Met Office (Figure 4.14). A similar series, beginning in 1766, is available for rainfall. On a global scale, temperature compilations are available extending back to 1850.

(a)
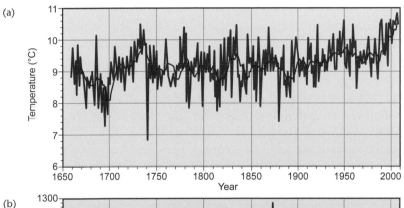

(b)
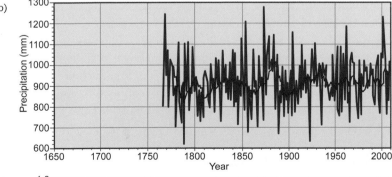

(c)
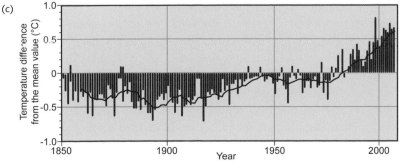

Figure 4.14

(a) Mean annual temperature for Central England, 1659–2007, and (b) annual precipitation for England and Wales, 1766–2007. (c) Changes in the mean global temperatures, 1850–2007. The red lines smooth out the short-term fluctuations and show the trends. In each plot they show the 10-year moving average.

Questions

28 a) Suggest reasons for the fluctuations in the values recorded in the top two graphs of Figure 4.14.
b) What, if anything, can you conclude from these two graphs?

29 Refer to the bottom graph in Figure 4.14
a) In which period did the mean global temperature seem to remain steady?
b) In which periods was there marked global warming?

Figure 4.15

Documentary records of changing climate: (a) a mid-nineteenth century picture of the Lex Blanche glacier in the European Alps (b) a late-twentieth century photograph of the same glacier.

Question

30 How does Figure 4.15 suggest that the climate has changed since the mid-nineteenth century?

Documentary records

Meteorological records can be extended using documentary evidence of past climate. Documentary sources include maps, old photographs, paintings, reports of crop yields, archives, ships' logs and diaries. Such sources, while not direct records of climate, may contain information that can be used by historical climatologists to infer past climatic conditions. One good example is the use of documentary archives to reconstruct fluctuations in the size of Alpine glaciers. Glaciers may advance and retreat over the years in response to changing climate conditions, especially in response to varying winter snowfall and summer temperature. Glaciers advance during times of colder temperature and increased snowfall. They retreat during drier and warmer times. By using documentary evidence along with more recent monitoring, scientists can piece together a record of glacier fluctuations and use this to draw conclusions about changing temperature and/or snowfall (Figure 4.15).

Other documentary sources can be used in the same way, and in some cases have extended information about climate change back well over 1000 years. Not surprisingly, the richest and longest sources of documentary evidence come from parts of the world with a long history of record keeping: especially good records are available from Europe and from China.

Data from natural archives

Despite the extended record from documentary sources, even a record dating back for several centuries is not long enough to capture the full range of variability in the Earth's climate system. In addition, large parts of the Earth lack good documentary records. Scientists therefore turn to natural records of climate either to extend their records further back in time or to fill geographical 'gaps'. Such natural records, or natural 'archives' as they are often called, include sediments laid down in the oceans, in lakes and on land, ice preserved in glaciers and ice sheets, trees rings and fossil corals.

Scientists who look at climate from these natural archives are called palaeoclimatologists. Natural archives can extend the records back many hundreds of thousands, or even millions, of years and so give us a much longer record of climate change and variability. However, scientists cannot extract climate information directly from these archives. Instead they have to look for clues in the records. They examine any fossils, including pollen, and measure the chemical composition of samples. From the data they can then infer information about climate such as temperature and rainfall. These estimates of past climate usually carry quite large uncertainties, certainly larger than meteorological data. Also, natural archives may be difficult to date precisely and there may be gaps in the records when, for example, sediments are eroded. Despite these problems, natural archives are the only sources of evidence we have for long-term changes in climate.

Sediments from the deep oceans

Deep ocean sediments contain a wealth of information about past changes in the oceans as well as conditions on land. The type and particle size of sediments can tell scientists about ocean circulation. Fossils preserved within the sediments, especially remains of microscopic plants and animals, provide information about water temperature and ocean circulation. The variations in the oxygen isotopes found in the calcium carbonate of ocean sediments can be interpreted to provide a record of variations in volume of ice in the world (Figure 4.16). This is closely linked to global temperature. As a result, scientists have been able to use their studies of sediments from the deep ocean to provide a long and often continuous record of changing climate extending back millions of years in some places.

The recovery of cores of sediment from the deep sea has been an increasingly important source of palaeoclimatic information. Work has continued for nearly 50 years starting with the Deep-sea Drilling Program in the mid-1960s, followed by the Ocean Drilling Program in the mid-1980s and, more recently, by the International Ocean Drilling Program, which began in 2003. Although the recovery of sediment cores from the deep oceans is expensive and complex, the study of these cores has revolutionised our understanding of climate change over timescales ranging from thousands to millions of years. The data have provided firm support, for example, for the theory that changes in the Earth's orbit around the Sun have caused the cycles of the ice ages of the past few million years.

Questions

31 Why is calcium carbonate common in ocean sediments?

32 a) What features of Figure 4.16 can be used to see if the data in the graph are consistent with the data plotted in Figure 4.10 on page 106?
b) To what extent are the data in Figure 4.16 consistent with the data in Figure 4.10?
c) Why is it important in science to be able to compare data produced by one method with similar data produced by a different method?

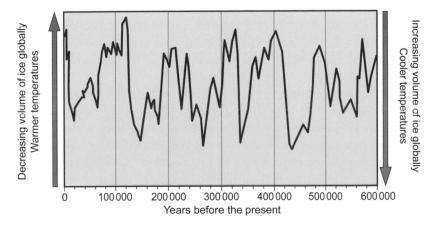

Figure 4.16

Changes to the global volume of ice and the mean global temperature deduced from oxygen isotope variations measured in the calcium carbonate of microfossil shells from the Pacific Ocean near the equator. These changes mainly indicate alternations between periods with glacial and non-glacial climates over the past 600 000 years.

Questions

33 Suggest natural processes in the environment that could be responsible for slightly changing the ratio of oxygen isotopes in water or calcium carbonate.

34 Suggest a method that scientists could use to check that they are using the correct formula when translating the oxygen isotope ratio in Antarctic ice to the temperature of the clouds when the snow formed.

35 Why are there no instrumental records of the composition of trace gases in the atmosphere that are more than about 50 years old?

36 Suggest assumptions that have to be made in using bubbles of gas in ice to measure the concentration of gases in past atmospheres.

37 What sorts of contamination of Greenland ice might give rise to carbon dioxide?

38 Suggest a method that scientists can use to determine the ages of the different layers of ice.

Oxygen isotopes in the study of past climates

Isotopes are atoms of an element that have a nucleus with the same number of protons but different numbers of neutrons. Oxygen has two major isotopes. Most of the oxygen in the world consists of oxygen-16, with eight protons and eight neutrons. A trace amount consists of oxygen-18, which has two more neutrons. Scientists can measure very small variations in the ratio of oxygen-18 and oxygen-16 in a range of environmental and geological materials. From the results they can work out important information about climate.

Polar ice sheets form from snow. In the water frozen in the ice sheets, the oxygen-18 to oxygen-16 ratio varies with the temperature in the clouds at the time the snow fell. A lower oxygen-18 to oxygen-16 ratio indicates that the temperature was lower.

In the calcium carbonate ($CaCO_3$) formed in the deep oceans, the oxygen-18 to oxygen-16 ratio is determined by the ratio of the two isotopes in seawater. This, in turn, is controlled by changing global ice volume. During glacial periods, when more of the world's water is frozen in large ice sheets, the ocean water becomes relatively enriched in oxygen-18, and this is recorded as calcium carbonate precipitates. During warm stages, the oxygen-18 to oxygen-16 ratio of deep-ocean carbonates decreases. For carbonates that formed close to the sea surface, such as coral skeletons, the ratio of oxygen isotopes in calcium carbonate is mainly related to sea surface temperature.

Ice cores

Like deep-sea drilling, the recovery of cores of ice from the world's great ice sheets is expensive and challenging. The Greenland ice sheet is around 3 km thick. Its ice contains a climate record extending back over 100 000 years. The Antarctic is colder and drier than Greenland so the ice there accumulates more slowly. This means that the 3.2 km thickness of ice in Antarctica preserves a climate record that is about 800 000 years long. The oxygen-18 to oxygen-16 of the frozen water in the ice is a record of changes in air temperature.

In addition, gas bubbles trapped in the ice give 'snapshots' of past atmospheres and can be used to measure their composition. Indeed, analyses of such gas bubbles are the only direct means we have of measuring greenhouse gas concentrations in the atmosphere earlier than about 50 years ago. There are problems, however. The bubbles in ice take time to close off from the atmosphere. This means that the gas within them is somewhat younger than the surrounding ice. Scientists cannot, therefore, simply assume a direct relationship between the concentrations of greenhouse gases in the gas bubbles and temperature from oxygen isotope analysis of the ice surrounding the bubbles.

To complicate matters further, the difference in age between gas and ice varies through time, depending on the rate that ice accumulates. Furthermore, reliable records of carbon dioxide concentration cannot be obtained from the Greenland ice sheet. This is because high concentrations of impurities have led to the formation of carbon dioxide within the ice itself. Reliable records are available from the Antarctic ice cores, however, and reliable methane data can be obtained from both.

Pollen grains

Most pollen grains fall to the ground close to the plant that they came from. As a result, pollen found in lake sediments or peat deposits can give scientists a good indication of the local vegetation at the time when the deposit formed. The best records come from bogs and lake sediments where there has been little oxygen to support the growth of bacteria that decompose pollen grains.

Pollen grains make good fossils because they have tough outer coatings that are resistant to decay. Also the pollen grains from different plants are highly distinctive so that it is relatively easy to identify the plant that they come from.

By studying pollen grains, scientists (called palynologists) can reconstruct the distribution of plants in the past. They can then use their deductions as clues to changes in the climate. This assumes that the scientists can show that a species has not changed its ability to tolerate environmental conditions such as minimal rainfall or extreme temperatures. Studies of pollen in peat allow scientists to find out about climate at least as far back as the last ice age, which ended about 11 500 years ago.

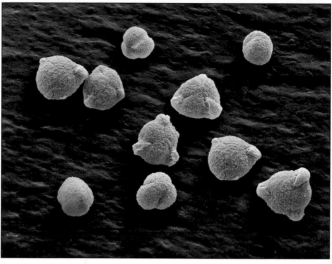

 Figure 4.17

Distinctive pollen grains from an oak tree magnified about 200 times. Oak trees are moderately sensitive to frosts in spring and require 4 months of the year with temperatures above 10 °C.

Tree rings

Most trees produce annual growth rings. The thickness of these rings changes according to climatic factors such as temperature or rainfall. Scientists study the relationship between the widths of recent tree rings and the records of the climate where the tree grew. In this way they calibrate the widths of rings in terms of modern climatic variables. They can then use these calibrations for different trees to reconstruct the past climate for the period before the instrumental record started. The reconstruction of past climate using tree rings in this way is called dendroclimatology. Although the oldest living trees, the Bristlecone pines of the White Mountains, California (Figure 4.18), are less than 5000 years old, dendroclimatic records have been extended back to just over 10 000 years (in Southern Germany) by using dead, or fossil, wood.

Figure 4.18

Bristlecone pines from the White Mountains, California.

Question

39 Scientists use the term 'proxy data' to described the data deduced from studies of natural archives. Why is this an appropriate term?

40 The nickname 'hockey stick' is used to describe the curve in Figure 4.19.
a) Why is this an appropriate name?
b) What is the most striking feature of the curve and what are the implications?
c) Suggest why the degree of uncertainty narrows over the period covered by the data.
d) Why was it only possible to create this plot in the final years of the twentieth century?

The 'hockey stick'

Palaeoclimatic data have been used to reconstruct changes in climate over a variety of timescales. Of greatest interest to those concerned with our present climate and its possible future behaviour, however, is the past millennium.

The first quantitative reconstructions of climate over the past millennium were constructed and published in the late 1990s. These were based on a range of datasets from natural archives together with documentary evidence for the earlier part of the record, and on instrumental data for the past 150 years or so. There have been a number of studies, each of which differs in detail; nonetheless, they all show the same basic pattern (Figure 4.19).

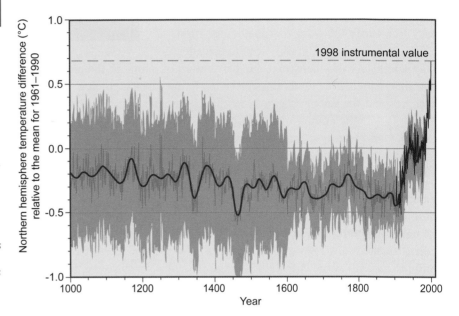

Figure 4.19

Reconstructions of Northern hemisphere climate over the past millennium from a range of instrumental (red), documentary sources and natural archives (blue). Grey shading represents uncertainty. The purple line smoothes out the short-term fluctuations in the data from documentary sources and natural archives to show the trends. It shows the 40-year moving average.

The ice-core scientist

Dr Liz Thomas works at the British Antarctic Survey, based in Cambridge. Her work focuses on the study of ice cores as archives of past climate. Liz has analysed ice cores from Greenland as well as from Antarctica (Figure 4.20). Following training as an oceanographer, Liz had originally planned to work on coral records of past climate, but somewhere along the way she became diverted from warm tropical oceans to the polar regions and a career in ice cores.

"Working in the Antarctic requires some special personal qualities" she says. "A good sense of humour, not minding the cold and the ability to do without all but the basics, are important."

In the field

A field season in Antarctica may last anything from 6 weeks to 4 months. It usually begins with a flight to the Falkland Islands, either direct from the UK or via South America. From here, scientists fly to one of the Antarctic bases: in Liz's case, she flew to the Rothera Research Station, located on Adelaide Island, approximately 1860 km south of the Falkland Islands. This is the base that supports the bulk of fieldwork in Antarctica.

Figure 4.20

Dr Liz Thomas drilling at Berkner Island, Antarctica.

Base life is fairly sophisticated compared with life in the field. The base has comfortable rooms with en suite facilities and wireless Internet access amongst other things. Up to a hundred people may be stationed at the base in the Antarctic summer months, but only a handful remain over the winter to maintain the base and carry on some of the science projects. Ice coring, which is just one of several scientific activities supported by the base, only takes place in the Antarctic summer.

From Rothera Station, scientists are transported to their field sites in Twin Otter aircraft and from this point the comforts of the base are left behind, although this is more than compensated for by the excitement of the science. Some deep drilling projects involve quite large teams. In contrast, Liz's Antarctic ice-coring season in 2007, on Berkner Island, was a two-person operation. She describes the coring work as physically tough and very tiring. Because of the 24 hours of daylight in the Antarctic summer, the working day is determined by the need for rest and food, not that the latter is anything much to look forward to. Dehydrated meals are the order of the day, with plenty of fat-rich food to help keep out the cold, although the ration of a bar of chocolate per day is a little more enticing. The weather can be a real problem. If gales set in, scientists cannot work and are confined to their accommodation – tents – with little to do but sleep, although the demanding nature of the work means that sleeping is rarely a problem.

Once the fieldwork is over, the scientists, their equipment and the ice cores are transported back to base. Before the scientists leave their base, they carefully describe and log the cores before cutting them into 55 cm lengths to fit into insulated boxes that were originally designed to transport tubs of ice cream. The cores are then taken back to the UK by sea while the scientists head for home by air. Once again, the weather can cause problems, delaying their journey by several weeks in some cases.

In the laboratory

Once back in Cambridge, Liz still cannot escape from the cold. Over the past few years she has spent well over 2000 hours working in a giant freezer back at the British Antarctic Survey (BAS). She has had to cut samples of one of the Greenland ice cores. In some cases, she had to cut slices very accurately with the help of a specially designed ice-cutting machine to make sure that they were exactly 2 mm thick. Thin samples are needed to give one sample for every couple of months of the period during which the ice formed back in the last ice age. Such thin samples allow detailed information to be obtained about the month by month changes to the climate at that time.

The sampling process is long and tedious. Once complete, the analytical work can begin and this involves many more hours in the laboratory. Liz undertakes analytical work using a technique called ion chromatography. She uses her instrument to measure the concentrations of calcium, magnesium, sodium, chloride and sulfate ions (Figure 4.21). Although there is no need to carry out this work in a freezer, it is important to avoid any contamination of the samples, so she has to wear special protective clothing, including a face mask, when in the laboratory.

The calcium and magnesium content of the ice originally came from atmospheric dust carried by winds from the continents, especially Central Asia. There is more dust to be swept up by the winds when the continents are dry. Some of the dust makes its way to Greenland and becomes incorporated into the ice. This means that variations in the calcium and magnesium content of the ice through time give scientists clues about the extent of rainfall in the Northern hemisphere during the period studied.

Sodium and chloride ions come from sea salt. Measuring the concentrations of these ions in ice provides information about windiness and the atmospheric circulation around the Arctic. Finally, sulfate ions come from volcanoes and tell scientists about past volcanic activity.

Figure 4.21

Dr Liz Thomas measuring the ion composition of melted ice core samples at BAS using an ion chromatograph.

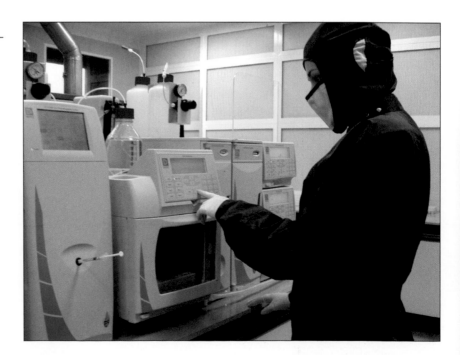

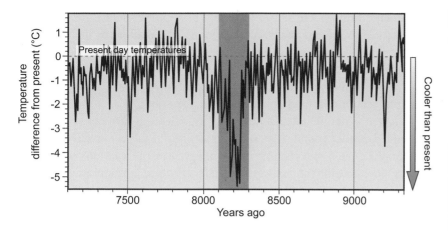

Figure 4.22

An abrupt period of cooling recorded in a Greenland ice core around 8200 years ago (grey shaded area).

Teamwork

Given the time, effort and expense of collecting ice cores, it is important to analyse them in as many different ways as possible (Figure 4.22). While Liz's own work concentrates on the concentrations of dissolved ions in the ice, other labs undertake other analyses including measurements of stable isotopes and trace gases. Because the reconstruction of past climate involves looking at all of the data, work on ice cores is usually written up and published by teams of scientists, often working in many different institutions in several countries. It is rare for scientific papers based on ice cores to be written by only one author.

4.4 Climate modelling

The future has not yet happened so unlike the past, which we can reconstruct using geological evidence, the future can only be the focus of long-term forecasts. The climate system is highly complex so these forecasts involve the use of climate models run on extremely powerful computers. Given the prominent role that climate models now play in the study of future climate, it is interesting to note that the first models were not developed to predict the future; rather, they were designed to help improve understanding of the climate system.

The nature of climate models

Climate models are based on the physical laws that describe transfers of mass and energy within the climate system. Their operation involves solving very large numbers of mathematical equations that describe the climate system. Because of their complexity, the computing power needed to run the most state-of-the-art models is considerable and the most complex models are therefore run on the most powerful computers available.

Climate models used to forecast future climate are called general circulation models, or GCMs. Models of this kind are also used to forecast the weather over a much shorter timescale. This type of model was first developed in the 1970s. Since then they have grown in complexity as scientists have improved their understanding of the climate system and as computers have become more powerful.

The first models represented the atmosphere in a simple way. They took into account the radiation from the Sun and the effects of carbon

Questions

41 Explain why particular care has to be taken to avoid contamination of the ice cores and the samples cut from the cores for analysis.

42 Suggest reasons why more dust accumulates in Greenland ice when the climate is arid.

43 Suggest reasons why there is a connection between the concentration of sodium and chloride ions in ice samples and the windiness of the climate when the ice formed.

44 What are the possible implications for today of detecting the period of cooling in Greenland over 8000 years ago, as shown in Figure 4.22?

dioxide and rainfall, but not much else. Through the 1980s, the models were refined to include the effects of clouds and changes to the surface of the land that affect albedo. Then the models were adapted to feature a simple ocean and, by the mid-1990s, ocean models had greater sophistication. Towards the end of the last century the models could also take into account particulate matter from volcanoes.

In recent years the models have also included the carbon cycle and added further complexity to the modelling of the oceans. The most sophisticated models now incorporate chemical reactions in the atmosphere, and the interactions that couple the oceans and atmosphere. These are described as fully coupled atmosphere–ocean GCMs (AOGCMs). However, even the most advanced models cannot properly represent small-scale or highly complex phenomena or processes, such as clouds.

The three-dimensional resolution of GCMs has also increased. The earliest models simulated climate on a grid with squares measuring 600 km × 600 km and with only five vertical levels within the atmosphere. Today the most advanced AOGCMs have 135 km × 135 km grid squares, with the atmosphere represented by 38 vertical levels and the oceans by 40. Modern GCMs incorporate details of important feedbacks within the system.

Despite the increasing complexity of GCMs, more simple climate models are still used and can be invaluable in certain circumstances. Such models typically have larger grid sizes and much reduced complexity in the way in which the climate system is represented. As a result, they are less demanding on computer time and power and therefore quicker and cheaper to run. They allow researchers to undertake much longer runs than is possible with fully coupled, state-of-the-art AOGCMs and to vary initial conditions slightly and thereby perform many series of runs, which are invaluable in assessing and quantifying uncertainties.

How are models validated?

Models are the only means that scientists have of forecasting the future. A challenge for scientists is to test the reliability of their models. When forecasting weather, scientists can simply wait and see what happens and compare the actual weather with their forecast. Studies of this kind have shown that modern weather forecasts are quite accurate, especially for the next 3 to 5 days.

Scientists using models to simulate the changes to climate for many decades into the future cannot wait to see what happens. However, it is vital that future climate simulations can be tested in some way, because these may form the basis of policy decisions. Fortunately, there are several ways to validate climate models. These are as follows:

- By comparing the results of simulations of past climates to the measured climate over the past 150 years – with particular emphasis on the mean values of climatic variables such as temperature and precipitation (Figure 4.23).
- By comparing model simulations of past climate over longer timescales with climate data deduced from geological records.
- By comparing model simulations of large climatic events with meteorological records – such as the climatic response to major volcanic eruptions.

Questions

45 Why is there a big increase in the computing power needed in moving from a model based in a 600 km × 600 km grid with only five vertical levels in the atmosphere to a model based on a 135 km × 135 km grid with 38 vertical levels in the atmosphere and 40 levels in the oceans?

46 Suggest two examples of feedbacks in the climate system which climate models need to take into account.

Key term

In meteorology, **precipitation** is water that condenses from the atmosphere and falls to the ground as rain, snow, hail, fog or sleet.

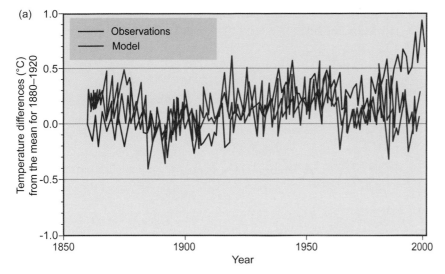

(a)

Figure 4.23

Changes in the global mean surface temperature relative to the mean temperature between 1880 and 1920 from the instrumental record compared with simulations with a coupled ocean–atmosphere climate model (a) taking into account the natural effects of solar radiation and volcanic eruptions only, and (b) taking into account both natural and anthropogenic effects of greenhouse gases including ozone and the effects of aerosols.

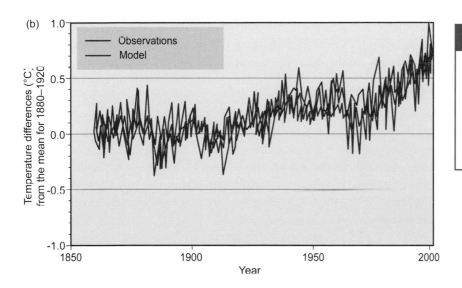

(b)

Questions

47 What can you conclude by comparing parts a and b of Figure 4.23?

48 Suggest which of the three ways of testing climate models provides the severest test of the models. Give your reasons.

Climate sensitivity and projections of future climate

One of the key issues for climate modellers is to explore how sensitive the Earth's climate is to natural events and human activities. One way of exploring this issue is to use models to estimate the extent of global warming that would take place if the concentration of carbon dioxide in the atmosphere were to rise to double the value before industrialisation started.

Models are the tools most usually used to measure sensitivity, although attempts have been made to estimate sensitivity by looking back into the geological past. Values of sensitivity vary between models. Recent studies suggest that climate sensitivity is likely to lie between 2 °C and 4.5 °C, with a best estimate of about 3 °C. The largest source of uncertainty in estimates of sensitivity lies in the feedback mechanisms associated with clouds, which are still imperfectly understood.

Key term

A measure of **climate sensitivity** is the average change in the mean surface temperature of the Earth resulting from a doubling of the concentration of carbon dioxide in the atmosphere from its pre-industrial level.

Figure 4.24

The results of modelling the mean temperature change of the air just above the ground in the Northern hemisphere from 2000–2100, assuming greenhouse gas emissions continue to rise as they did in the early 1990s.

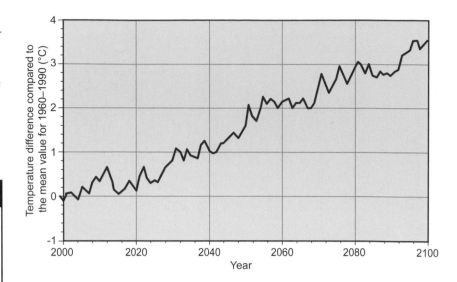

Key terms

A **prediction** is a statement of what we think will happen in future. A weather forecast is an example of a prediction.

A **projection** is a statement of what could happen in future based on a set of assumptions about possible changes to variables such as the level of greenhouse gas emissions.

Questions

49 Why is it very important to be able to put an accurate value on climate sensitivity?

50 Why is it not straightforward to estimate climate sensitivity by studying data from natural archives in the Earth's geological past?

51 What, according to Figure 4.24, is the climate sensitivity of the Northern hemisphere if the modelling is based on the expectation that the carbon dioxide concentration in the atmosphere will be double the pre-industrial value by 2080?

It is not possible to predict future changes of climate. Rather, modellers use a number of different projections of how greenhouse gas emissions will change through time and model the climatic response to the changes. Figure 4.24 shows an example of such a projection.

The climate modeller

Dr Alan Haywood is a climate modeller at the University of Leeds. His research focuses on the modelling of past climates. However, the modelling of past climates and the use of models to project future climate are closely related tasks. As he says: "Models are the only means we have of finding out about possible future climate, simply because the future hasn't happened yet! However, we also need models to help us understand the past. The Earth's climate system is extremely complex and we have imperfect knowledge of past climate because of gaps – both in geographical terms and in terms of time – in our records. Climate models help us to fill these gaps and improve our understanding of how our climate system works."

Figure 4.25

Dr Alan Haywood examines a climate model simulation of past climate in his office in Leeds.

The nature of climate models

Regarding models, Alan Haywood reminds us that: "Models are, by their very nature, imperfect representations of reality. Even the largest and most complex climate models are a simplification of reality. We have no choice, because the climate system is almost unimaginably complex. Also, if models did not simplify reality then they would no longer be models, but exact replicas of the real thing.

"Because models are simplifications of reality, their representation of climate is always 'wrong' to some degree. By this we mean that the real climate and the description of climate from our models are not the same. Perhaps surprisingly, this need not necessarily be a problem. The important question is whether a model provides a sufficiently adequate representation of the climate system for it to be useful. Weather forecasting for 3 days into the future requires a different degree of accuracy than is required for the reconstruction of past climate, say 18 000 years in the past. The demands on the model are therefore different in each case."

Teamwork

"Modern climate models are very large and complex and they have to be developed by multidisciplinary teams rather than individuals. These teams consist of environmental scientists concerned with different aspects of the Earth's climate system, backed up by computer programmers. Although some of the early model development was carried out in universities, over the past decade most of the actual building of models, at least in the UK, has been concentrated in the Hadley Centre, focussing on the Met Office Unified Model (Figure 4.26). The Hadley Centre is a world-renowned centre for climate prediction and modelling and a part of the UK Met Office based in Exeter."

Questions

52 Why are the results of climate modelling of value even if the projections of future climates are 'always wrong'?

53 Where in the world, according to the Hadley Centre Model, will global warming be greatest when the carbon dioxide concentration in the atmosphere is twice its pre-industrial level?

Figure 4.26

Results of a climate simulation for the future using the Hadley Centre Model. The map depicts the difference between simulated mean annual temperatures at the Earth's surface for a doubling of atmospheric carbon dioxide concentration compared to the level before the onset of the industrial revolution. This is just one of a range of projections from the model.

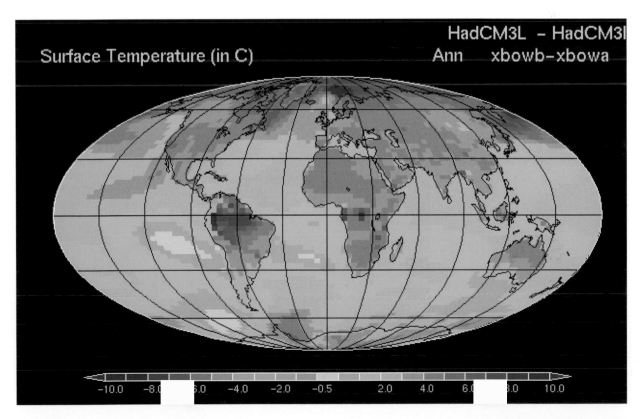

Computing power and costs

"Although simple models can be run on modern desktop computers, more complex modelling needs high-performance computers. In the United Kingdom, suitable computers are housed at the Met Office. They can also be found in a number of universities, although here, climate modellers compete with people from other disciplines, mainly in the sciences, for computer time.

"Such high-performance computers are extremely powerful in terms of processing power (equivalent to about 1000 dual-core processor PCs) and storage capacity (up to several hundred terabytes, Tb, where $1\,Tb = 10^{12}$ bytes). They are also very expensive, costing somewhere in the region of a million pounds, with a bill for maintenance and upgrading of around several hundred thousand pounds every few years. Such computers need to be housed in ultra-clean and temperature-controlled conditions.

"This means that climate modelling is an expensive business. It can take up to a day of computing time to run 3 to 5 model years: that's up to about 160 days to run a 500-year simulation. For example, to run the HadCM3 model for 500 simulated years can cost between £10 000 and £20 000 for a single run on the UK's national computing facility."

Modelling and forecasting

Modelling of past climate and projections of future climate use the same type of models that are used for weather forecasting. One question that people often ask is: "How can you hope to simulate climate 50 to 100 years in the future if even the weather forecasts are sometimes wrong?". As Alan points out, weather forecasting and climate prediction are not the same thing, even though they are undertaken using similar models (Figure 4.27).

"Weather forecasts are based on simulations giving a lot of detail over a relatively small area and in just a few days. Future climate simulations and past climate reconstructions, on the other hand, are concerned with climate, which is the average weather. In climate simulations, the short-term variability that we call weather is averaged out to give mean values. So, even though weather forecasts become less accurate beyond about 3 days, it is still possible to simulate the average weather – what we call climate – far into the future or way back in the past."

Question

54 Where in the world, according to the Hadley Centre Model, is the increase in summer rainfall greatest compared to 9000 years ago?

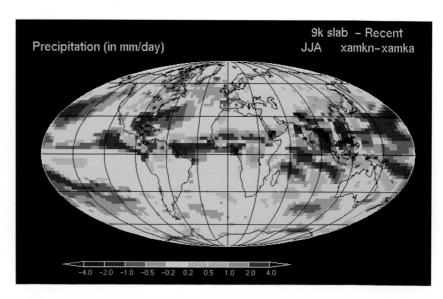

Figure 4.27

Results of a climate simulation for the past using the Hadley Centre Model. The map depicts the difference between summer precipitation (rainfall and snowfall) 9000 years ago compared to present.

4.5 The Intergovernmental Panel on Climate Change (IPCC)

Much research on climate change and related issues is happening worldwide. This work is sometimes carried out by individual scientists but more usually by teams, mainly working in universities and research establishments. The work is funded by governments, a range of national and international funding bodies and also by industry. The results of the work are generally published in the scientific literature following a process of peer review.

Most of this work, although publicly available, remains largely 'invisible' to all except specialists within the specific scientific fields. This is partly because the relevant scientific journals are held in specialist libraries and are only available to others on subscription. It is also the case that the papers themselves are largely incomprehensible to lay people.

The challenge is to bring together the vast body of literature in a form that is more widely accessible so that it can be used to inform international political debate about climate change. For the past two decades, this has been the task of the Intergovernmental Panel on Climate Change, or IPCC.

The IPCC was established in 1988 by the World Meteorological Organization (WMO) and the United Nations Environment Programme (UNEP), in response to growing evidence that human impact was altering climate. The IPCC was set up to bring together relevant information from existing peer-reviewed literature. The IPCC is not itself a research organisation that undertakes or funds primary research. There are three working groups to review and assess the work of others (Figure 4.28). In addition, there is a separate task force charged with helping nations to compile inventories of their greenhouse gas emissions.

Questions

55 Why is it important that the work of climate scientists is published in journals?

56 Why is peer review crucial to science in general and to the work of the IPCC in particular?

Figure 4.28

The organisational structure of the Intergovernmental Panel on Climate Change, IPCC.

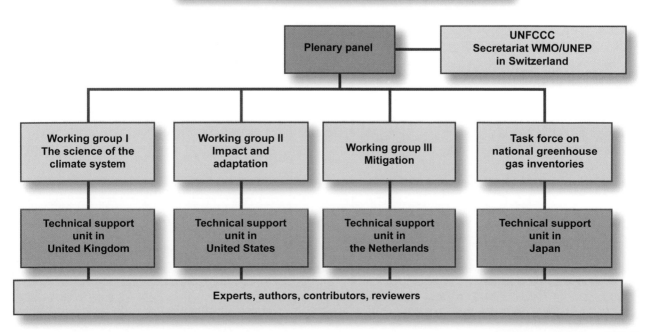

Intergovernmental Panel on Climate Change (IPCC)

Plenary panel

UNFCCC
Secretariat WMO/UNEP
in Switzerland

Working group I
The science of the
climate system

Working group II
Impact and
adaptation

Working group III
Mitigation

Task force on
national greenhouse
gas inventories

Technical support
unit in
United Kingdom

Technical support
unit in
United States

Technical support
unit in
the Netherlands

Technical support
unit in
Japan

Experts, authors, contributors, reviewers

The main outputs from the work of the IPCC are the assessment reports. These are the major syntheses of research work. The most recent assessment report (AR4) was published in 2007. It includes the full technical reports from each of the working groups, a technical summary and a summary for policymakers for each of the working groups; a synthesis report covers all of the working groups' findings.

The IPCC scenarios and their implications

There are simply too many uncertainties surrounding future greenhouse gas emissions to be able to predict climate nearly 100 years in the future. Rather, the IPCC has based its projections for future climate on a number of scenarios.

Originally the word 'scenario' meant the outline of a play or film. Here it means a set of assumptions that can be used to build up a picture of what the future might be like. Climate models explore the implications of scenarios. Scenarios are not predictions or forecasts but they offer images of possible climates in the future.

The IPCC scenarios

The IPCC greenhouse gas emission scenarios currently in use were published in 2001. Although there are 40 individual scenarios, they all follow one of four main 'storylines' associated with different projected social and economic circumstances around the world. Two of the main storylines are as follows.

A1 – Very rapid economic growth worldwide; peak in population by the middle of this century followed by a decline; rapid introduction of new and efficient technology across the globe. The individual scenarios within this storyline largely reflect energy use: A1F1 assumes intensive use of fossil fuels; A1T assumes the adoption of alternative energy sources; while A1B is based on a balance of sources.

B1 – Similar changes in population and economic growth to A1, but with reductions in use of materials coupled with shifts to 'clean' and efficient technologies and the adoption of global solutions to sustainability.

In addition, one of the earlier emission scenarios published in 1992 (IS92a) is still in use since it has featured widely in many climatic impact studies. This is often known as 'business-as-usual' since it is thought to provide a realistic picture of what would happen to emissions under a continuation of conditions that prevailed in the early 1990s.

Figure 4.29

Emissions of carbon dioxide under a range of IPCC emission scenarios, along with projected atmospheric concentrations of the gas.

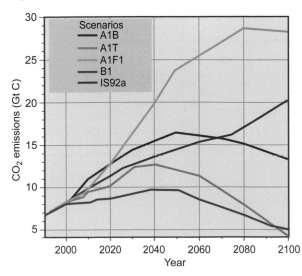

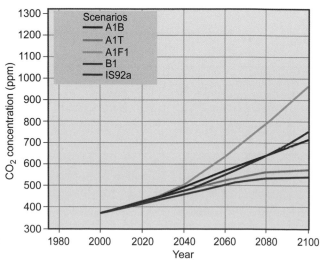

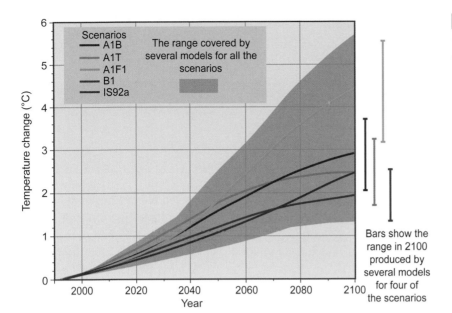

Figure 4.30

Global mean temperature change simulated by a range of climate models for selected IPCC greenhouse gas emission scenarios.

Model simulations project a global mean temperature change of between about 1.4 and 5.8 °C by 2100 (Figure 4.30).

4.6 Impacts of climate change

It is important to distinguish between global warming and climate change. Warmer temperatures will bring other alterations to climate, such as changes to rainfall patterns and increases in the frequency and intensity of extreme weather events.

The warming will be not be even across the world. The harmful effects of climate change are likely to be concentrated in the countries that are less able to adapt and respond. According to the projections of climate models, climate change will be greatest at high northern latitudes and least over the southern oceans and parts of the north Atlantic. In the northern latitudes, this will lead to reduced snow cover, sea ice and permafrost.

Changes in precipitation will be even more variable. The projections suggest that there will be increases in some areas, including high latitudes and the parts of Asia affected by monsoons. In other places, such as the sub-tropical land regions, there will be less precipitation.

Questions

61 What would you say to someone living in England who thinks that global warming is a good thing because it will lead to long hot summers and warmer winters?

62 Give examples of extreme weather events likely to become more common and more intense as the mean global temperature rises.

Sea level rise

According to the models, there are likely to be significant rises in sea levels by 2100.

Figure 4.31

The best estimate of the projected rise in mean sea level by 2100. The projected values vary according to the assumptions fed into models and are subject to considerable uncertainty. These values are based on IPCC estimates. Some sea level specialists are suggesting that the rise will be more substantial than these figures suggest.

Changes arising from global warming	Contribution to rise in mean sea level/metres
Expansion of the water in the oceans	+0.28
Melting of glaciers and the Greenland ice sheet	+0.22
Increased precipitation on the Antarctic ice sheet	−0.01

Many coastal regions of the world are vulnerable to future sea level rises. These include the coastal, delta regions of large river systems, some of which are heavily populated and already susceptible to regular flooding. One example is Bangladesh, on the delta of the River Ganges and other large rivers.

Small, low-lying tropical islands are also vulnerable to sea level rise. Several such islands are in danger including the Pacific Islands of Tuvalu and Vanuatu, and the Maldive Islands in the Indian Ocean.

Higher mean sea levels not only increase the risk of damage from storm surges but also make it more likely that salty sea water will contaminate fresh water aquifers in coastal regions.

In countries such as the Netherlands, elaborate sea defences currently protect low-lying areas of the country. Sea level rise in this century will require these sea defences to be improved, at great cost, if inundation of the land is to be avoided.

Figure 4.32

The melting of large ice sheets as well as mountain glaciers, such as the one shown in the photograph, will make a significant contribution to future rises in sea level.

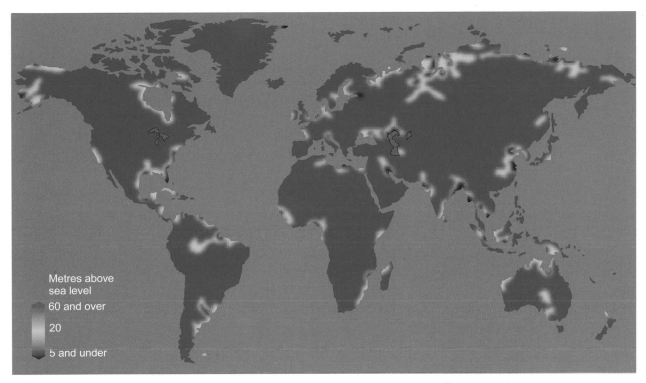

Metres above
sea level

60 and over

20

5 and under

Figure 4.33

Areas of the world's coastal zone that are
potentially vulnerable to future rises in sea
level.

It is difficult to estimate with real certainty just how many coastal
dwellers might be at risk from future sea level rises. Recent studies
suggest that, around the world, the area of land that is less than
10 metres above sea level is home to around 10% of the world's population;
that is over 600 million people, and 13% of its urban population. Around
two-thirds of the world's large cities with more than 5 million inhabitants
occupy zones on the coast that are only a little above sea level.

Water resources

Since the 1940s, there has been a four-fold increase in the global
demand for fresh water. Today, more than a billion people worldwide
still have no access to safe water, and more than double that number
have little or no sanitation. Climate change is likely to complicate this
already difficult situation.

There is considerable uncertainty in the projections from models
about future rainfall. Some areas may receive more rainfall in the
future, while others are set to become drier. The combination in some
areas of reduced rainfall with higher temperatures will worsen the
problem of supplying fresh water.

Model projections suggest that precipitation will increase in certain
key areas, notably the northern high latitudes in winter and the regions
affected by the Asian summer monsoon. Areas where precipitation is
expected to decrease include southern Europe, Central America, southern
Africa and Australia.

There is also good evidence to suggest that there will be more
extremes of precipitation, leading to floods or droughts. In drier areas
that are already marginal for agriculture, this could have serious
consequences for food production.

> ## Question
>
> **63** a) Which change is expected to
> make the greatest contribution to
> sea level rise?
> b) What is the projected rise in
> mean sea level by 2100?
> c) Why are the consequences of
> a rise in sea level potentially so
> serious?

Figure 4.34

The Huang He (Yellow River), China. Projected strengthening of the Asian summer monsoon may increase the flow in this and in similar rivers.

Agriculture and food production

Patterns of agriculture are generally adapted to the local climate. Farmers in Jamaica do not try to grow oats; those in Scotland do not grow bananas. Without large inputs of energy and capital, it is difficult to grow crops in places to which they are not suited.

Crops have well-defined temperature limits and rainfall requirements for successful growth. Climate change may make areas that are already marginal for particular crops no longer suitable for their growth. Climatic extremes, such as floods and drought, are also likely to have damaging effects.

The world is currently facing a food crisis, and this is likely to get worse in part as a result of climate change. In 2008, the secretary general of the UN, Ban Ki-Moon, established a high level task force to address the crisis in global food security. The impact of climate change on food production is one of the topics to be considered.

Non-agricultural ecosystems

Agriculture takes up about 10% of the world's land surface; the remainder is in a more natural state, although much is affected by human activities to a greater or lesser degree (see Chapter 6).

Natural, or semi-natural, ecosystems, are also susceptible to climate change. This is especially the case for forests. Trees live for a long time, which means that forests are much less able to adapt to changing conditions than other ecosystems. Trees in forests start to die back when

Questions

64 Suggest beneficial and harmful consequences of increased flow of water in rivers such as the Huang He in China.

65 Apart from climate change, suggest other possible causes of the crisis in global food security.

66 Suggest emergency measures to deal with food supply in the short term which might worsen the problem of climate change in the longer term.

Figure 4.35

Forest in north-west Canada, showing bare-looking areas where there has been 'die-back' of some trees. In this forest the die-back has been caused by an increase in the mountain pine beetle population.

they are stressed. This makes them susceptible to pests and disease, which may become more prevalent as the climate changes. In north-west Canada, for example, the forests have been affected by the mountain pine beetle, which is thriving in the warmer climate of the area.

Human health

Climate and human health are strongly linked. Humans, as a species, are adapted to a wide range of climatic conditions but people can suffer when there is a change in climate in a particular region. The extreme heat in Europe in the summer of 2003 is a good example. During this heatwave, there were an additional 21 000 deaths recorded.

Indirect effects of climate change can also include a change in the distribution of insects and microorganisms that cause disease.

Economic development

The Stern Review was a thorough attempt to assess the economic consequences of climate change: this report was produced in 2006 by Sir Nicholas Stern at the request of the British Government.

The review took into account the findings of the IPCC. A key conclusion was that in the long term the cost of inaction would be far higher than the cost of tackling climate change now. It also made clear that the costs will be lowest if nations act together.

The review took into account the economic costs of the impacts of climate change, and the costs and benefits of action to reduce the emissions of greenhouse gases. In doing so the review considered the

Questions

67 Suggest reasons why die-back of trees in forests leads to positive feedback in the climate system.

68 Suggest reasons why the impacts of global warming could lead to more deaths from cholera or from malnutrition in some parts of the world.

69 In what ways might human societies have to adapt to cope with the health risks in a warmer world? What are the implications of the changes?

Questions

70 a) Suggest possible responses to climate change in the UK that would be very costly to implement.
b) Suggest what the benefits of these responses would be.

71 Why are some countries in a better position to respond to climate change than others?

practical effects of climate change on the economy, human life and the environment. It also took into account the costs of technologies and strategies to reduce greenhouse gas emissions.

The report suggests that a rise of 2–3 °C in global temperature might decrease global economic output by around 3%. A 5 °C rise could reduce it further, up to 10%, and rather more in some nations. Stern suggests that about 1% of global wealth would need to be spent to reduce emissions to a level where they are stabilised over the next 20 years and reduced thereafter. Although the details of *The Stern Review* have been criticised by some economists, the overriding message is that the effects of climate change are likely to be serious, and widely felt.

4.7 Policy responses to climate change

The topic of climate change has been high on the political agenda ever since the publication of the first IPCC reports in 1990. International negotiations, generally led by the UN, have led to the signing of a number of important agreements aimed at reducing greenhouse gas emissions. International agreements are complemented by a number of policies to cut emissions that have been implemented at national or regional scale by the governments or, in some cases, on a small scale in states or even cities.

The United Nations Framework Convention on Climate Change

The United Nations Framework Convention on Climate Change (UNFCCC) was a product of the United Nations Conference on Environment and Development, popularly known as the 'Earth Summit'. This was held in Rio de Janeiro, Brazil, in 1992. The framework convention came into force on 21st March 1994. It was signed by representatives of 194 nations. The ultimate objective of the convention is to stabilise concentrations of greenhouse gases in the atmosphere to levels that do not pose a threat to society.

The countries involved agreed to collect data on greenhouse gas emissions and to formulate strategies for cutting down their emissions. They also agreed to prepare for the impacts of climate change.

The convention distinguishes between industrialised nations and those countries undergoing industrial and economic development. It states that the industrialised nations should take most of the responsibility for reducing emissions because they have been responsible for most anthropogenic emissions in the past. However, the convention includes no mandatory targets for cutting emissions, only encouragement to pursue them.

Parties to the convention meet once a year. Probably the most significant of these was the conference held in Kyoto, Japan, in 1997. It was at this meeting that the Kyoto Protocol was negotiated and agreed, though it then took 3 years of detailed discussions before agreement was finally reached.

The Kyoto Protocol

The Kyoto Protocol finally came into force in February 2005, when ratification by Russia meant that there were enough signatories. The first phase – called the commitment period – extends from 2008 to 2012. One-hundred and seventy-eight parties had signed the protocol by April 2008. The most significant absence from this list in terms of greenhouse gas emissions, was the USA, which, under the leadership of President George Bush, had no intention of ratifying the treaty.

The key feature of the Kyoto Protocol, distinguishing it from the UNFCCC convention, is that it places a legal obligation on countries to meet agreed emissions reduction targets. As with the UNFCCC, these reduction targets apply only to 27 industrialised countries and all the countries in the European Community. The only obligation on the other nations that have signed is that they monitor their emissions and submit regular reports. The protocol commits the industrialised nations to an average 5% reduction of greenhouse gas emissions compared with 1990 levels, over the commitment period.

At a UNFCCC conference, held in Bali in 2007, negotiations began to develop a successor to the Kyoto Protocol. The aim was to start a process that would lead to a new treaty by the end of 2009, in time for the end of the first commitment period of the Kyoto Protocol in 2012.

Although actual reduction of emissions by the industrialised countries is the primary means of meeting Kyoto Protocol targets, the treaty recognises the fact that many industrialised nations already possess relatively efficient industry, making further reductions difficult. It therefore allows these nations to offset some of their emissions by paying other nations to reduce theirs. This process is called carbon offsetting and it has led to the development of a relatively new, but fast emerging, carbon trading market.

The targets imposed on the industrialised nations are legally binding. They are enforced by the threat of penalties for non-compliance. What this means is that a country that fails to meet its target will have to make up the shortfall, plus 30%, and will additionally be unable to participate in emissions trading programmes.

The United Kingdom, along with the rest of the European Community, is a strong supporter of the Kyoto Protocol. Uniquely amongst nations, the UK is making climate change a legal commitment. The Climate Change Bill will make a 60% reduction in carbon dioxide emissions by 2050 a legally binding target. The bill received royal assent in November 2008.

Not surprisingly, the Kyoto Protocol has attracted criticism. Some critics have argued that it is a UN scheme to slow economic growth in industrialised nations and a means of transferring wealth from the global rich to the global poor. Yet others have argued that it is unwieldy and unworkable and that any benefits that might be accrued will be far outweighed by the costs.

Questions

72 The Kyoto Protocol offers three ways for industrialised countries to offset some of their emissions. Explain why these examples of the three ways can be effective:
a) helping to pay for reforestation or investment in energy schemes such as solar power
b) investing in schemes to replace or improve inefficient, fossil-fuel-powered, energy generation
c) buying emissions 'allowances' from nations that are in a position to exceed their targets under the Kyoto Protocol.

4.8 Public engagement with climate change

Climate change is not simply a scientific issue. It is the job of scientists to reconstruct past climate, monitor the climate now and make projections about possible future climate. Social sciences, including economics and politics, come into play when it comes to preparing for the impacts of the changes and developing strategies to deal with them.

There are numerous groups, some with vested interests, that have strong views about the nature and scale of any responses to climate change. It is not an easy task for policymakers to take into account the views of governments, large commercial organisations, campaigning pressure groups and the general public.

Public awareness and concern

A number of studies have been undertaken to assess people's awareness and understanding of the issues arising from climate change. These have mainly taken the form of studies similar to opinion polls carried out in politics. Some small discussion forums, called focus groups, have also been held to examine the issues.

A report from the UN Development Programme in 2007 suggested that awareness of climate change and global warming was generally high at the time, although less than 50% of those in some developing countries were aware of the issues. Overall, people accept that human activity is altering climate, but are confused about the mechanisms. This latter finding was supported by the results of a focus group promoted by a Canadian environmental organisation, which found that awareness of climate change was accompanied by limited technical knowledge. In particular, participants often muddle up the greenhouse effect and the problem of the hole in the ozone layer.

Worries about the impacts of climate change have been found to be widespread in many studies, especially within the European Union. Concern is lower in the USA but successive polls have shown it to be increasing. Despite these findings, climate change generally seems to be low on people's lists of major anxieties. Furthermore there is, at present, little information about what people might be prepared to do themselves to combat climate change.

Some might argue that scientific issues like climate should be left to scientists and policymakers to sort out. Social scientists would dispute this. They find that public perception of risk, and how people respond to environmental hazards, are both important considerations for policymakers when they address specific environmental issues.

Media coverage

Within the mainstream, peer-reviewed scientific literature, there is much debate about climate change. This is not surprising, because the climate system is extremely complex. Studies shed additional light on its workings almost on a daily basis. However, very, very little of this literature challenges the finding that humans are having a significant effect on our climate.

> ## Question
>
> **73** Give examples of vested interests that might affect the decisions taken to respond to the impacts of climate change.

> ## Question
>
> **74** How would you explain to a friend the difference between global warming and the formation of the hole in the ozone layer?

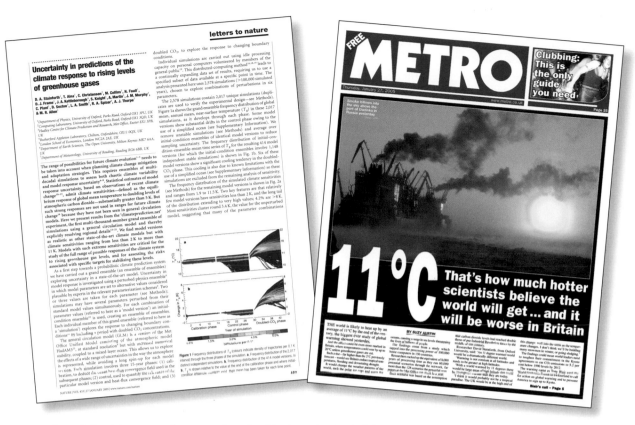

Figure 4.36

Front page of the Nature paper by David Stainforth (University of Oxford) and colleagues, which discussed results of climateprediction.net experiments, along with a headline from Metro newspaper, one of many that reported the story.

Stephen Schneider, a professor at Stanford University in California and an author of the IPCC assessment reports, has suggested that the media tends to place climate scientists into one of two camps: the pro-global warming camp or the anti-global warming camp. This approach is unsuited to scientific debate since it ignores the spectrum of opinion that usually exists about a scientific issue. The problem is made worse by the tendency of some journalists to seek eye-catching headlines. Such headlines attract readers and may help to sell newspapers, but do not always report the issues accurately.

The problem is illustrated by the reporting of findings from a project called climateprediction.net. This research project uses the 'spare' processing power of thousands of desktop computers to investigate the impact of small differences in approximations made in climate models. In a paper published in *Nature* on 27th January 2005, the range of climate sensitivities quoted was from less than 2 °C to more than 11 °C, although most of the model runs had sensitivities closer to 3 °C. Media coverage of the story was widespread, picking up on the upper range of sensitivity values in the model runs yet with limited qualification.

Dissenting views

The near-universal participation in the UNFCCC shows that there is general agreement amongst the world's governments about the seriousness of climate change. The widespread ratification of the Kyoto Protocol also suggests that many of the world's nations regard action to reduce greenhouse gas emissions as a priority as well. Within the science area, all credible national or international scientific bodies agree that human activity is modifying climate. There are, however, a number of influential scientists and non-scientists who dissent from this consensus.

> ## Question
>
> **75** To what extent, in your experience, do the popular media set the agenda and influence opinion on issues such as climate change?

76 Suggest reasons why someone might dispute the existence of anthropogenic influence on climate and put forward counter-arguments to each of the reasons you suggest.

The term 'dissenter' presents problems, however, because it suggests that scientists and others either agree with the majority view about climate change or dissent from it. In fact, debate amongst those connected with the science and policy of climate change is vigorous. This is despite the accusations from some commentators that there exists an absolute scientific consensus from which no divergence is allowed without the dissenter being branded a 'sceptic' or 'climate change denier'.

There is also a range of views among those who are sceptical about the mainstream views about climate change. Some take the extreme view that humans are having no effect on climate at all and that observed change is due to natural causes. Others argue that humans probably are having an effect on climate, but any attempts to address it are too expensive or futile because they will have no effect. Some in this group suggest that it would be much wiser to invest in new technologies to alleviate harmful impacts of climate change as they arise.

Review Questions

77 Use examples drawn from the scientific explanations of the greenhouse effect and global warming to illustrate these ideas:
  a) A common way of explaining an observation is to show that it is an example of a more general law.
  b) A scientific theory is not just a summary of the data, but an explanation that goes beyond the data.
  c) Scientists are more confident about theories that include a plausible mechanism to account for the events observed.
  d) A convincing scientific theory leads to predictions that are precise and are detailed enough for it to be possible to show that they are false.

78 a) Explain why instrumental records of climate do not provide enough data to help scientists understand the global climate system.
  b) Explain an example of negative feedback in the climate system which has to be taken into account by climate models.
  c) Explain an example of positive feedback in the climate system which has to be taken into account by climate models.
  d) Explain, with examples, the main sources of uncertainty in climate simulations for the year 2100.
  e) Why are estimates of the sensitivity of the climate system to greenhouse gas emissions based largely on climate models?

79 a) Why is much of the research into climate change carried out by interdisciplinary teams?
  b) To what extent, if at all, do the interests of groups in society influence the direction of scientific research into climate change?
  c) What factors should be considered when deciding whether to trust a new scientific finding or claim about climate change?

80 a) What aspects of the findings of climate change scientists make it hard for policymakers to decide how to respond to the consequences of global warming?
  b) What does it mean to adopt a precautionary approach to policy-making and to what extent is this approach appropriate when implementing measures to reduce the impacts of climate change?

81 Why is international cooperation so important in the field of climate change:
  a) in understanding the science?
  b) in attempting to reduce greenhouse gases?

82 If you felt strongly that not enough was being done by your local authority to combat climate change, what actions might you take to attempt to influence their policies?

Chapter 5

Energy futures

Figure 5.1

Urban and industrial development in China is leading to a rapid rise in the use of energy in a country with a population of over 1.3 billion, making up about 20% of the people in the world.

- How are patterns changing worldwide in the use of energy resources?

- What are the implications of the rapid growth in the use of energy resources by countries such as China and India?

- Will it be possible to meet the rising demand for energy resources sustainably?

- How can we reduce the risks to health and the environmental impacts of generating electricity?

- What can national and international organisations do to plan for a more sustainable energy future?

Figure 5.2

A micro-hydro scheme on the River Fechlin near Fort Augustus in the Scottish Highlands. Similar small-scale schemes provide energy for rural homes and can be used in countries like Kenya in which 96% of people do not have access to grid electricity. Village hydro schemes can be used for charging batteries or for activities that generate income, like grain milling.

5.1 Standard of living and quality of life

People and energy resources

The way that people live their lives depends to a great extent on fuels. The higher a person's standard of living, the more goods and services he or she can buy (Figure 5.3). Making these goods and providing these services requires fuels or other energy resources. In almost every country, people use more energy today than they did in the past.

The high standard of living of people in countries such as the UK is largely the result of technological developments, many of them based on scientific ideas. But the demands this makes on fuels, particularly fossil fuels, has rapidly depleted a precious finite resource, while leading to emissions of gases that damage the environment (see Chapter 4). The UK is one of the countries that belong to the Organisation for Economic Co-operation and Development (OECD). This organisation includes the USA, most European countries, Korea, Mexico, Canada, Australia, New Zealand and Japan. The OECD countries produce and consume close to 80% of global economic output (measured by gross world product), while they account for less than 20% of global population.

The global inequalities in fuel use and the impact of climate change all over the world raise serious moral questions. While technical developments can contribute to tackling these problems, they cannot provide a complete solution. Economic, environmental and ethical considerations are often involved, and decisions involve balancing different considerations against each other.

There are over two billion people in the world today with no access to modern energy services (Figure 5.4). They depend on types of biomass such as wood, charcoal or dung to meet their energy needs at home. These energy resources do not generally feature in the official world energy statistics, yet wood and dung are estimated to provide an amount

Key terms

The term **standard of living** describes the quantity and quality of goods and services to which people have access. Income per capita is a common measure of the standard of living. Other measures include the level of access to good healthcare and education. A high standard of living has been associated with the use of relatively large quantities of raw materials, requiring a large supply of energy and leading to lots of waste.

Quality of life is not necessarily the same as standard of living. It is not possible to measure quality of life in the way that standard of living can be measured using per capita income. It is possible, though, to identify factors that increase or reduce people's quality of life, though some of these are matters of personal choice about which individuals disagree.

Figure 5.3

This US family has a high standard of living.

Figure 5.4

Young women carrying firewood towards a market at Kalemie in the Democratic Republic of the Congo.

of energy equivalent to one billion tonnes of oil each year. This is over one and a half times more energy than is provided worldwide by nuclear power. Unfortunately, climate change and economic developments are a threat to the provision of biomass in these forms.

Homes where biomass burns are often polluted by the smoke from cooking fires. Many people in developing countries spend up to one-third of their income on energy resources and women may spend three or more hours a day walking many kilometres to collect wood to burn.

Without basic, clean energy it is not possible to meet the development goals that have been set by the United Nations and to provide the essentials of food, healthcare and education in a sustainable way for the poor of the world.

One way to compare the energy use in different regions or countries is to work out the average amount of energy used by each person in a year. This is the annual per capita energy consumption. Three countries are compared in this way in Figure 5.5.

Country	Total energy use in 2005/TWh	Population/millions
USA	29200	297
UK	2920	60
Democratic Republic of the Congo	210	58

Figure 5.5

Energy consumption in three countries. The figures for energy use include fossil fuels, nuclear power and renewables such as hydroelectricity but not biomass such as fuelwood.
1 TWh (terawatt hour) = one thousand million (10^9) kilowatt hours.

Energy units

The scientific unit for measuring amounts of energy is the joule (J). A joule is a small amount of energy. One million joules equals 1 megajoule (1 MJ).

Power is measured in watts. One watt (W) represents the transfer of 1 joule of energy per second.

A thousand watts is a kilowatt (kW). The power of a hairdryer on a high setting is typically about 2 kW.

A million watts is a megawatt (MW). The power of a formula one car is about 0.5 MW and the power of a high-speed train is about 4 MW.

One gigawatt (1 GW) is a thousand megawatts. The power of the nuclear power station at Sizewell is 1.2 GW, while the largest coal-fired power station in the UK, Drax, has a maximum output of about 4 GW.

Multiplying the power of a device by the time the device operates indicates the amount of energy that has been supplied or used. A kilowatt hour (kWh) is a measure of the energy needed to run a 1000 W device for 1 hour. Running a 1 kilowatt device for 1 hour leads to the supply or use of 3.6 megajoules (MJ).

Questions

1 Work out the average per capita energy consumption per year for each of the three countries in Figure 5.5.

2 How many times greater is the per capita energy consumption in the USA than in the Democratic Republic of the Congo?

3 Suggest differences in the life of people in the Democratic Republic of the Congo compared with people in the USA that help to explain the differences in average per capita energy consumption.

4 Suggest reasons why it can be misleading to use average values of per capita energy consumption when comparing life in different countries.

5 Give examples to illustrate the distinction between standard of living and quality of life.

6 Give an example of a modern technology that enhances your quality of life that:
a) needs a relatively large amount of fuel or electricity
b) does not need you to use a large amount of fuel or electricity.

7 How can you account for the fact that supplying the food we eat makes a large contribution to the per capita use of energy resources in the UK?

8 Some science-based technologies have unintended and undesirable impacts on people or the environment. Give two examples to illustrate this statement, choosing technologies that involve energy resources.

Energy consumption in different countries

World energy statistics collected by the International Energy Agency (an independent body linked to the OECD) help to highlight the considerable differences from country to country.

With the world population growing and people everywhere wanting as high a standard of living as they can achieve, the worldwide demand for energy is increasing quite rapidly. The main source of this energy continues to be fossil fuels. Figure 5.6 shows the amounts of energy supplied, worldwide, in 1973 and 2005 by different fossil fuels and by other energy sources.

Questions

9 Identify from Figure 5.6, for the world's total energy supply in 1973 and 2005:
a) two features of the pattern of supply that are essentially unchanged
b) two significant changes.

10 In the period from 1973–2005 what was the increase in world TPES:
a) in Mtoe?
b) as a percentage of the 1971 figure?

11 What percentage of world TPES came from fossil fuels:
a) in 1973?
b) in 2005?

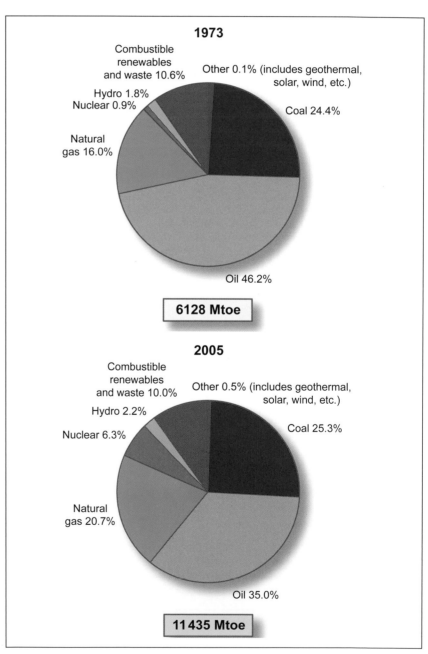

Figure 5.6

Where the world's total primary energy supply (TPES) came from in 1973 and in 2005.

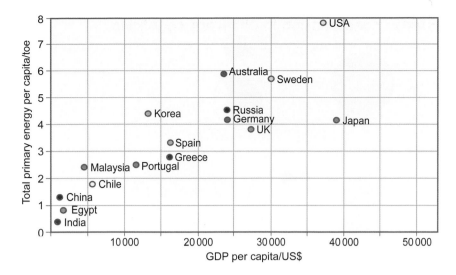

Figure 5.7

The link between primary energy consumption and GDP, based on figures from the International Energy Agency's Key World Statistics 2008.

In energy statistics, the gross domestic product (GDP) of a country is often used as a measure of how wealthy or poor the people are on average. The scattergraph in Figure 5.7 shows that there is a rough relationship between a country's GDP per capita and its energy consumption. However, this relationship can change as countries find ways to make more efficient use of energy. Some countries need less energy than others to produce the same added value to GDP.

5.2 Fuels and energy

Fuels are useful because they are concentrated energy sources. When we burn a fuel, we release energy that we can then use to do other things (such as heating things up, making things move, and so on). Most of the energy for the manufacturing industry, agriculture, transport and our homes comes from burning fossil fuels – coal, oil and natural gas. At present fossil fuels are available on a large scale, but they are becoming increasingly expensive as the world demand for energy resources rises. Also, the consequences of their greenhouse gas emissions are becoming more and more serious.

Some energy also comes from nuclear fuel (enriched uranium and plutonium), which is used in nuclear power stations to generate electricity. In some parts of the world, wood or dried animal dung (biomass) is the main fuel (Figure 5.8, page 140).

Questions

12 Since 1992 the energy intensity of the USA economy has fallen by an average of 2% per year. Suggest changes in the country that might account for this decline.

13 Give two general conclusions that can be drawn from Figure 5.7.

14 Suggest reasons to account for the position of Japan on the graph in Figure 5.7.

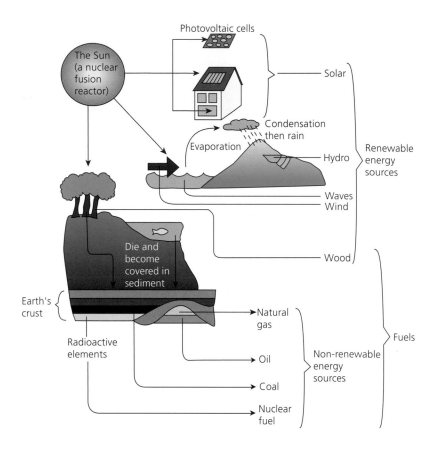

Photovoltaic cells

The Sun
(a nuclear
fusion
reactor)

Solar

Condensation
then rain

Evaporation

Hydro

Renewable
energy
sources

Waves
Wind

Wood

Die and
become
covered in
sediment

Earth's
crust

Radioactive
elements

Natural
gas

Oil

Coal

Nuclear
fuel

Non-renewable
energy
sources

Fuels

Figure 5.8

Fuels and other energy resources.

Key terms

The original meaning of a **fuel** was 'a material for burning'. More recently, the term has been extended to include **nuclear fuel**, which is used in nuclear power stations, though it is not literally 'burned'. **Fossil fuels** are the fossilised remains of prehistoric rainforests or tiny marine animals, and have formed over millions of years. A **renewable** energy source is one that is being (or can be) replaced as it is used.

But fuels are not our only energy sources. The Earth receives a great deal of energy directly from the Sun, in the form of solar radiation. Solar radiation can be used directly for heating, or to generate electricity using photovoltaic (or solar) cells. The Sun also drives the water cycle, which raises water into high dams for hydroelectric schemes, and causes wind and waves, which can also be used as energy sources.

Fossil fuels take so long to produce that the current reserves are effectively all we have. They are non-renewable energy sources. On the other hand, wind, water and sunlight are renewable energy sources. So is wood, provided it is not used faster than trees can re-grow.

Primary and secondary energy sources

When fossil fuels burn in air they produce a flame that can be used for heating on a small or large scale. Sometimes we use the energy directly, for example to heat our homes or cook food, or to make a car engine run. But we can also use it to make steam to drive turbines in power stations, which then turn generators to generate electricity (Figure 5.9). Electricity is then used in factories, homes and businesses to run a wide range of appliances. Electricity is said to be a secondary energy source. It has to be generated using a primary energy source (such as a fossil fuel, nuclear fuel or one of the renewable energy sources).

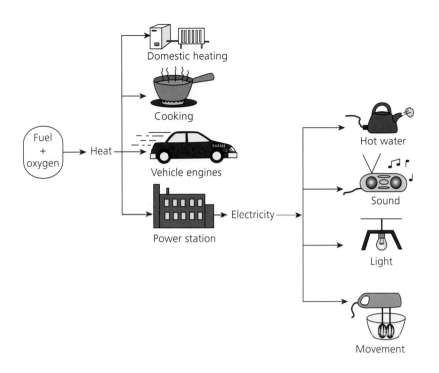

Question

15 Natural gas is a fossil fuel made up mainly of the hydrocarbon methane.
a) What happens to the elements in methane when gas burns?
b) In what ways can the products of burning be harmful?

Key terms

Primary energy is the energy directly available from fossil fuels, nuclear fuels and any other direct energy inputs including renewables.

Conversion processes turn energy resources into different forms such as electricity or cleaner fuels (for example hydrogen). These are examples of **secondary energy resources**.

Figure 5.9

Different pathways from primary energy resources to end use.

5.3 Generating electricity

At present, most of the world's electricity is generated using the energy released from burning fuels (Figure 5.10). This is having a serious effect on the Earth's atmosphere because of the release of greenhouse gases (see Chapter 4).

In some high-income countries, such as France, a significant proportion of electricity is generated in nuclear power stations (see Section 5.7). Although these do not release large quantities of polluting gases into the atmosphere, they cause other environmental problems, because of the radioactive waste they produce.

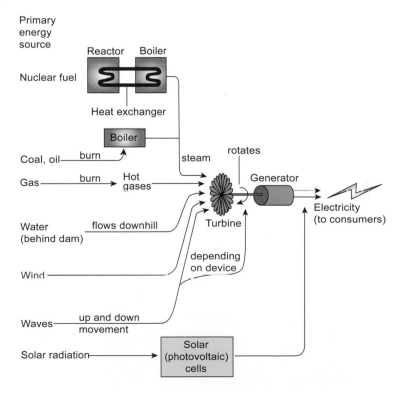

Figure 5.10

The steps involved in generating electricity from primary energy sources.

Figure 5.11

The mix of primary energy sources used to
generate electricity in the UK, 2007.

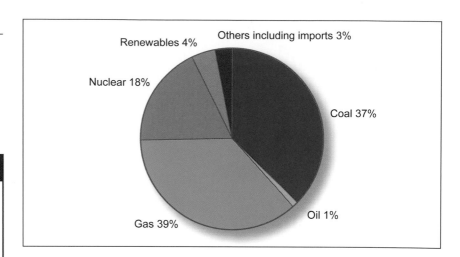

Key term

Cost-benefit analysis is a
process used in decision-making
by governments, and other
organisations, which involves
weighing up the costs and benefits
of a particular course of action. This
can be controversial because of the
basis on which monetary values for
the size of the costs and the value of
the benefits are estimated now, and
in the future.

Figure 5.12

Drax power station is the largest coal-fired
power station in the UK. It supplies about
7% of the country's electricity. Hot gases
from burning coal leave from the flue on the
right. Steam from the cooling water rises
from the cooling towers on the left. Cooling
towers have been described as monuments
to the inefficiency of large power stations.

There is an increasing interest in the use of renewable energy sources
to generate electricity (Figure 5.11). Until recently, however, electricity
from most renewable energy sources has been much more expensive.
Furthermore, methods of generating electricity from renewable energy
sources also have environmental impact.

If people want all the benefits of a readily available supply of
electricity, they must balance the cost of each method of generation
against its environmental impact, to decide which methods to use.
Decision-makers carry out detailed cost-benefit analyses when planning
energy policies.

Using fossil fuels to generate electricity

In a coal-fired power station, energy is given out as the fuel burns. This
is used to heat water to turn it into steam that drives a turbine. Once
the steam has passed through the turbine blades, it is condensed back to
water, to draw more steam through. The cooling water
used to do this is heated in the process (Figure 5.12).
In any fuel-burning power station, a lot of the energy
produced by burning the fuel is carried away by this
cooling water. As a result, the efficiency of the power
station is low (Figure 5.13).

The efficiency of fuel-burning power stations can be
increased to some extent by improved technology, for
example, with better turbine design. But no device that
uses energy for heating to produce movement (that is no
'heat engine') can ever achieve anything approaching
100% efficiency. The reason is that some of the energy
always has to be transferred to a cold reservoir (like
the cooling water) to keep the process running. And
this energy is usually wasted. In fact, the maximum
theoretical efficiency for a technologically perfect heat
engine using steam at 500 °C is around 60%. In practice,
the most modern power stations using gas turbines can
achieve an efficiency of about 50%, but coal, oil and
nuclear power stations that use steam to drive turbines
are at best 40% efficient.

Efficiency

In any process it is important to know how much of the energy goes where we want it to. In a conventional power station much of the energy from the burning fuel ends up heating cooling water and the surrounding air. The efficiency of the process is the percentage of the energy available from the fuel that ends up where we want it to be, as electrical energy.

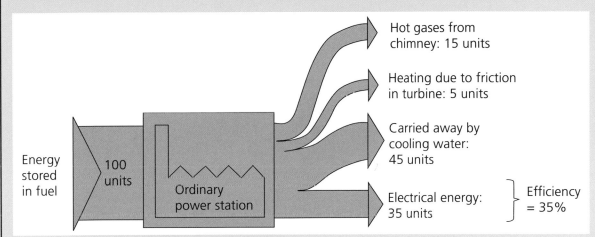

The low efficiency of a power station can be improved if the 'waste' energy in cooling water is re-used by pumping the hot water round local housing. Used in this way, the power station becomes a combined heat and power (CHP) station and the energy efficiency rises to 70–80% because, at least in theory, the energy is no longer wasted but used to heat the buildings. The problem is to ensure a steady demand for the energy available for heating. This is easier to achieve on industrial sites where the energy for heating can be used in manufacturing.

Figure 5.13

The efficiency of an ordinary fossil fuel power station.

Coal is found in many parts of the world and it is relatively easy to mine and transport. This means that about 40% of all the world's electricity is generated in coal-fired power stations. The problem with burning coal is that to give the same amount of energy it produces much higher emissions of the greenhouse gas carbon dioxide than burning natural gas.

There are three principal methods for reducing carbon emissions from coal-fired power generation.

- Improving coal-fired power station efficiency

Developers of new power stations are using advanced boilers, improved turbines and other technologies to reduce the fuel needed to generate power. This increased efficiency of coal power stations can reduce emissions of carbon dioxide by up to 20% compared with less efficient power stations.

- Co-firing coal with biomass

Efficient coal power stations can also combine their fuel with biomass, such as wood chippings, and decrease emissions by a further 10%. A number of power stations in the UK have now been co-firing for several years. However, a review of biomass policy for the UK (published in 2007) advised that it is generally more cost-effective to use biomass as a fuel for heating rather than generating electricity.

Questions

16 Coal consists of up to 90% carbon, C, mixed with minerals that do not burn and small amounts of other elements including hydrogen, oxygen and sulfur. Natural gas consists of methane, CH_4, which contains 75% carbon and 25% hydrogen. Why does coal give higher emissions of carbon dioxide than natural gas when both fuels supply the same amount of energy?

17 Explain how programmes of energy efficiency help to cut greenhouse gas emissions.

18 Why does co-firing a power station with wood chippings and coal help to cut the total emissions of carbon dioxide?

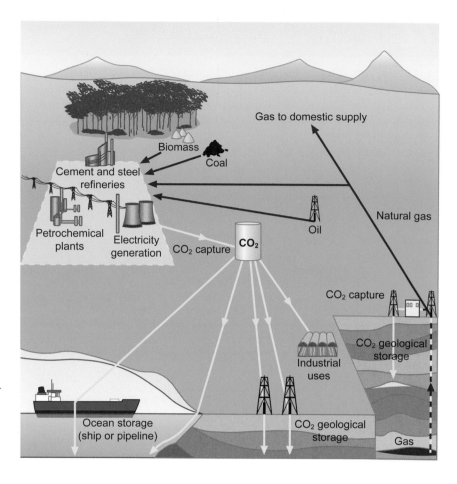

Figure 5.14

Options for carbon dioxide capture and storage: storage in deep geological formations (such as depleted oil wells or aquifers containing salt water) and injection deep in the oceans.

- Carbon capture and storage (CCS)

Carbon capture and storage (CCS) is another approach being explored for cutting emissions of carbon dioxide from coal-fired power stations. This type of approach is only feasible where the power station is fairly close to where the carbon dioxide is to be stored. It is then possible, in principle, to capture between 85% and 90% of the gas (Figure 5.14).

Injection of carbon dioxide into the deep oceans is still in the research phase. Injecting carbon dioxide into oil and gas fields is now feasible and economically viable in some circumstances. However, the technology is still at an early stage. New infrastructure will be needed on a very large scale to make this technology effective. A study at the Massachusetts Institute of Technology in 2007 estimated that capturing as much as 60% of the carbon dioxide from US power stations would involve handling a volume of the gas of the same order of magnitude as the total volume of oil now moved around the world each day. It will take 10 to 20 years for carbon capture and storage to become widespread, even if the technology can be made to work.

5.4 Generating electricity with nuclear power

The energy to produce steam in a nuclear power station comes from the fission of atomic nuclei such as uranium-235 (Figure 5.15). The atoms break up when bombarded with neutrons and as they do so they give off two or three more loose neutrons and quite a large amount of energy. In principle, each of the neutrons produced could then hit another uranium atom and cause another fission, thus creating a chain reaction. An uncontrolled chain reaction is what happens in an atomic bomb. However, for nuclear power generation the chain reaction is controlled with the help of materials that absorb the neutrons rather than letting them hit another uranium atom.

Figure 5.15

Atoms of uranium-235 split when bombarded with neutrons. Fission produces two atomic nuclei of roughly the same size together with several neutrons and a large amount of energy. Uranium-235 and the fission products are radioactive.

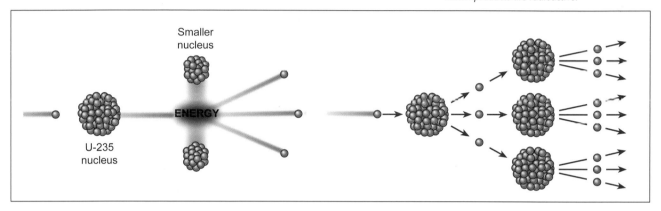

Fission happens in the core of a reactor that is heavily shielded to prevent any radiation escaping (Figure 5.16). The energy released by fission is continually removed from the core by a 'coolant', which can be a liquid or a gas. The coolant is very hot as it leaves the reactor so it can be used to boil water and convert it to steam. It is this steam that is used to drive the turbines that generate electricity.

Figure 5.16

Sizewell A nuclear power station (right) started generating electricity in 1966. It consisted of two reactors. The power station was shut down at the end of 2006 and is now being decommissioned. Sizewell B (left) is still the UK's newest nuclear power station. It was built between 1988 and 1995.

When the nuclear fuel has been in the reactor for some time, the fission products build up and the fuel is not as efficient as it should be. However, it still contains most of the original uranium. At this point, the fuel in the reactor is replaced and the used fuel can be reprocessed.

Benefits and risks of nuclear power

Since burning fossil fuels inevitably releases large quantities of carbon dioxide into the atmosphere, nuclear fuels offer what appears to be a 'greener', more environmentally friendly option. This advantage of nuclear power has been emphasised by the nuclear industry. Since the 1950s, nuclear power, fuelled by imported uranium, generated a significant proportion of the UK's electricity. This reached a peak of nearly 30% of electricity output in the 1990s. In the last 10 years, nuclear power has provided about one-fifth of the country's electricity needs. Had the industry built fossil fuel power stations in place of nuclear power stations, the UK's total carbon emissions might have been 5% to 12% higher in 2004.

However, no new nuclear power stations have been built in the UK since the Sizewell B station started operating in 1995. Public opinion has been strongly opposed to the nuclear industry. The public has been very concerned by radiation risks that include exposure to radiation from leaks, from waste and from accidents. Another worry is the threat of a terror attack using a 'dirty bomb'. A dirty bomb is one designed to use conventional explosives to scatter radioactive material so that it contaminates a large area.

Low-level leakage from nuclear plants

Very small amounts of radioactive material routinely escape from nuclear stations into the immediate environment. The main concerns about any routine leakage of radioactive materials into the environment are about the levels that are permissible and the extent to which the radioactive materials accumulate. Regulations about permitted levels have been progressively tightened up since the introduction of nuclear power stations in the late 1950s and only materials with a relatively short half-life may be released. Nevertheless, these may become more concentrated as they move up natural food chains.

The problem of radioactive waste

Nuclear power stations produce three main types of radioactive waste, which are classified as high-level, intermediate-level and low-level wastes (Figure 5.19, page 148). At present most of the high-level and intermediate-level waste is stored in constantly cooled tanks at the site where it is produced. This type of storage is only designed to be short term, and some more permanent storage will eventually be needed.

Any discussion of risk must take three things into account:
• the type of harmful event
• the probability that the event will happen
• the seriousness of the consequences if it does happen.

The Health and Safety Executive in the UK distinguishes between hazard and risk:
• a hazard is anything that can cause adverse effects
• a risk is the likelihood that a hazard will actually cause its adverse effects, together with a measure of the severity of the effect.

Different kinds of risk have to be compared in different ways. Most people are exposed to some kinds of risk, such as being killed by lightning or in a road accident. So in these cases it is reasonable to measure the risk by the chance per million people per year.

Cause of death	Annual risk in the UK
Cancer	1 in 387
Injury and poisoning	1 in 3137
Road accidents	1 in 16800
Gas incident (fire, explosion, carbon monoxide poisoning)	1 in 1510000
Lightning strike	1 in 18700000

Figure 5.17

Health and Safety Executive estimates of the risk of death averaged over the whole UK population.

Other kinds of risk, such as rock climbing or travelling by air, are compared in a way that takes account of the extent to which the risk is being run. For air travel, for example, the risk is expressed as a proportion of the number of kilometres travelled or the number of journeys.

Activity	Annual risk in the UK
Scuba diving	1 in 200000 dives
Rock climbing	1 in 320000 climbs
Fairground rides	1 in 834000 rides
Rail travel	1 in 43000000 passenger journeys
Air travel	1 in 125000000 passenger journeys

Figure 5.18

Health and Safety Executive estimates of the risk of death as a consequence of taking part in a range of activities.

People's attitudes to risk very much depend on whether they can judge the hazard directly from their own experience, or whether the cause of the danger is not well understood or is particularly dreaded. This means that public expectations about the levels of protection required, or the level of risk that can be tolerated, may differ according to the nature of the hazard in question and people's knowledge or feelings about it.

A distinction is made between the tolerance and acceptance of risk. People tolerate a risk when they are willing to live with the risk so long as they can see the benefits and are confident that it is being kept under control. Society keeps tolerable risks under control and seeks to reduce them when possible. An acceptable risk is one that people take for granted as part of normal life and work.

Questions

24 Suggest reasons why many people have a particular fear of radioactive materials and the radiations they give off.

25 Give examples from your experience to distinguish between a risk you accept and a risk you tolerate.

Figure 5.19

Quantities and radioactivity of nuclear wastes in store in the UK (2007). 1 TBq = 1 million, million becquerels. The becquerel is the basic unit of radioactivity, equal to 1 nuclear disintegration per second. High-level waste (HLW) is highly radioactive liquid waste that is produced when spent nuclear fuel is reprocessed. Intermediate-level waste (ILW) is sufficiently radioactive to require shielding during its handling and transportation. Low-level waste (LLW) consists of lightly contaminated materials and is disposed of by burial at approved sites.

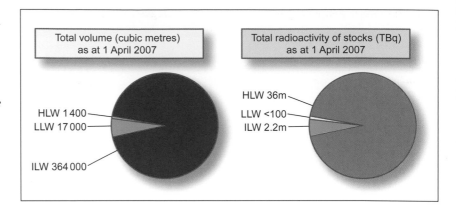

Total volume (cubic metres) as at 1 April 2007

HLW 1 400
LLW 17 000
ILW 364 000

Total radioactivity of stocks (TBq) as at 1 April 2007

HLW 36m
LLW <100
ILW 2.2m

Question

26 What can you conclude from Figure 5.19?

Nuclear accidents

A major reason for opposition to nuclear power is the fear of serious accidents and the scale of radioactive contamination that these might cause. This fear is based on two sorts of reason.

First, there have, in fact, been quite a number of nuclear accidents. The two most serious of these, in terms of the amount of radioactive pollution released, were the fire and resulting leakage at Windscale (now known as Sellafield) in England in 1957, and the explosion at Chernobyl in the Ukraine in 1986 (Figure 5.20). A terrorist attack on a nuclear site could have similar consequences.

Second, with any complex technological process, it is never possible to anticipate all of the things that might conceivably go wrong or to make every aspect of the process completely fail-safe. Nor can we ever be completely sure that any software that is used to control the process is completely free of 'bugs'.

Figure 5.20

Sheep farmers in parts of Wales and Cumbria are still affected by the contamination of their land by radioactive caesium from the Chernobyl disaster. The sheep have to be monitored and checked before they are allowed to be sold into the food chain.

Furthermore, people are involved at various stages in the process and it is never possible to rule out the possibility of human error. Nor is it desirable to eliminate human involvement in the technological process altogether because, if something happens that was entirely unforeseen by the designers of the plant, a sensible response to the situation will necessarily involve human judgement. Unfortunately, however, neither the judgement that something has happened that requires human intervention, nor the judgement about how precisely to intervene, can be guaranteed to be correct. In science and technology, as in life generally, there can be no absolute certainties. The possibility of accidents in nuclear plants can never be entirely eliminated. In fact, human error played a significant part in both the Windscale and the Chernobyl accidents.

Terrorist attack

Ever since terrorists flew airliners into the Twin Towers of New York in September 2001, there have been heightened fears of what might happen if an aircraft were crashed into a nuclear power station. For example, the shielding for a new nuclear power station under construction in Finland was redesigned and strengthened as a result to be certain that it could resist the impact of a large commercial airliner.

The ALARP principle and cost-benefit analysis

People responsible for controlling industrial risks have to decide whether or not:

- a risk is so great and the consequences of an accident so severe that the process must be banned
- a risk has been made so small that no further precautions are needed
- a risk lies between the two extremes and must be reduced to a level that is as low as is reasonably practical (ALARP).

In the case of major and uncertain risks, the application of the ALARP principle involves cost-benefit analysis. The consequences of a nuclear accident would be so serious, widespread and long lasting that the industry has to spend very large amounts of money to make it very unlikely that there will be a serious accident while minimising the other risks of exposure to radiation during operations.

In an analysis of a safety system, the 'benefit' is the reduction of risk while the money spent on installing the system is the 'cost'. To weigh up the gains and losses, ways have to be found to put a monetary value on the risks. This means that those doing the analysis have the difficult task of estimating the values for human life, for health and for all the other possible consequences of a major nuclear accident.

Some of the consequences of a nuclear accident for health and the environment are likely to affect future generations as well as those alive now. This means that the analysis also has to translate the costs of future harms into modern values. This process, which economists call discounting, involves assumptions that can often be controversial. The discount rate is the rate at which society is willing to trade future benefits against current costs.

Operators of processes must bear the cost of reducing risks unless the cost of doing so is grossly disproportionate when compared with the benefits.

The process of cost-benefit analysis does not allow for the fact that it is generally the case that those people who pay the costs of a particular measure are not the same as those who receive the benefits. However, decisions based on the analysis need to take this into account.

Questions

27 Identify groups of people that might be likely to be affected by exposure to radiation from a nuclear plant:
a) from routine leaks
b) from stored nuclear waste
c) from nuclear accidents.

28 Suggest reasons why it is hard to assess the risks associated with the long-term storage of nuclear waste.

29 Suggest four issues that need to be taken into account when assessing the risk of sabotage of nuclear facilities by terrorists.

30 There are serious risks to human life associated with all forms of generating electricity. What is it about the risks from nuclear power that means that the public in the UK is particularly opposed to this technology?

31 a) Who are the main beneficiaries when a new nuclear power station is built and operated?
b) Who are the people who face increased risks from a new nuclear power station?
c) How might the nuclear industry compensate those who face increased risks?

Nuclear waste at Sellafield

Sellafield is one of the most complex and compact nuclear sites in the world. It is home to two reprocessing plants, plants that produce nuclear fuel for new reactors and a variety of plants used for the treatment and storage of nuclear waste.

Managing nuclear waste

Low-level waste makes up 80% of all nuclear waste and is only slightly radioactive. This category includes protective clothing, laboratory equipment, paper towels and gloves and other items that have been used in the controlled areas of a nuclear site, or in hospitals or nuclear research centres.

This type of waste is treated at Sellafield by placing it inside a drum that is then compacted down to a quarter of its original size using a high-force compactor. These 'squashed' drums are then placed inside a freight container and transported a short distance to the low-level waste repository near the village of Drigg (Figure 5.21). At the repository, the freight containers are filled with cement before being placed into a purpose-built concrete lined vault.

Only 50% of the solid low-level radioactive waste disposed of at this repository is from Sellafield. The rest comes from hospitals, universities, research establishments and industries around the UK.

Intermediate-level waste includes fuel cladding material and sludges that come from nuclear treatment processes. At Sellafield, there are two encapsulation plants where this sort of waste is placed in stainless steel drums and then mixed with cement. The drums then have a lid put on them; before being washed and monitored and placed into a special storage facility on the Sellafield site. The decision as to where this waste will be stored long term will be made by the government.

Figure 5.21

The Drigg low-level nuclear waste repository in Cumbria with Sellafield in the background.

The most radioactive high-level waste accounts for just 1% of all nuclear waste and it is not actually created in nuclear power stations. High-level waste is produced when fuel that has come out of a reactor is reprocessed. At the moment this waste is stored above ground. A permanent solution to getting rid of the waste has yet to be found.

Reprocessing high-level waste

Linda McLean is a commercial manager at the Sellafield plant (Figure 5.22). Here she describes the work she does and how she sees the future for nuclear energy and what many see as its biggest drawback – nuclear waste.

"My job at Sellafield involves managing all the commercial activities for a whole range of departments – human resources, environmental health and quality, strategy, finance and information technology. This means that I get involved with the contracts we have with suppliers. I also have to help to work out the types of contract we need for future work. I also have to deal with the Nuclear Decommissioning Authority, our main customer. We have to be sure that the authority is happy with our performance. The job is incredibly varied, but that's what makes it exciting and interesting.

"Sellafield does not produce electricity any more, but is mainly focused around cleaning up old plants and reprocessing fuel. Reprocessing is done by very few countries in the world. As a result, fuel from reactors in Japan, Germany, Switzerland, Italy and other European countries has been sent to Sellafield to be reprocessed. Countries like Japan are now building their own reprocessing facilities but at the moment they have to rely on Sellafield and on plants in France to do it for them.

"Reprocessing fuel for overseas customers creates high-level waste. Clearly it is not fair for the UK to be stuck with this waste and so the contracts for reprocessing have a clause that makes the customers take any waste back. Determining the best technical strategies for actually returning this waste was my first job at Sellafield.

Questions

32 What are the implications for public policy and public opinion of the association between the peaceful and military uses of nuclear power?

33 Explain why high-level waste turns into intermediate-level waste with time.

34 Suggest reasons why the management and storage of intermediate-level waste might be a bigger challenge than dealing with high-level waste.

Figure 5.22

Linda McLean studied Maths and then IT at the University of Glasgow before she started work in the High Level Waste Plant department at the Sellafield reprocessing plant. She is chair of the British Nuclear Energy Society's Young Generation Network (BNES YGN).

Reprocessing nuclear waste

Reprocessing is a way of separating out useful chemicals from the waste products that are making the fuel less efficient. The aim is to recover the valuable parts of used fuel, which includes the unused uranium together with the plutonium that formed in the reactor. This is done by a complex series of chemical processes that begin with dissolving the used fuel in acid.

Once the process is complete, the recovered uranium and plutonium can be used to make new nuclear fuel. The high-level waste product is turned into a solid glass. This process of vitrification evaporates the water from the liquid waste to produce granules. These are mixed with small pieces of glass and heated to over 1150 °C inside a melter.

The mixture of molten glass and waste is then poured into stainless steel containers and allowed to cool. When the glass cools it solidifies and encapsulates the nuclear waste. The containers are then lidded, washed and monitored before being placed into a specially designed store at Sellafield. This process reduces the volume of waste to one-third of its original volume. It also makes it more stable as the waste is now in a solid form rather than a liquid form.

"This was a really interesting job because of all the challenges it presents. In simple terms, the first thing is to get the waste out of the store, which is actually more difficult than it sounds because the waste is highly radioactive and has to be handled remotely. It then needs to be checked to make sure it's suitable for return to the customers and, if it is, it needs to be placed into specially designed transport flasks and then transported to the port at Barrow-in-Furness.

"Once we get it to Barrow the waste has to be loaded onto specially designed ships so that the containers can be shipped back. When I started, waste returns like this had never been done from Britain and so there were many technical issues to resolve, including the mathematical modelling of the radiation from these containers to make sure that they were safe."

Dealing with nuclear waste in the future

Linda continues:

"The key issues at Sellafield today revolve around nuclear waste. When the UK first started a nuclear programme, the goal was getting the power stations up and running and generating electricity. At the time no detailed thought was given to what would happen to any waste that arose as a result or how it would be possible to decommission the reactors when they got to the end of their operating life.

"For the future, the plans for waste management and decommissioning are considered at the outset of any new nuclear programme. We do not yet know what type of reactors will be built in the UK in future, but even so we can make an estimate of how much waste will be produced from experience in other parts of the world. It turns out that a new fleet of reactors in this country would add less than 10% to the existing waste.

"This reduction in the amount of waste that is produced is due to changes in the design of reactors and in the type of fuel that is used. For example, fuel for modern reactors produces much more energy per kilogram than in the past. This means that less fuel is needed in the reactor so that there is less waste in the end.

"Fuel for new reactors can also stay in the reactor and be used for much longer periods. This is because the new fuels can continue to work well even when there has been a build-up of fission products. Again, this means that less fuel is used over the life of the reactor, leading to less waste.

"The new reactors also have a much simpler design. This simpler design means that fewer raw materials are required to make them, so there is less to dispose of when a reactor comes to the end of its operating life. This cuts down the waste from decommissioning.

"The simplification has been achieved through having a much bigger reliance on passive safety rather than engineered components; for example using gravity rather than a pump to move fluids. As well as reducing the amount of decommissioning waste this also makes new reactors even safer than the existing ones – a pump might stop working, gravity won't."

Managing the wastes from the past

"However, although new reactors won't produce as much waste as the existing ones, it doesn't solve the problem of what we do with current waste and how we deal with all nuclear waste in the long term. This has been (and still is) the subject of a lot of debate about nuclear power.

"In order to solve the problem, the government initiated a complete review of radioactive waste management and appointed the Committee on Radioactive Waste Management (CoRWM) to come up with recommendations so that a carefully thought through decision can be made. The CoRWM has recommended that this waste should be stored in a repository deep under the ground (Figure 5.23). This is not a new idea; other countries have already demonstrated that the safe and secure long-term management and permanent disposal of nuclear wastes in deep geological repositories is technically feasible – the process for constructing radioactive waste disposal sites is already under way in countries such as Finland and Sweden.

"So, although the long-term storage and disposal of nuclear waste is an issue, it is not an issue for which we have no solution and, at the moment, all wastes are stored safely and securely while we await the final decision.

"However, even if we decide to go for a deep geological repository then we still need to decide where to put it. This is actually a fascinating question and will need input from all sorts of people. Some of the radionuclides in nuclear waste have very long half-lives and so the

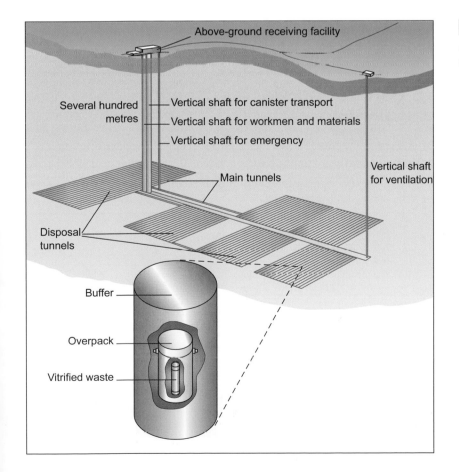

Figure 5.23

Plans for a deep repository for high-level nuclear waste.

waste will have to be kept safe for tens of thousands of years. The decision on where to put such a repository will therefore need input from geologists, who will need to determine how the site is going to change over thousands of years. Also, nuclear physicists and chemists will need to work out what will happen to the containers of waste over the years. Plus, because we can't just build a repository and see what happens, we will need to predict what happens by building mathematical models – so we will also need mathematicians.

"All these scientists will have to examine these issues and use their technical expertise to make sure that all the information is available and correct. Only then can the government make a fully informed final decision.

"We also need to consider the people aspect of it – even if we come up with a location that is great from a scientific point of view, what if the local community doesn't want it? All in all it's a very, very difficult question and I can understand why we don't yet have the answer."

A future for nuclear power?

"Many people don't like nuclear power. I'll admit that it's not perfect, there are still a number of issues particularly surrounding nuclear waste. However, personally, I think nuclear power must be included in the energy mix going forward. Nuclear is a virtually carbon dioxide-free source of energy that makes it a valuable contributor in the battle against climate change. Being able to generate our own electricity by way of new nuclear power stations will reduce our dependence on imported fuel. Including nuclear energy as part of a balanced energy mix together with things like renewables will help meet this country's energy goals and so in my mind it's simple – nuclear power must be part of the solution.

5.5 Generating electricity with renewables

Various ways of generating electricity with renewable resources are becoming increasingly important as a means to achieving a secure supply with reduced emissions of greenhouse gases (Figure 5.24).

Questions

36 These five methods for disposing of high-level nuclear waste have been used or discussed:
- dumping in a deep ocean
- burying under Arctic ice
- firing into space
- keeping on the surface in containers
- burying in an underground repository.

Which of these methods meet the requirements that storage should be secure, safe and permanent?

37 a) Linda McLean thinks that nuclear power must be included in the energy mix in future. Why do you think that she takes this view?
b) Do you agree with her? If you disagree, what arguments would you use to persuade Linda that she is wrong?

38 a) Which type of renewable energy supplied most electricity in 1990?
b) Why has this type of renewable energy declined in relative importance since 1990?

Figure 5.24

The growth in electricity generation from renewable sources since 1990. This includes electricity from co-firing with biomass in power stations, generation from waste incinerators and in power plants using gas from landfill.

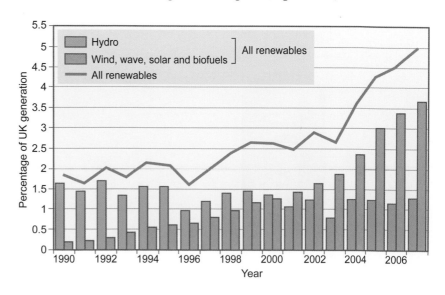

The tried and tested renewable technology in the UK is hydroelectric power. Most of the large-scale sites for hydroelectric schemes are already in use, but there are plans for more smaller scale schemes in Scotland (Figure 5.2).

An alternative way of using water to generate electricity is tidal power. This can involve building a barrage across a river estuary. Sea water is trapped behind the barrage at high tide and flows out through turbines as the tide falls. The largest tidal power station in the world, and the only one in Europe, is in the Rance Estuary in France. This was built in 1996 and generates on average about 68 MW for the French electricity grid. This is only about 0.012% of the country's electricity needs.

There are several estuaries in the UK where it would be feasible to build a tidal barrage. These include the Severn, Dee and Humber estuaries. Of these, the scheme that has been considered most seriously from time to time is the one to build a tidal power station across the Severn estuary. This has the potential to supply about 5% of the UK's electricity. A barrage would, however, destroy a habitat that is important to wading birds and other wildlife and so it is strongly opposed by the Royal Society for the Protection of Birds and other organisations.

The power of a tidal flow can also be harnessed by underwater turbines (Figure 5.25). The first turbine of this kind started supplying electricity to the national grid in 2008. The turbine acts rather like an underwater windmill. When running at full power, a turbine of this kind has an output of 1.2 kW. In the UK there is potential for more underwater turbines off the coast of Anglesey, in the Pentland Firth, around the Channel Islands and in the Severn estuary.

In the past the scale of electricity from renewables has been small in the UK because oil and gas from the North Sea have been readily available and cheap. Now the supply of North Sea gas and oil is in decline and pressure from government has brought about the increases in renewables as a way of cutting carbon emissions. Since 1989 there have been financial incentives to encourage the development alternatives to fossil fuels. At first much of the money was used to support nuclear

Questions

39 The Rance tidal barrage has a peak output of 240 megawatts (MW) but an average output of 68 MW. How can you account for the difference?

40 a) Explain why a tidal barrage across the Severn Estuary seems so attractive to policymakers seeking to ensure secure electricity supplies with low carbon emissions.
b) Why is there fierce opposition to the idea of a Severn barrage?

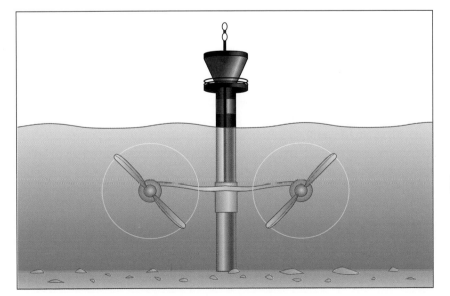

Figure 5.25

SeaGen is the first of a series of underwater turbines driven by the tides in Strangford Lough, Northern Ireland. The two turbine blades, each measuring 16 m from tip to tip, turn at around 14 revolutions per minute. The turbine drives a generator that supplies electricity to the grid.

power but since the introduction of the Renewables Obligation in 2001 a greater share has supported renewables. The Renewables Obligation requires electricity companies to obtain an increasing proportion of their electricity from renewable sources, or to pay a price if they fail to do so.

The UK government gives some support to wave energy, but the main area of growth in the near future is expected to come from on-shore and off-shore wind farms. Meeting government targets could require as many as 3000 extra 5 MW off-shore wind turbines and 4000 3 MW on-shore turbines, in addition to the 2000 turbines that have already been installed.

As well as bringing down the cost, renewable energy faces other challenges. One problem is to link wind farms and other sources of renewable electricity to the national grid of power lines. The transmission network was designed to receive electricity from large power stations and then distribute it to consumers. The grid has to be extended and redesigned to take in electricity from widely distributed, smaller sources of power.

Another challenge is that renewables such as wind, wave and tidal power are intermittent and, unlike fossil fuel and nuclear power stations, cannot be relied on to provide a steady supply of power.

5.6 Predicting future energy use

Scenarios

Research teams have explored and reported large numbers of energy scenarios, motivated by the fact that changes in the energy sector are essential to sustainable development. It takes many years to make substantial changes in complex energy systems and so energy scenarios often extend over periods as long as 100 years. These scenarios explore the interplay between changes in population, economic developments and technical innovation with ecological systems and the wider environment.

In advance of a world summit on sustainable development in 2002, the United Nations Development Programme and the World Energy Council commissioned a *World Energy Assessment*. This assessment explored the implications of scenarios developed by the International Institute for Applied Systems Analysis. These scenarios had been studied systematically over 5 years, with detailed work to build up databases and formal models.

The work focused on three cases, incorporating sets of assumptions about future technical, social and economic developments in the near term up to 2020 and then in the longer term up to 2100. The three cases were named A, B and C. Variants within the cases gave rise to six scenarios for analysis.

Case A: This assumes a high-growth future with vigorous economic development and rapid technological development. There are three variants of this case: A1, A2 and A3.

Case B: This is a middle course with modest economic growth and modest technological developments. This is the nearest to a business-as-usual scenario.

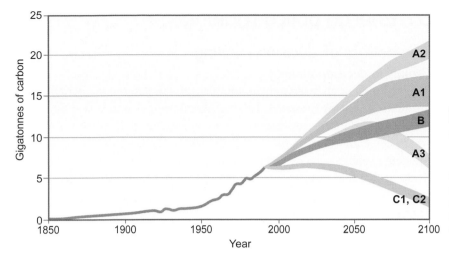

Figure 5.26

Global carbon emissions from fossil fuel use 1850–1990 and in six scenarios from 1990–2100. In each scenario, the range shows the difference between gross and net emissions. Gross emissions are actual carbon dioxide released into the atmosphere. Net emissions include deductions for carbon absorption.

Case C: Here the assumptions are based on policies to give environmental concerns high priority. Also in this scenario governments introduce environmental and energy taxes to protect the environment. They also transfer wealth from richer to poorer countries to bring about economic equity. Variant C1 assumes that new sources of renewable energy will be introduced and nuclear energy phased out by 2020. Variant C2 includes both new renewables and investment in new nuclear power.

The *World Energy Assessment* used the six scenarios to illustrate the options available for achieving the transition of energy systems towards sustainability. The implications of the scenarios for global carbon dioxide emissions are shown in Figure 5.26.

Analysis of the scenarios makes it possible to estimate the expected atmospheric concentration of carbon dioxide in the different scenarios, as shown in Figure 5.27. Only in the C scenarios do carbon dioxide concentrations in the atmosphere stabilise by 2100.

Date	Source of estimate	Carbon dioxide concentration in the atmosphere/ppmv
1800	Data	280
2008	Data	387
2100	Scenario A1	590
	Scenario A2	730
	Scenario A3	530
	Scenario B	620
	Scenarios C1 and C2	450

Figure 5.27

World Energy Assessment *estimates of future carbon dioxide concentrations in 2100 in six scenarios compared to historic data.*

Questions

45 Identify the variant of case A that:
a) is coal intensive
b) features changes to make the future more sustainable and equitable.

46 What processes mean that net carbon dioxide emissions are less than gross emissions as shown in Figure 5.26?

47 Which scenarios avoid a doubling of the carbon dioxide concentration in the atmosphere from 1800 to 2100?

48 According to Figures 5.26 and 5.27, can technological innovation help the world to achieve a sustainable energy policy whilst continuing to experience economic growth?

5.7 Energy policy making

The politics of decision making

Groups in decision making

The government civil servants and ministers who determine energy policy are subject to many pressures. It is not just during elections that citizens exert their influence. Governments regularly use opinion polls to find out what people are thinking on key issues. Major planning decisions related to energy supply, such as power stations or wind farms, can stimulate lively debate that local MPs then represent to ministers. Most MPs are not scientists but they do have access to some expertise, such as the regular briefings on technical issues from the Parliamentary Office of Science and Technology.

Citizens who feel particularly strongly about an issue can become activists as members of pressure groups such as Greenpeace or Friends of the Earth. Both of these organisations have vigorous campaigns to promote renewable sources of energy and to oppose the use of fossil fuels and nuclear power to generate electricity (Figure 5.28). These groups draw on the expertise of scientists to inform their campaigns.

Other organisations with large memberships also campaign on energy issues because of their impact on people and the environment. The World Wide Fund for Nature (WWF) pays close attention to energy policy as part of its campaign to promote sustainable development in defence of the natural world. The Royal Society for the Protection of Birds (RSPB) supports the development of wind farms but seeks to highlight the parts of the country where wind turbines could threaten large numbers of birds.

Organisations that represent industry, such as the Confederation of British Industry (CBI) and the Trades Union Congress (TUC), exist to

Questions

49 Under what circumstances might the implementation of energy policy in the UK change you from a concerned citizen to a campaigning activist?

50 In response to a government consultation about carbon capture and storage in 2008, the person in charge of the World Wide Fund for Nature's climate change policy said: "Reliance on an as yet unproven technology, however promising it may be, is a risky business. The future of the planet's climate cannot rely on good intentions." What does this mean and how could the statement be justified?

51 What practical steps could the RSPB take to help the developers of wind farms limit the damage they cause to birds?

Figure 5.28

Climate change activists marching towards Kingsnorth Power Station in Kent in 2008 as part of a campaign to stop a new coal-fired electricity station from being built.

influence government and industrial policy, including energy policy. Individual energy companies clearly have a big stake in plans for future energy supplies and so they lobby parliament to affect energy policy, but they also use public relations techniques to shape opinion in society.

Science and decision making

Like MPs, most government ministers and civil servants do not have an advanced education in science (Figure 5.29). As a result, government departments have a chief scientist to advise ministers. Governments also use scientists as experts in other ways, for example, to undertake inquiries into difficult policy problems.

There are leading scientists in the House of Lords, with life peerages, some of whom belong to the House of Lords Select Committee on Science and Technology. This committee produces influential reports on a range of issues including climate change and energy policy.

Scientists, like other sections of the nation, have their own independent organisations. When a new issue arises that concerns them, they may have to hammer out a combined 'professional' opinion that they can present to government. Most working scientists belong to an organisation related to their subject specialism, such as the Institute of Physics or the Institution of Civil Engineers. Particularly influential, in terms of reputation and policy, are two organisations that elect their fellows: the UK's national academy of science, the Royal Society, and the Royal Academy of Engineering.

European comparisons

France

In Europe, France has been exceptional in its adoption of nuclear power as the main source of its electricity. There are more than 50 working nuclear plants in the country and they generate about three-quarters of the nation's electricity.

Nuclear power is accepted in France, unlike in the UK where it is unpopular. France has relatively few natural energy resources. In the 1960s most of its oil power was generated by burning imported oil. The shock of the oil price rises in the early 1970s led French policy makers to adopt nuclear power as the means of achieving energy independence and security of supply (Figure 5.30).

| Figure 5.29

Prime Minister Gordon Brown with ministers John Hutton and Hilary Benn, unveiling the government's energy saving package at a press conference in September 2008.

Questions

52 In its response to a House of Commons inquiry 'Keeping the lights on', the Royal Society stated: "Renewables and energy efficiency measures are not sufficiently developed to make up for the shortfall in energy generating capacity caused by the phase out of nuclear power stations and older coal plants." If this is the case, what are the implications for policy?

53 In its response to a House of Lords Select Committee consultation on 'The Economics of Renewable Energy', the Royal Academy of Engineering stated that one of the main barriers facing most forms of renewable energy is the capital cost of installation – unlike the traditional thermal forms of generation where fuel costs represent a significant proportion of costs. Why is this the case and does it apply to all forms of renewable energy?

| Figure 5.30

French president Nicolas Sarkozy talking to workers at an EDF nuclear power station in Normandy in 2007. Sarkozy gave a speech arguing that nuclear energy is safer for the environment.

In a country where independence is valued, politicians were able to persuade most French citizens to accept a nuclear policy given the absence of indigenous coal, gas and oil. The government was helped by the French tradition of embracing ambitious, technological projects such as high-speed trains and supersonic aircraft. Also, France is a country where scientists and engineers have high status and are generally trusted.

Opinion surveys have shown that French people share with other Europeans the negative images and fears of radiation, but that nevertheless most citizens recognise the benefits of electricity generation from nuclear power and see that it makes their modern lives possible.

Figure 5.31

German chancellor Angela Merkel holding a mock-up of a wind turbine at a technology fair in 2008. The German chancellor actively promotes policies to deal with the challenges of climate change.

Germany

As in France, there was strong support for nuclear power in Germany after the oil price rises in the early 1970s. However, only one nuclear station has opened since the 1986 nuclear accident at Chernobyl. Following reunification in 1990, all the nuclear stations built by Soviet engineers in the east of the country were closed down and dismantled. In 2001 the government decided to phase out the 17 nuclear power stations that generated one-third of the country's electricity over a period of about 30 years.

Green campaigners have been active in Germany since the 1960s. Damage to the country's valuable forests by acid rain from fossil fuel power stations was one of the issues that raised the profile of green politics. The electoral system in Germany has since allowed green politicians to gain seats in the Bundestag (the German parliament). In 1998 they won 7% of the national vote and were sufficiently established to become part of a coalition government.

In this political context, Germany managed to cut its greenhouse gas emissions by 18% between 1990 and 2005. The government has implemented a range of policies that include a tax on fuel, laws that encourage waste reduction and recycling, and subsidies that encourage people to retrofit their homes with solar panels.

A key feature of energy policy has been the 'feed-in' law to encourage renewables. This law subsidises anyone that produces their own energy from renewables and it allows them to sell any surplus electricity to the grid. One consequence has been a rapid increase in the percentage of electricity generated from renewables, doubling to 12% between 2000 and 2006. Another consequence has been that renewable energy technologies in Germany have become an important industrial sector, employing about a quarter of a million people.

Questions

54 What have been the decisive events related to energy supply that have helped to shape people's attitudes to sources of energy in the UK?

55 Why is a 'feed-in' law an effective way of stimulating the development of renewable sources of electricity?

UK government energy policy

In contrast to the implementation of energy policy in other countries, such as Germany, the UK government has deferred decisions while carrying out a series of reviews and issuing consultation and policy papers on energy issues. All this activity is driven by the fact that the country can no longer meet its need for energy from its own resources. The coal industry has contracted dramatically, while production of oil and gas from the North Sea is now in decline. So the UK is having to rely on imported energy resources at a time when oil and gas prices are rising steeply as demand for energy resources is increasing worldwide, especially as a result of economic growth in countries such as China and India.

At the same time, the country has signed up to international agreements to cut emissions of greenhouse gases. So the government faces the challenge of devising feasible policies to ensure security of energy supplies while responding to the issue of climate change. These changes are also happening at a time when many of the large coal and nuclear power stations in the country are nearing the end of their lives.

A major influence on UK thinking about energy policy has been the review carried out by Lord Stern of Brentford (see Chapter 4). As a result of the analysis, Lord Stern argued that three elements of policy are essential for an effective response to the challenge of climate change:

- carbon pricing through taxation, emissions trading or regulation should show people the full social costs of their actions – with the ultimate aim of establishing a global carbon price across countries and sectors;
- support for technologies designed to encourage the large-scale development and use of a range of low-carbon and high-efficiency products
- steps to foster energy efficiency.

Some economists have criticised the *Stern Review*. The main criticism has focused on the procedure Lord Stern used to estimate the costs and benefits occurring in the future. Nevertheless, the report has had an important impact by showing that the need for action on climate change is not just an issue arising from the scientific consensus agreed by the IPCC but also has severe economic implications that call for action now.

In its 2007 White Paper, the UK government set out policies to respond to these challenges with the aims of:

- saving energy
- developing cleaner, low-carbon energy supplies
- securing reliable energy supplies at prices set in competitive markets.

As a step towards cleaner, low-carbon energy supplies, the government has announced plans to develop renewable energy sources, not only to generate electricity but also for transport and heating. In 2007 the UK signed up to an agreement with other EU member states to an EU-wide target of 20% of energy resources coming from renewables by 2020. The UK contribution is to supply 15% of its energy needs from renewables by that year. The size of the challenge this presents is shown by Figure 5.32 (page 162).

Questions

56 Suggest reasons for the delayed decisions about energy policies in the UK compared to other countries, such as Germany.

57 Natural gas resources are more widely dispersed than oil, but 56% of proven reserves are found in just three countries: Russia, Iran and Qatar. What are the policy implications of this for the UK?

58 The UK government thinks that it is very important to the UK that technologies necessary to make generating electricity with coal become low carbon are developed and introduced as rapidly as possible.
a) What technologies are available to do this?
b) Why is this so important to the UK?

59 Suggest benefits to the UK of signing up to international agreements that impose constraints on its energy policies.

60 Currently 99% of road transport relies on petrol or diesel from oil. Identify two renewables that can help the UK to reach the 15% target by 2020 in the transport sector.

61 Explain how encouraging investment in renewables for heating, road transport and generating electricity can help the government reach its policy targets.

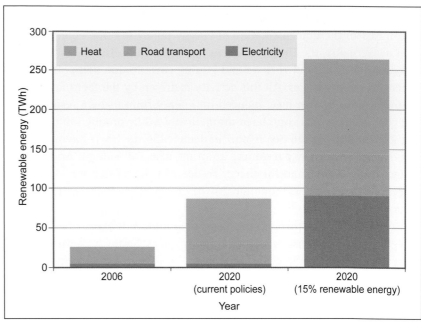

Figure 5.32

A possible scenario to reach 15% renewable energy in the UK by 2020.

A wide range of technologies is available that will have to be exploited to reach the ambitious 15% target, as shown in Figure 5.33.

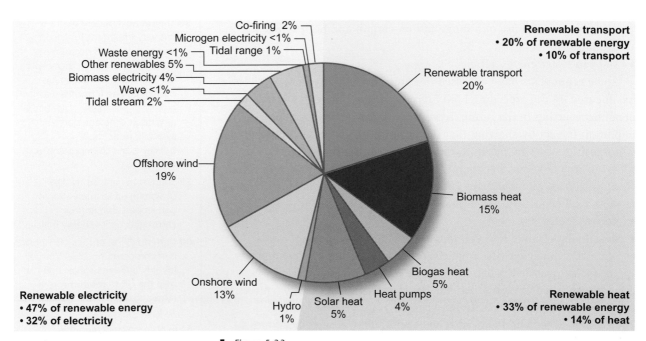

Figure 5.33

A possible breakdown of the renewable technologies to be introduced by 2020 to meet the target of 15% renewables by that year.

5.8 Meeting policy targets through energy conservation

Saving energy can help to reduce carbon dioxide emissions and at the same time reduce the need for the UK to import energy resources.

Energy saving in homes

Science and technology are helping to reduce energy consumption in homes, for example by developing more efficient methods of lighting, refrigeration, cooking and washing (Figure 5.34). But improved technology is not the only, or even the most effective, way of reducing energy consumption in homes. More careful use of lights, heating and hot water can help to save energy. Still more energy can be saved by more effectively retaining the heat in homes by means of effective insulation and draught proofing.

The UK government target is to make all homes carbon neutral by 2016.

Key term

A process is **carbon neutral** if the carbon dioxide released is balanced by actions that remove an equivalent amount of carbon dioxide from the atmosphere.

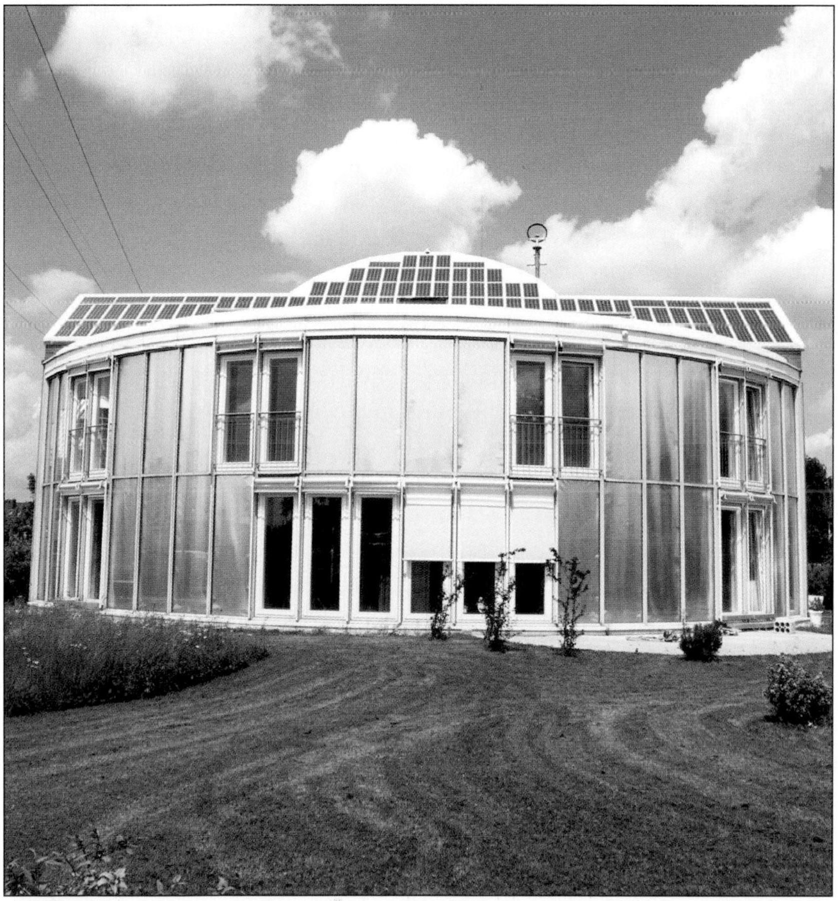

Figure 5.34

This house uses solar energy to be completely self-sufficient for heating and electricity. The building has a wall of transparent insulation on the south side for direct heating by the Sun (passive solar heating). It heats its water with solar collectors and uses solar panels (photovoltaic cells) to generate electricity. Electricity is used to split water into hydrogen and oxygen by electrolysis. These gases are stored and used for cooking or to generate electricity in a fuel cell when there is not enough solar energy available. This demonstration house was completed in 1992 in Freiburg, Germany.

Questions

62 Why are international agreements necessary if the UK is to introduce cars and domestic appliances that are more energy efficient?

63 The Energy Saving Trust estimates that homes in the UK waste over £900 million per year by leaving appliances on when not in use. Why do people waste energy resources in this way?

64 The government is encouraging the development of smart meters and real time displays that enable people to track their energy use more conveniently in their homes. Suggest reasons why this should help people to change their habits and make more efficient use of energy.

65 Friends of the Earth argues that energy companies should change to make money from selling less energy, not more.
a) Why would this be a desirable approach?
b) Is it practicable, and how could it be done?

The breakdown of average carbon dioxide emissions by individuals in the UK. In 2005 the average per capita emission was 1.16 tonnes of carbon per year.

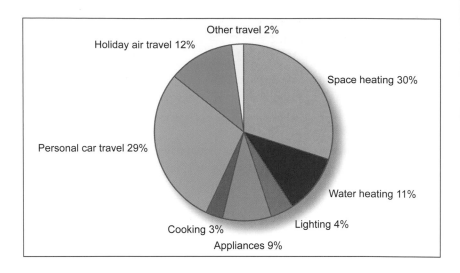

Energy saving in transport

Personal car travel makes a substantial contribution to the average carbon emissions, as shown by Figure 5.35.

There is a range of technologies that might be introduced that could make a significant contribution to carbon reduction from transport. These technologies include more advanced versions of hybrid vehicles, including 'plug-in' hybrids, fully electric vehicles, second generation biofuels (see Section 5.9), and hydrogen-fuelled vehicles, whether powered by an internal combustion engine or a fuel cell (see Section 5.9). However, the success of hydrogen- or electricity-based technologies in delivering low-carbon transport will rely heavily on the way that electricity is generated in the UK in future.

Really significant reductions in carbon emissions from transport cannot be achieved by science and technology alone. It is also necessary to persuade people to change their travel habits, both in the amount of travelling they do and the way they do it.

Public transport is more fuel efficient than private motoring. New investment in public transport combined with the rising cost of fuel is encouraging a shift to public transport, especially in big cities.

The government has tried to encourage changes towards more sustainable patterns of travel behaviour using a range of measures that include workplace, school and personalised travel planning and travel awareness campaigns. One example is the scheme to encourage more primary school children to walk to school through 'walking buses'. Others include the various initiatives to encourage more cycling such as the designation of Bristol as the first cycling city. The government also hopes that schemes of this kind will help tackle growing levels of obesity in the UK by building physical activity into everyday life.

Energy saving in business

The main policy instrument for encouraging energy efficiency and the reduction of carbon dioxide emissions is the EU Emissions Trading Scheme (ETS). This applies to all companies that make intensive use of energy. In the first phase the scheme applied to the businesses across Europe that were responsible for about 50% of the EU's carbon dioxide gas emissions. These businesses include combustion plants, oil refineries,

Questions

66 The Stern Review noted that:

"Transport is one of the more expensive sectors to cut emissions from because the low-carbon technologies tend to be expensive and the welfare costs of reducing demand for travel are high."

Give reasons to explain the two points made in this statement.

67 When deciding which policy is most appropriate in addressing environmental challenges, the government must use the most effective instrument: regulation, voluntary agreements or taxation. Give one example from the field of transport to illustrate each type of instrument.

coke ovens, iron and steel plants, and factories making cement, glass, lime, brick, ceramics, pulp and paper. The aim of the EU ETS is to help the countries that belong to the EU to comply with the commitments that they agreed to when signing the Kyoto Protocol (see Chapter 4). The scheme is an attempt to put a price on carbon emissions and to provide financial incentives for businesses to innovate and save energy.

5.9 Meeting policy targets through new energy technologies

A group of scientists at Bath University is working on improving ways of making 'green' energy. None of these forms of energy individually provides the answers to all our energy needs – each has strengths, weaknesses and drawbacks.

Biofuels – a short-term alternative to fossil fuels

The move to greater sustainability includes the shift towards alternative energy resources to replace finite resources such as fossil fuels. The chemical industry is helping to supply alternative fuels such as biofuels. The apparent advantage of biofuels is that they are carbon neutral. The crops grown to make the fuel take in carbon dioxide during photosynthesis as they grow. In theory, the same quantity of carbon dioxide is then given out as the biofuel burns.

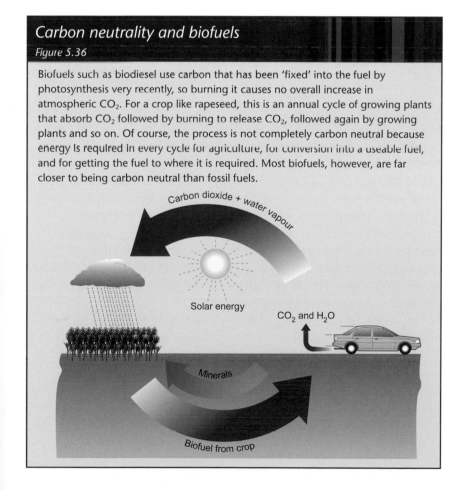

Carbon neutrality and biofuels
Figure 5.36

Biofuels such as biodiesel use carbon that has been 'fixed' into the fuel by photosynthesis very recently, so burning it causes no overall increase in atmospheric CO_2. For a crop like rapeseed, this is an annual cycle of growing plants that absorb CO_2 followed by burning to release CO_2, followed again by growing plants and so on. Of course, the process is not completely carbon neutral because energy is required in every cycle for agriculture, for conversion into a useable fuel, and for getting the fuel to where it is required. Most biofuels, however, are far closer to being carbon neutral than fossil fuels.

Carbon dioxide + water vapour

Solar energy

CO_2 and H_2O

Minerals

Biofuel from crop

Figure 5.37

Matthew Davidson is a chemistry professor at the University of Bath with a particular interest in developing new catalysts.

Improving production of biodiesel

Matthew Davidson is a chemistry professor who leads a team working on converting vegetable oil (usually rapeseed oil) into biodiesel (Figure 5.37). Here he describes his work to improve the production of biodiesel.

"The large molecules in vegetable oil make the oil thick so that it would clog up diesel engines if used without processing. The molecules need to be broken into single chains by a chemical process When this is done the molecules resemble those in mineral diesel.

"Processing of this sort costs money and requires energy. We are investigating ways of speeding up the reaction and using less energy. This is done using a catalyst to speed up the reaction. In the past many catalysts were toxic chemicals, but we specialise in 'green chemistry' and the designing of catalysts that are non-toxic."

Will biodiesel answer all our energy needs?

"Biodiesel can never meet all our energy needs, but it can help mitigate the problems caused by fossil fuels. It is a very useful technology for transport because it can be used alongside petrochemical diesel without the need for major changes in infrastructure or engine design. However, it would be very difficult to 'grow' enough biodiesel to replace the vast amount of oil that we currently consume.

"Biodiesel is best thought of as one of a whole range of possible solutions for replacing fossil fuels. We think of it as an important transitional technology for transport while more radical technologies, such as fuel cells and solar power, are developed to a stage where they can be widely used."

Should we be growing rapeseed and other crops for fuel? Shouldn't the land be used to grow food?

"Increasing competition between food and fuel is a complex social and political issue that cannot be solved by new technology alone (Figure 5.38). Using land to grow non-food crops is not a new phenomenon – cotton and rubber are two examples of widely grown non-food crops. However, as the world's population increases and gets richer, there is increasing demand for both food and fuel and if their production relies on the same limited resources this can cause conflict and can lead to the destruction of important natural habitats.

"One important technological advance that could help is the production of biofuels from biomass. This need not compete with food production. 'First generation' biofuels have relied on the direct use of food crops to produce fuel; examples are biodiesel from rapeseed and bioethanol from corn starch. A 'second generation' of biofuels is now being developed that can use either the waste parts of food crops (such as straw from corn and wheat) or use crops grown on marginal land that cannot be used for food production. Jatropha is an example of a drought-resistant plant that can give high yields of oil when grown on marginal land.

Figure 5.38

Food or fuel? Oil-seed rape growing in fields next to a motorway. Rapeseed is grown to make animal feed, vegetable oil for human consumption and biodiesel.

"Another intriguing possibility is the use of microalgae for the production of biofuels. These tiny aquatic organisms use photosynthesis very efficiently and can produce high quantities of oil whilst absorbing carbon dioxide. The potential yield of biodiesel from microalgae is many times that possible from land-based crops, suggesting that they may develop into a significant source of biofuels (and other chemicals) in the future.

"Although first generation biofuels have been important to prove the technology, second generation biofuels will provide a far more sustainable source of transport fuels in the future. These developments are made possible by advances in technology, but they can only be effective in combination with social, political and economic developments that lead to the implementation of sustainable production and use of fuel."

Fuel cells – a medium-term solution for generating electricity with very high efficiencies

Professor Saiful Islam leads another team at the University of Bath (Figure 5.39). The group is designing new materials for fuel cells of the future. Here he explains the potential of fuel cells and describes his work.

Questions

68 Suggest reasons for and against the view that the use of biodiesel for transport should be thought of as a transitional technology and not a long-term solution to the problem of developing sustainable energy resources.

69 Why is the potential yield of biodiesel from microalgae many times that possible from land-based crops?

70 New biofuel technologies "can only be effective in combination with social, political and economic developments that lead to the implementation of sustainable production and use of fuel." Explain and illustrate this statement.

Figure 5.39

Professor Saiful Islam.

"Like a combustion engine, a fuel cell uses some sort of chemical fuel. But like a battery, the chemical energy is converted directly to electricity, without the polluting combustion step.

"The ideal fuel for a fuel cell is pure hydrogen (H_2) but other hydrogen-rich fuels can also be used, such as methane (CH_4) and methanol (CH_3OH). When hydrogen is used, no CO_2 is produced and the only by-product is water, H_2O."

Types of fuel cells

There are a number of different fuel cell types being developed around the world. Today, two types generally stand out as the most promising: solid oxide fuel cells and polymer-based fuel cells.

- Solid oxide fuel cells (SOFCs) are made from inorganic, crystalline materials and operate at temperatures above 800 °C. This makes them suitable for heat and power generation in homes, hospitals, office buildings, and other stationary applications (Figure 5.40).
- Polymer-based fuel cells – also known as proton exchange membrane fuel cells – are suitable for use in cars and buses, and mobile applications such as laptop computers. They use organic polymers that operate well at or near room temperature.

Where does the hydrogen come from and is it safe?

"Hydrogen is a secondary energy source that is made mainly from natural gas and steam. It can also be made by electrolysis, which involves passing an electric current through water. There is extensive research being carried out to develop more sustainable ways of making hydrogen. One approach is to use renewable solar power as the source of electricity. New methods of hydrogen storage are also going to be very important to its use as a safe energy source."

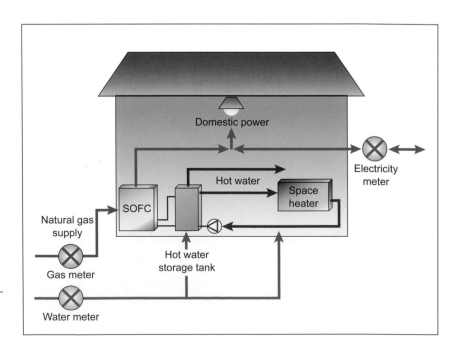

Figure 5.40

A solid oxide fuel cell (SOFC) can provide heating as well as electricity. This can be a very efficient way of using a fuel in a building.

How do you use computer modelling to design new materials for fuel cells?

"I do not work in a laboratory but with a supercomputer. My research involves designing computer models of crystal lattices. The models are based on real minerals that occur in nature. I use the models to predict how the oxygen ions might move through the lattice in solid oxide fuel cells – the faster the better. Modelling can reveal information that is difficult to extract from experiments alone, such as predicting the motion of ions in crystalline solids."

Solar panels – are they the long-term solution for energy?

Solar panels producing electricity are with us already, but they are very expensive. They use crystalline silica or other costly materials that are generally non-renewable. The energy put into making the panels is high compared with the energy they generate.

Halina Dunn is working in a team investigating the possibilities of a new generation of solar voltaic cells that mimic an important process in nature – photosynthesis (Figure 5.41). Halina explains:

"Like photosynthesis, this type of cell harvests light from the Sun. The cells are made with intensely coloured purple dyes spread as a single layer of molecules on the surface of titanium dioxide nanoparticles. These are tiny particles that are 10 nanometres (that is 10^{-9} m) in diameter. When the dye absorbs visible light, it produces electrical power rather than the sugar formed during photosynthesis.

Questions

71 Why is hydrogen a secondary rather than a primary source of energy?

72 Why does a building with a fuel cell make more efficient use of the energy from natural gas than a building with a gas boiler and a mains electricity supply?

73 What are the risks of using hydrogen as a fuel for fuel cells:
a) in a home?
b) in a motor vehicle?
c) Compare the risks you have identified in parts a and b with the risks of using gas and petrol.

74 Why do fuel cells have the potential to provide a more sustainable way of using energy resources?

Figure 5.41

Halina Dunn read Physics for her first degree but is now doing a PhD with the Renewables team in the Chemistry department at the University of Bath. She has always felt strongly about environmental issues, and so, when she graduated and found out about the possibility of being involved in renewable projects at the University of Bath, she jumped at the opportunity.

75 Why are solar cells at best only a solution to the challenge of developing sustainable energy resources in the long term?

76 Suggest two applications of solar cells made from thin, transparent films laid down on the surface of plastic.

77 Suggest reasons for and against the view that using less energy in all aspects of life should be given greater priority than research into new energy technologies.

"In a dye-sensitised solar cell, dye molecules act rather like chlorophyll in a leaf by absorbing photons and exciting electrons to a higher energy state. The electrons are then collected on the porous titanium dioxide support. My research is all about studying what happens to the electron in the titanium dioxide. For the solar cell to work, the electrons have to complete a perilous journey through the crystal lattice. The danger is that the electrons get stuck in traps, or react with the wrong component.

"Cells of this type have already exceeded 10% efficiency. They have the great advantage that they can be printed on sheets of conducting glass or on flexible plastic films suitable for mounting on windows for power generation.

"We hope that cells like this can be part of the answer to domestic energy, along with other types of renewable energy. The cells are not yet efficient enough but industry is starting to get involved.

"It is too early to be able to predict which type of solar cell will be commercially successful. As well as our dye-sensitised cells, there are many other technologies in the pipeline, including cells based on polymers, and thin-film cells that are similar to silicon cells, but based on different materials.

"Of course for all of us, using renewable fuels is only part of the answer. I think using less energy in all aspects of our lives has to be a priority."

78 Use examples from the supply and use of energy resources to illustrate these statements about risk:

a) New technologies based on scientific advances often introduce new risks.

b) It is difficult to assess the risk of a new technology because there are no available data for estimating the probability of harm.

c) When taking a decision about the management of a given risk, people need to take into account both the probability of the event occurring and the seriousness of the consequences if it did.

d) Reducing the risk of a given hazard costs more and more the lower we want to make the risk.

e) People and governments have to decide what level of risk is acceptable by weighing up the probability of harm and the cost of reducing it further.

79 Give examples to illustrate these statements about policy and practice in the context of the supply and use of energy resources:

a) Official regulations apply to many kinds of scientific activity and there are regulatory bodies to monitor practice and enforce the controls.

b) Much of the evidence available to the people who make decisions is often uncertain.

c) Many decisions about new technologies involve economic considerations.

d) Some decisions about science and technology need to comply with international agreements.

e) Policy makers are influenced by the mass media, special interest groups and public opinion.

f) Vested interests can affect the interpretation and evaluation of evidence by the people involved in making decisions.

80 a) Greenpeace argues that nuclear power is a relic of an out-of-date, centralised and wasteful energy system. What is the basis for this aspect of Greenpeace's case against nuclear power?

b) Greenpeace campaigns for a decentralised system that, combined with renewable energy and energy efficiency, could deliver larger carbon dioxide savings than building new nuclear power stations. What would this mean in practice and what would be the benefits and risks?

81 The EU wants to cut greenhouse gas emissions by 60% by 2050. The EU also has a binding target to cut them by 20% by 2020. The following extract is from the 2008 Budget. It announces that the government wants to make it easier for households and communities to generate energy from renewable sources for their own use, and to feed any excess into the national grid.

> The UK is committed to tripling the contribution made by renewable electricity by 2015. The European Commission has now brought forward an EU-wide target for 20% of energy production to come from renewable sources by 2020, and the government will consider a wide range of measures to enable the UK to play its part. In the summer, the government will launch a full consultation on what more the UK should do to increase renewable energy use and meet its share of the EU target. The government will also consult on the most appropriate support mechanism for microgeneration at individual and community level, including the option of a feed-in tariff. The government will also consider how to address barriers such as planning and grid access.

Read the extract and write a clearer account, suggesting examples of energy generation that might be used in this way:

a) in a south-facing council building in London

b) on a hillside in West Wales

c) on an arable farm in Norfolk.

Chapter 6

Sustaining the variety of life on Earth

- How did the huge variety of life on Earth come about?
- Are we approaching a sixth mass extinction, and does this matter?
- Can anything be done to reverse the current trends in extinctions and habitat destruction?
- Do short-term economic gains threaten long-term ability of the Earth to support a growing population?
- How do we balance human need in poorer countries and the desire to preserve natural ecosystems? Is this an imposition of Western values?
- What are the roles of new technologies in either reducing or increasing our impact?

Figure 6.1

Bonobos, sometimes known as pygmy chimpanzees, are thought to be the closest living relatives to humans. This species is in danger of extinction. Bonobos live wild only in parts of the Democratic Republic of the Congo such as the Salonga National Park. The only true enemies of bonobos are humans. The main threats to bonobo survival are hunting and habitat destruction.

6.1 Relationships between living organisms

You have probably visited a zoo at some point in your life. Reasons for visiting a zoo range from a serious interest in conservation, to just wanting to see unusual and interesting animals from all over the world.

Each animal comes originally from an ecosystem, consisting of a complex community of animals, plants and microbes which interact with each other and their physical environment. Some of these ecosystems are now threatened, and many of the species the ecosystems support are likely to become extinct in the near future.

The history of species

The concept of species is still debated by scientists. A species is often defined as 'a group of actually or potentially interbreeding populations that are reproductively isolated from other such groups'. So, for example, chimpanzees and gorillas belong to different species; they cannot interbreed. This definition relies on a knowledge of reproductive behaviour, so it is impossible to apply it to fossil species or organisms that do not reproduce sexually.

Knowing how closely related organisms are is an important part of being able to classify groups. In the same way that close relatives in a human family have common ancestors, related species have evolved from common ancestral species. The evolutionary hypotheses about species are constantly revised as evidence from DNA sequencing is cross-referenced with knowledge of the biology of different species, and the fossil record.

The animals most closely related to human beings are the apes. One species of ape, the pygmy chimpanzee or bonobo, is our closest relative. This is no surprise to anyone staring at the chimp enclosure in a zoo. Chimps look like small hairy humans; their behaviour leads us to conclude that they are intelligent and sociable; they have emotions and sensitivity to other members of their community. They use tools, communicate in squeaks and grunts and often stand upright on two limbs.

Collecting evidence of the relationships between organisms from species currently alive on Earth is a massive task. Scientists have only identified a tiny fraction of living species. Collecting evidence from extinct species relies on the careful identification of fossils in collections all over the world.

Behind the scenes at the Natural History Museum

The Natural History Museum is well known as a very special venue for a day out in London. What most visitors do not know is that behind heavy wooden doors tucked away in the corners of the galleries, there are vast halls packed with millions of specimens of dried plants, pickled animals and fossils. Most of these have been allocated a two-part Latin name, the first indicating the genus and the second the species.

Everything is organised into a system of classification, showing what group it belongs to and from what it is descended.

Key terms

Species names are used for both living and extinct organisms. For instance, modern humans, known as *Homo sapiens*, are distinguished from the extinct *Homo neanderthalensis* species that died out 24 000 years ago. *Homo* is the genus name, and the species name is *sapiens* (meaning 'wise'). No other species of the group *Homo* still exist.

Fossils are the imprints of parts of organisms that have become preserved in rocks after death.

Question

1   Explain why only a very small fraction of living organisms are ever likely to be preserved as fossils.

Key term

The science of **classifying** living organisms is called taxonomy. Modern classification systems put organisms into groups or 'taxa'. The taxa range from 'Kingdom', which divides up animals, plants and three other major categories, through increasingly closely related groups: phylum, class, order, family, genus and species. The groupings imply evolutionary relationships between organisms.

Since the eighteenth century, when Linnaeus founded the modern binomial (two-name) system of classifying plants and animals, the ultimate goal for taxonomists has been the classification of every living species on Earth.

The Species 2000 project coordinates the global collection and publication of species data. One of the challenges in this immense project is the shortage of scientists with the expertise to identify species accurately. New technologies and equipment may help the task of collecting and recording specimens, but there is no substitute for the taxonomists who can classify the millions of unidentified specimens already in museums, and those found in the field.

Web technologies, GPS systems and three-dimensional imaging allow scientists to share data on species, so the task of cataloguing biodiversity becomes an international collaboration.

Questions

2 Suggest reasons why it is important to be able to identify and name all the different species on Earth.

3 Scientists have been recording and classifying species since the eighteenth century. Why is it that there are still a large number of unknown species?

Figure 6.2

Taxonomy is a key activity for Zerina Johanson and Peta Hayes, who both work in the palaeontology department of the Natural History Museum where scientists study fossil animals and plants.

Question

4 Why does the Natural History Museum keep many specimens of the same fossilised species?

The immense, cool halls of the palaeontology department have rows of very high and wide specimen cabinets. Zerina Johanson (Figure 6.2) slides open a door to reveal tray after tray of fossil fish. She explains:

"To monitor whether species are at risk of extinction, you need to know which species are alive now, and compare this with what you had in the past – that's why we need this pile of fossils.

"I am one of the curators responsible for the health and cataloguing of the collection. We have to make sure nothing is broken or deteriorating. Since its beginning, the Natural History Museum has been a repository for fossils from around the world; the scale of the collection is unsurpassed. Scientists can come here to study the specimens they need, without having to travel all round the world.

"This set of drawers contains one hundred specimens of the same species of ancient armoured fish from Scotland. You may wonder why we have so many. Actually, I wish we had a thousand. Each specimen is different. Different fossils have different features preserved – some are young individuals and some old, and there are variations within the species. These armoured fishes are particularly interesting as they survived one of the mass extinctions during the Devonian, but the whole group was suddenly wiped out a few million years later. No one knows why, but it could be that a different group, the ray-finned fishes, out-competed them.

"Fossil fish allow us to tell an exciting story about vertebrate evolution. If you grab your upper arm, then your forearm and hand, you are touching the same kind of bones we find in the ancient bony fossil fish in the collection. We think that the fish must have carried many of the same genes that we do."

Peta Hayes (Figure 6.2) trundles past with a huge and heavy fossil palm frond on a trolley. This is for her research studying the plants that grew on the Isle of Wight 30 million years after the extinction of the dinosaurs. She explains:

"There are over a quarter of a million plant fossil specimens in the Museum and over 30 000 microscope slides. These specimens belong to the nation – they are yours and mine.

"Science moves on and ideas change, and we often have to re-label things. As plants fossilise, the different parts get separated, so you usually find the roots, stems and leaves have been allocated different species names.

"Some of the specimens have green dots on them. These are type specimens, the single specimen which defines the species. These are really important, and scientists come to compare them with other specimens they have collected."

Peta has fulfilled a childhood dream of working with fossil plants: "I visited the Museum when I was nine and there was an event where you could watch scientists at work. I was shown a fossil plant like the one that had helped the famous scientist Wegener piece together his hypothesis of continental drift – the fossil was found in both South America and Africa.

"Fossil plants also provide important information about past ecosystems and climate changes. For example, toothed leaves tend to have grown in cooler climates, and smooth-edged leaves in tropical climates. Fossil plants surprised scientists by showing that there was no ice at the poles in the age of the dinosaurs, and the whole Earth was much warmer then."

Zerina is now holding two rounded nodules of rock from Western Australia. "Inside these rocks are perfectly preserved fossil fish, 380 million years old. My dream for the future is that, having been encased in a protective layer of limestone, the fish inside have some of their soft parts preserved. While I don't think we could get DNA from these – they are mineralised – we should be able to see detail that will enable us to learn a lot more about how they lived and where they sit on the evolutionary tree."

"Botanists have extracted DNA from living plants" says Peta. "One of the jobs for museum scientists is working out the dates where one species diverged from another. Using DNA information and the shapes of fossils, we can extrapolate back in time and see where the 'branches' of the evolutionary tree start."

Classification and evolution

Common structures such as limbs, eyes and hair can suggest that animals might be closely related. The trouble with using only this approach is that animals that are not closely related may have evolved similar structures. Fish and dolphins, for example, look superficially very similar but are only very distant cousins. Dolphins are mammals, like humans (Figure 6.3). Fish have some similarities with humans, such as having a backbone, but they are more closely related to frogs and toads than mammals are (Figure 6.4). Modern taxonomy uses similarities between the DNA of organisms as evidence of their relationships.

Questions

5   Identify advantages of having a large collection of specimens from all over the world, including type specimens, in one place.

6   Suggest reasons why the Natural History Museum not only uses its collection of specimens for scientific research but also puts them on display to the public.

Question

7   List three characteristics common to dolphins and humans, which are not shared with fish.

Figure 6.3

Bottle-nosed dolphins.

Figure 6.4

Sharks and dolphins look more similar than humans and dolphins, but this does not mean they are more closely related.

DNA analysis in classification

In the same way that DNA fingerprinting can provide evidence in a paternity case, or can help convict a murderer, DNA contains the evidence of relationships between living organisms.

DNA analysis allows scientists to make hypotheses about family trees for any organism, going right back to their first simple, single-celled ancestors. Each time DNA is copied to form sex cells (e.g. eggs and sperm), there is a chance of a copying error. This type of mutation is passed on from one generation to the next. Environmental factors such as ionising radiation also cause mutations. If the basic rate of DNA mutation is assumed to be steady over time, an analysis of accumulated differences in DNA makes it possible to work out the relationship between two individuals or two groups of organisms. Scientists can use similarities and differences in DNA to calculate how long ago different groups diverged from each other during evolution.

Natural selection relies on the great variety of possible combinations of genes that can result when a species reproduces sexually. Your DNA is more similar to the DNA of any brothers or sisters than to the DNA of your cousins. You have some genes in common with your grandparents, uncles and great aunts, but the more distant the relative, the less DNA you have in common.

Question

8 Why is sexual reproduction important in the theory of evolution by natural selection?

Evolutionary trees

A family tree showing the species that are closely related to humans goes back millions of years. Over time, the many changes to DNA eventually meant that different populations could not interbreed, and they looked increasingly different from one another.

Evolutionary trees help scientists to work out how species evolved from common ancestors (Figures 6.5 and 6.6). Groups of organisms occurring close together on branches of an evolutionary tree are closely related, just as in a human family tree.

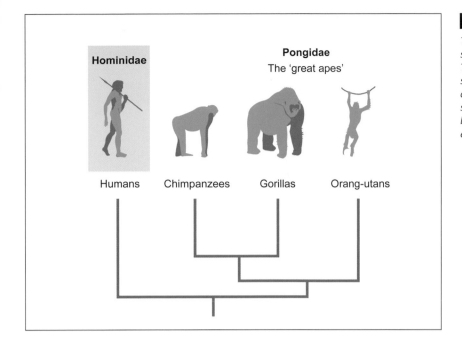

Figure 6.5

Traditional classification was based on similarities in the anatomy of organisms. The great apes were grouped into one family separate from humans and their immediate ancestors. Both great apes and humans shared a common ancestor which existed before these two main groups split off during evolution.

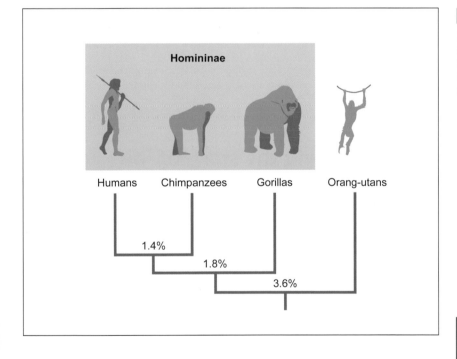

Figure 6.6

This evolutionary tree of apes is based on similarities in DNA. The percentages show the size of the genetic differences between the groups based on evidence from DNA sequencing.

Recent evidence from DNA leads some scientists to argue that chimpanzees and bonobos, living humans and all fossil humans should be classified in a single genus, *Homo*, and that chimps and bonobos should be in a single species. Some fossil teeth found in 2007 are 10 million years old and appear to belong to a primitive gorilla. This suggests that the gorillas did not diverge from humans and chimps 6–8 million years ago as previously thought. Over time, biological classifications and evolutionary trees change as new fossils are found, and as techniques for analysis improve.

Questions

9 What percentage of the DNA in humans is the same as the DNA in chimpanzees?

10 Explain why the data given in Figure 6.6 are incompatible with the evolutionary tree shown in Figure 6.5.

11 Explain why, from time to time, scientists have to revise the classification of groups of living organisms.

DNA analysis can be carried out on tiny quantities of DNA. A reaction called the polymerase chain reaction allows billions of DNA molecules to be produced from one original molecule in a few hours. The process uses enzymes similar to those involved in DNA replication in cells.

The polymerase chain reaction is useful when studying the genetics of specimens such as a 40 000-year-old mammoth, or an insect found frozen in amber. The technique only needs minute samples containing DNA.

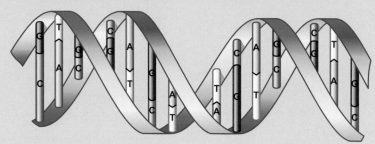

A diagram of a DNA molecule showing the position of the four bases C, T A and G.

The bases C, T, A and G in a DNA molecule spell out the genes which determine the activities of cells and the characteristics of organisms. A strand of DNA can be analysed to map the exact sequence of the four bases C, T, A and G. Base sequences are compared between DNA molecules from different sources.

The human genome contains over 20 000 genes, made up of three billion base pairs. Any two persons' genomes are only expected to vary by around 1000–1200 base pairs.

6.2 Interpreting the story of life on Earth

Deep time

The fossil remains of animals, plants and microbes provide powerful evidence for the evolutionary relationships between species, and for the types of organisms and habitats which existed in the past. There are fossil sea shells at the top of Mount Everest, which must originally have been deposited on an ancient sea floor. Remnants of tropical species remain in Arctic rocks, while the coral rag limestones of England are the remains of a coral reef which once covered most of the country. Rocks, and the fossils they contain, tell the story of how climates change over geological time, how continents move and how mountains rise and fall as rocks fold and sink.

Geological time is measured in a scale of thousands of millions of years (Figure 6.9). The relative timescale of the periods such as Cambrian, Cretaceous and Jurassic are determined by the distribution of the living organisms which have survived as fossils. Other events such as mountain building, volcanic eruptions, ice ages, the covering of the land by sea and meteorite collisions also make a clear mark in the rock sequence (Figure 6.8).

Question

12 Suggest how the type specimens of fossils in the Natural History Museum (see pages 174–175) could be used to determine the relative age of rock strata.

Figure 6.8

These layers of rock in the cliffs near Lyme Regis in Dorset are rich in fossils. Studying the position of the fossils in rocks like this allows scientists to identify organisms which lived together during the same periods of geological time.

Figure 6.9

The story of the Earth in geological time.

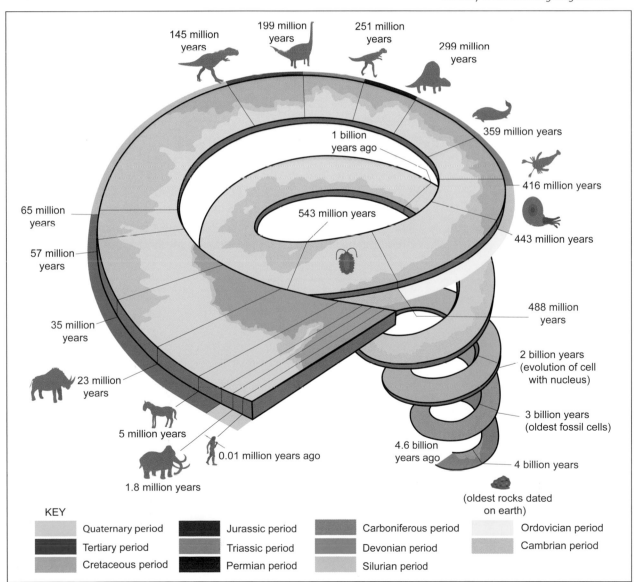

145 million years

199 million years

251 million years

299 million years

359 million years

1 billion years ago

416 million years

65 million years

543 million years

443 million years

57 million years

488 million years

35 million years

2 billion years (evolution of cell with nucleus)

23 million years

3 billion years (oldest fossil cells)

5 million years

4.6 billion years ago

4 billion years

0.01 million years ago

1.8 million years

(oldest rocks dated on earth)

KEY

Quaternary period

Jurassic period

Carboniferous period

Ordovician period

Tertiary period

Triassic period

Devonian period

Cambrian period

Cretaceous period

Permian period

Silurian period

Questions

13 What is it about the half-life of a radioactive element, such as uranium, that makes it possible to use it to calculate the age of a rock sample?

14 The carbon-14 isotope has a half-life of about 6000 years.
a) Why is this a suitable isotope for determining the age of remains of living things but not of rocks?
b) Suggest precautions that would be necessary to give an accurate result when sampling and dating a bone discovered during an excavation.
c) Why is carbon-14 dating not likely to be accurate when dating a sample that is 60 000 years old?

The absolute dating of the geological periods is based on precise measurements of the concentrations of radioactive elements in rocks and of the products of their radioactive decay. There is a well-established technique based on rocks such as zircon which contain uranium atoms. Uranium-235 atoms decay to lead-207 with a half-life of about 700 million years; while uranium-238 atoms decay to lead-206 with a half-life of about 4.5 billion years. Modern techniques allow smaller and smaller samples of material to be analysed. As a result, the age of rocks and of the Earth can be estimated with increasing accuracy.

What fossils tell us about the past

Darwin realised that extinction is a likely result of evolution by natural selection. Over 99% of the species that have ever lived have become extinct, as they fail to adapt to changes in the environment or to compete with other organisms. Around 95% of all past extinctions are probably due to a continuous series of background extinctions occurring over time. The normal background rate represents a few species becoming extinct every year. The fossil record confirms that over time, the normal 'background rate' has been interrupted with five major peaks in extinctions.

Two-hundred and fifty million years ago, around 95% of marine species and 70% of land species on Earth were wiped out by an extinction event. We know this from the fossil record, along with evidence for what might have caused this mass extinction, and four other similar events in the past (Figure 6.10).

According to the data, the background extinction rate works out at around eight families of species becoming extinct per million years. Calculation of the background rate depends on which organisms are included. Any conclusions from fossil data must bear in mind that only certain organisms with hard parts become preserved as fossils.

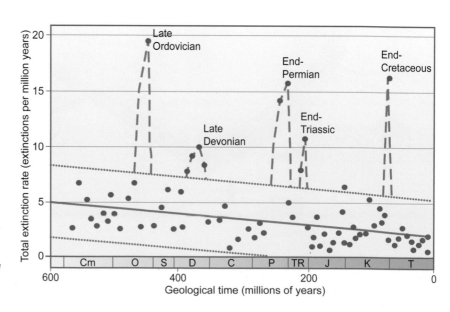

Figure 6.10

The graph shows 76 points where extinction rates were calculated for marine vertebrates and invertebrates, and plotted against geological time.

Outlier or real event?

It is clear that most of the points in Figure 6.10 are clustered together in a band with a downwards trend. A few points fall outside this clustering. Scientists have to decide whether these are significant mass extinction events or just random variations in the background extinction rate.

The trend is shown by a best-fit line, which in this case was calculated excluding the outliers. The dotted lines either side of the best-fit line show the 95% confidence band. There is a 95% chance that any points within this band are part of the trend represented by the best-fit line. Scientists agree that the outlying points which do not fall into the 95% confidence band are statistically significantly different from the best-fit line. The clustering of the points – how separate the outlier is from other points – also affects whether an outlier is considered statistically significantly different from the trend. Four of the outlying peaks are statistically significantly different, whereas the late Devonian extinction peak is not.

Key term

An **outlier** is a data point which is separate from the rest of the data. When interpreting data, scientists must consider the possibility that outliers represent errors in the data collection. Alternatively, an outlier can indicate a problem with the theory being applied to interpret the data. Statistical tests can be carried out to determine whether outliers are significantly different from the rest of the data.

The great dying

The extinction event that occurred 250 million years ago is sometimes referred to as 'the great dying'. It forms the boundary between the Permian and Triassic geological periods (Figure 6.11). Whole groups of organisms, including many sponges and ancient corals, disappeared for ever, while other groups suffered only minor losses. The explanation seems to be that flooding and deforestation occurred as trees and other plants died. The evidence suggests that this happened when tonnes of soil poured into the sea and the oceans stagnated and became devoid of life.

Questions

15 Explain how the decision to remove a very high value outlier would affect:
a) the value of the mean
b) the estimate of the best-fit line of the data.

16 If you find an outlier in experimental data, how can you check whether the outlier is due to a 'real' effect?

17 What are the implications of the downward trend of the best-fit line in Figure 6.10?

18 What can you conclude from Figure 6.11 about the changes over time of:
a) the extinction rate
b) the rate of evolution of families of organisms
c) the difference between background extinctions and mass extinctions?

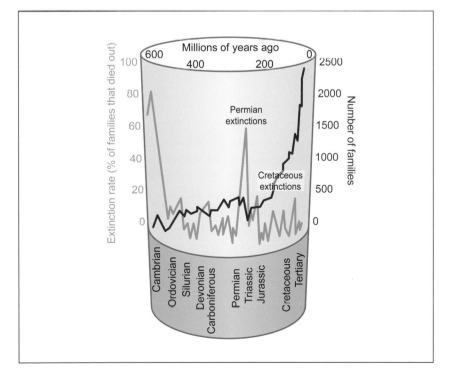

Figure 6.11

Graph showing mass extinctions over geological time since the Cambrian period.

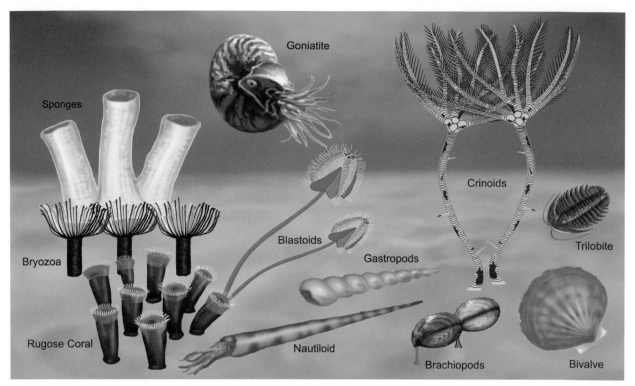

Goniatite

Sponges

Crinoids

Blastoids

Gastropods

Bryozoa

Trilobite

Rugose Coral

Nautiloid

Brachiopods

Bivalve

Figure 6.12

This illustration of the ocean floor before the end-Permian mass extinction shows several simple, fixed organisms, such as corals and large sponges.

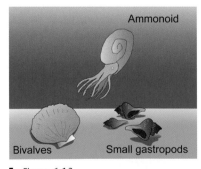

Ammonoid

Bivalves   Small gastropods

Figure 6.13

In the early Triassic period, after the devastating mass extinction at the end of the Permian, marine ecosystems were reduced to simple systems dominated by a small number of species.

At the end of the Permian, before the mass extinction, life on land included a large variety of reptiles and amphibians, and many plants, including ferns, conifers and gingkos. Complex coral reef ecologies existed in the oceans (see Figure 6.12), but there was a roughly equal balance between simple and complex marine ecosystems.

Directly after the Permian extinction, the fossil record shows mainly one species of reptile on land; a medium-sized herbivore called *Lystrosaurus*. Sea life was also dominated by a small number of species (see Figure 6.13).

It took about 50 million years for life on land to fully recover its complexity, with the rise of many species of dinosaurs, pterosaurs and aquatic reptiles during the Mesozoic (i.e. Cretaceous, Jurassic and Triassic periods). Nothing resembling a coral reef shows up until 10 million years after the Permian extinction, and full recovery of marine life took about 100 million years. By the Cretaceous, the ocean floor was dominated by complex ecosystems that had largely displaced the simple post-extinction ecosystems (Figure 6.14).

The change from roughly equal numbers of simple and complex ecosystems before 'the great dying', to a gradual dominance by complex ecosystems, permanently changed the types of ecosystems that exist on Earth. Ecosystems dominated by stationary organisms with low metabolic rates (such as lamp shells and sea lilies that filter nutrients from the water) gave way to more active, mobile organisms (such as snails, clams and crabs). Evidence for this major change became available early in the twenty-first century, through an international scientific collaboration, the Paleobiology Database. This huge repository brings together information about the entire fossil record of plants and animals from all over the world, allowing an overview which was not previously possible.

Figure 6.14

In the Cretaceous, many millions of years after the end-Permian mass extinction, the complex ocean ecosystems had many free-swimming, complex organisms, including ammonites, Nautilus, mobile clams and snails.

The death of the dinosaurs

The most well-known extinction event is probably the fifth mass extinction, which occurred 65 million years ago at the boundary of the Cretaceous (K) and the period previously known as the Tertiary (T). The fossil record shows that all the terrestrial dinosaurs and all the ammonites were wiped out, along with many other species across the existing habitats.

Evidence for theories about the mass extinctions

Explaining the death of the dinosaurs

Theories on the causes of the five mass extinctions include major climate changes, along with massive volcanic and collision events. Most scientists agree that the K-T extinction event was caused by collisions between Earth and one or more asteroids a few kilometres across (Figure 6.15).

Figure 6.15

Artwork of a large asteroid colliding with Earth. The energy released as a massive asteroid collided with the Earth is equivalent to several million atomic bombs. The dust cloud produced could block out sunlight for several years.

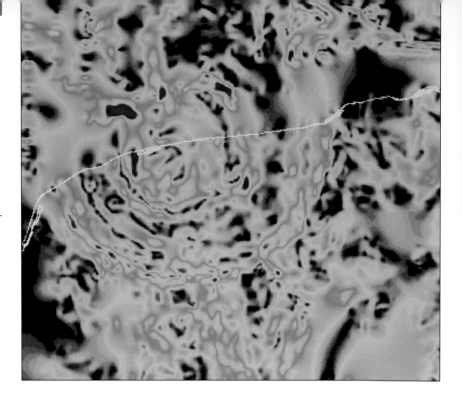

Figure 6.16

A gravity map of the Chicxulub impact crater, showing variations in gravity at the Earth's surface. The colours show the degree of difference between the measured gravity in small areas caused by deep concentrations of rock, compared to the general gravity for the whole region. This is evidence of an ancient crater more than 180 kilometres in diameter. The crater rim is seen as the larger green, yellow and red ring. The white line indicates the coast; land is in the lower half of the frame.

Questions

21 Suggest evidence that scientists could look for to link the existence of the Chicxulub crater with 'the great dying'.

22 Why is there widespread popular interest in competing theories to explain the death of the dinosaurs?

In 1980 a team of researchers, including the Nobel prize-winning physicist Luis Alvarez, discovered that layers of rock found at the K-T boundary anywhere in the world contain levels of iridium many times the normal level for the Earth's crust. As iridium is rare on Earth, but common in many asteroids which hit the Earth, the team concluded that an asteroid collided with the Earth at this time. Ten years later, the theory was supported by the discovery of the massive Chicxulub impact crater off the coast of Mexico (Figure 6.16).

Explaining 'the great dying'

Theories about the causes of 'the great dying' at the end of the Permian include single or multiple meteorite collisions at the same time as an increase in volcanic eruptions (Figures 6.17 and 6.18). Either of these alone could have caused major climate changes.

Figure 6.17

These rocks surrounding the River Jokulsa in Iceland shows distinctive steps as a result of a succession of flood basalt flows. Prehistoric volcanic eruptions causing flood basalts were associated with sudden increases in carbon dioxide levels in the atmosphere.

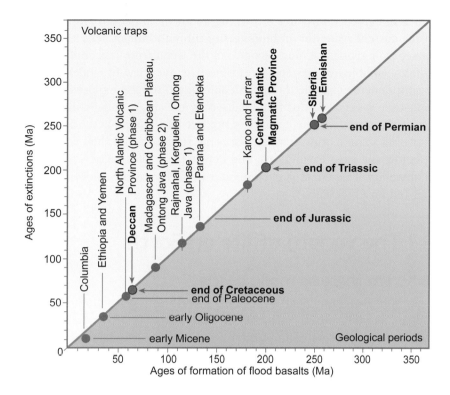

Y-axis: Ages of extinctions (Ma)
X-axis: Ages of formation of flood basalts (Ma)

Volcanic traps

Columbia
Ethiopia and Yemen
North Alantic Volcanic Province (phase 1)
Deccan
Madagascar and Caribbean Plateau, Ontong Java (phase 2)
Rajmahal, Kerguelen, Ontong Java (phase 1)
Parana and Etendeka
Karoo and Farrar
Central Atlantic Magmatic Province
Siberia
Emeishan

end of Permian
end of Triassic
end of Jurassic
end of Cretaceous
end of Paleocene
early Oligocene
early Micene

Geological periods

Figure 6.18

Flood basalts or 'traps' are large areas of volcanic rocks formed by giant volcanic eruptions. The timing of the eruptions can be dated using radioactive isotopes. The graph shows the ages of the main volcanic traps and mass extinctions. The traps, shown as dots on the graph, show good correlation with the mass extinctions. The main geological period are shown, with a scale of 'millions of years ago' (Ma).The data suggest that major environmental changes caused by these massive natural air pollution events, caused, or at least strongly contributed to, the extinctions. Uncertainties in the dating are shown by error bars. Error bars are not shown where they are smaller than the dots.

Lessons from past extinctions

Geologists can inform us of the timings, effects and recovery from large-scale extinctions. These data are all we have on how biological systems recover after large-scale global disruptions.

It is difficult to predict the consequences if the current rates of climate change and habitat destruction go unchecked. Deciding whether or not our current and recent data are part of a long-term trend is an important challenge for scientists (see Chapter 4). Extrapolating data on changes in ecosystems into the future, when such a large number of interdependent factors is involved, requires complex modelling and careful interpretation.

Many scientists believe that we are heading for the sixth great extinction, as species become extinct at a far greater rate than ever before. Human activities and global climate change are undoubtedly squeezing species out of existence. In many cases it is not just individual species which are under threat: entire ecosystems such as coral reefs, heathland and rainforest are being destroyed – each the home of thousands of species.

It is clear that, over geological time, dominant species can became extinct, allowing previously less successful species to flourish. Rapidly changing conditions at certain times drove evolution in a particular direction and at an increased pace; animals and plants which were able to adapt quickly, and happened to have characteristics favoured by the new environment, became dominant. The changes at these times of mass extinction were too rapid to allow most organisms to adapt and change.

Question

23 Refer to Figure 6.18.
   a) Identify the examples which do not fit the pattern.
   b) What can you conclude from the graph?
   c) What can you *not* conclude from the graph without further evidence?

24 What do you understand by the term 'background rate of extinction'?

25 Why is it plausible that 95% of all extinctions have happened at the background rate rather than during mass extinctions?

26 Explain why extinction is a natural result of evolution by natural selection.

27 Which human activities contribute to returning some marine ecosystems to the situation they were in before the explosion of biodiversity?

28 Explain the importance of taxonomy in the protection of biodiversity.

29 Why is there uncertainty about the effects of the current trends in biodiversity?

30 Why was it over 20 years before Darwin published his book *On the Origin of Species*? What prompted him to publish when he did?

31 For what resources do organisms in an ecosystem compete?

Key terms

Biodiversity stands for biological diversity, and is the variety of life on Earth.

An organism's **habitat** is the physical environment where it normally lives. Many species may share the same habitat but, if so, they occupy different ecological niches.

An **ecosystem** is made up of a variety of organisms interacting with each other and the environment in which they live. An ecosystem may encompass many habitats.

A **niche** describes an organism's position and needs within an ecosystem. This environmental space is defined by habitat, climate, competitors, position in the food chain, space, shelter and so on.

Fossil evidence provides a warning about the potential effects of the current reduction in biodiversity through human activities. Palaeontologists have long recognised the trend from less complex to more complex ecosystems over time. The overview of evidence recently made available by the Paleobiology Database exposed the long-term reversal of this trend caused by the single end-Permian mass extinction. Marine ecologists suggest that human activities are returning some marine ecosystems to the situation that they were in before the mass extinctions, and before the explosion of biodiversity. This effect is even greater than that of the asteroid that fell on Chicxulub.

6.3 The variety of life on Earth

Why are there so many species?

Figures for current numbers of species on Earth vary depending on their sources, and they are all estimates. There are probably between 20 and 100 million species on Earth. Around two million species have been identified and catalogued, and new species are being classified at a rate of about 15 000 a year. Most species are inconspicuous microorganisms and tiny invertebrates, and many species remain undiscovered because they live in inaccessible environments.

During his travels round the world on HMS *Beagle* from 1831 to 1836, Charles Darwin marvelled at the great diversity of species. Years later, in 1859, he published *On the Origin of Species*, in which he set out his explanation of evolution.

Darwin's theory of natural selection explains how competition for limited resources creates the conditions for species to evolve. Some individuals in a species have a feature that gives them a better chance of surviving. This means that the individual is more likely to reproduce and pass on their genes to future offspring compared with other members of their species. For example, Darwin explained the large variety of finches living on the Galapagos Islands by suggesting that they must have originated from a single ancestral finch which evolved into many species. Each species of finch is adapted to a different niche on the islands; they avoid competition with each other because they have different food sources and live in different habitats.

Species evolve to fit a niche

Natural selection has resulted in a wide variety of organisms, each evolving to fill a specific niche. Survival depends on this specialisation, as it helps species avoid competition with one another, and makes optimum use of the resources present in an ecosystem. Evolution of structural adaptations, physiology and behaviour contribute to fit the organism to its niche (Figure 6.19).

Figure 6.19

Mangroves have evolved to survive in the salty coastal swamps of the tropics. The trees have structural adaptations which include far-reaching, exposed roots. Some species have roots above ground, filled with spongy tissue that allows oxygen to be transferred to the roots below ground. The roots are able to stop the intake of a lot of the salt from the water before it reaches the plant. Mangroves turn their leaves to reduce the surface area of the leaf exposed to the hot sun.

After the K-T extinction, niches were vacated which then favoured the evolution and dominance of many species of birds and mammals. If the K-T extinction had not occurred, you would not be around to learn about its effects from this book.

How do new species evolve?

Distributions in populations

Many characteristics of a species are the result of the contribution of several genes and their interaction with the environment. These characteristics show continuous variation and a normal distribution.

The distribution of characteristics such as giraffe neck length, body mass in sharks and flowering time in plants may stay the same for many thousands of years if the environment stays constant. Natural selection selects against individuals with genes that result in versions of a characteristic at either extreme of the range (Figures 6.20 and 6.21). A giraffe's niche includes grazing high up in trees. The ratio of neck length to body height has an optimum value

Question

32 Suggests reasons why the following features of mangrove trees help them to survive in salty coastal swamps:
   a) roots that reach out over wide areas of the swamp
   b) roots above ground that can take in oxygen
   c) leaves that can turn to limit exposure to the sun.

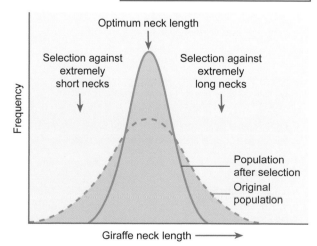

Figure 6.20

Any individual giraffe whose neck length deviates from the average is likely to be less well adapted if the environment is stable.

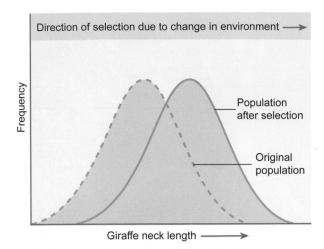

Figure 6.21

New niches become available as a population migrates into a different region or as a result of extinction of another species or climate change. The genetic make-up of a group of organisms changes if natural selection favours a different combination of genes to suit the new niche. This only produces a new species if the evolving group is prevented from breeding with the original species. Statistical tests can be used to decide whether two populations are actually different; the mean values of a characteristic (or more usually, of many characteristics) and spread of the data give an indication of whether differences in the two means are statistically significant. Defining these groups as two separate species involves additional information such as whether they can interbreed.

Question

33 Which of graphs A and B in Figure 6.22 has a higher value of standard deviation?

Representing data sets
Figure 6.22

If measurements of adult giraffe neck lengths are made in a sample population, a histogram can be plotted to show the number of giraffes within each range of neck lengths. This neck-length frequency distribution is spread between the highest and lowest values in a normal distribution.

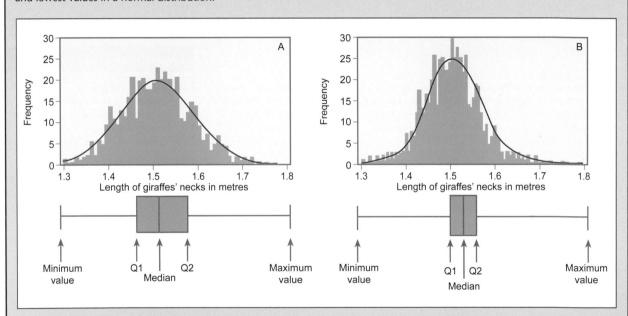

Graphs of giraffe neck length in two populations, A and B.

Comparing the giraffe populations A and B, it is obvious that, although the populations have the same mean neck length and the same range, the data are more spread out in population A. In population B, the data are more tightly clustered around the mean.

A full description of a set of data refers to the maximum and minimum values (the range of the data), the mean value and the spread of the data. The box and whisker plots below the graphs in the diagram show an alternative method for displaying the data, along with information about its distribution. The lower quartile, Q1, is the median of the lower half of the data. The upper quartile, Q2, is the median of the upper half of the data. The box shows the interquartile range, which is the middle 50% of all the data values. The line in the middle of the box shows the median value, and the two 'whiskers' either side of the box show the upper and lower ranges of the data.

In a box and whisker plot, data points are considered to be outliers if they fall more than 1.5 times the interquartile range below the first quartile or above the third quartile. More commonly, box plots show standard deviation rather than interquartile range. These plots use 'plus or minus two standard deviations' as a criterion for defining an outlier.

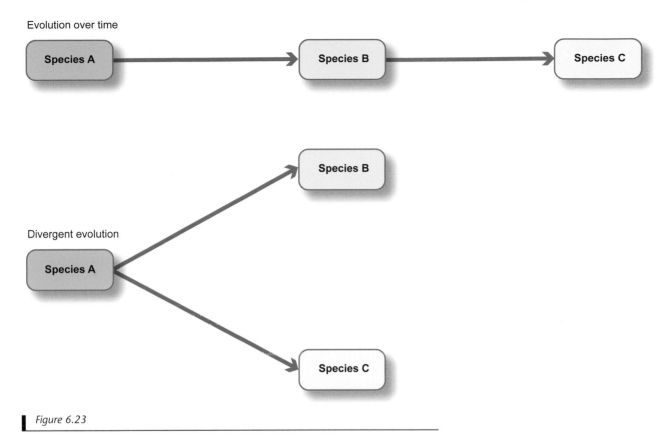

Evolution over time

Species A → Species B → Species C

Divergent evolution

Species A → Species B

Species A → Species C

Figure 6.23

If new niches become available or the environment changes, natural selection may favour different genes. One species may gradually evolve into another over time, or a species may split into two distinct species.

to allow for grazing, drinking, and changes in blood pressure as the head swings from tree top to ground. Individuals at the lower extremes in the range of neck length are not able to drink or compete for food. A baby giraffe with an extremely long neck risks problems during birth.

Fossils show that new species evolved as land masses split and moved around to form our modern continents (Figure 6.24).

One of the most dramatic demonstrations of the effects of continental drift on the formation of new species is the story of the split of marsupials from other mammals. Marsupials give birth to under-developed young and rear them in a pouch. Other mammals evolved from marsupials originally; their females have a uterus and develop a placenta to feed the embryo. DNA and fossil evidence show that the placental mammals divided from the marsupials around 100 million years ago. The start of this divide coincides with the split of the ancient continent Gondwanaland into land masses which became South America, Africa, Antarctica, India and Australia. Continental drift separated the ancestral mammals which then diverged into these two groups. Today there are many species of marsupials, some of these superficially similar to the placental mammals which evolved on different continents. None of them can mate with placental mammals. Their genetic and anatomical differences make them sexually incompatible.

Questions

34 Which of the following would you expect to show a normal distribution:
a) shark body mass frequency data
b) the number of moths caught in a trap at different times of year
c) the age distribution of a human population?

35 A student selected a sample of 25 people, measured their height and plotted the data onto a frequency histogram. He also calculated the mean and mode of the heights, and found these were not the same value.
a) What do the results tell you about the distribution of heights in this sample?
b) How should the student go about checking whether this is the usual distribution of height data in the human population?

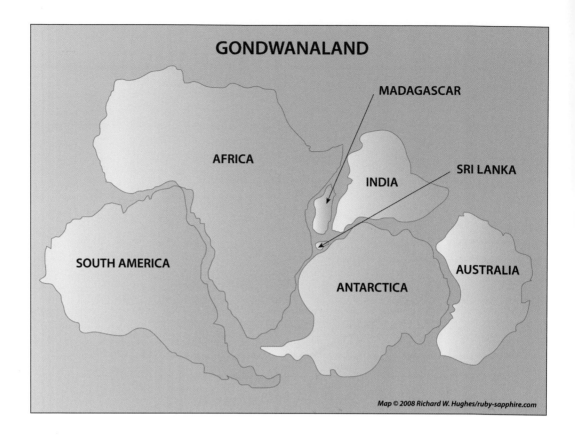

GONDWANALAND

MADAGASCAR

SRI LANKA

AFRICA

INDIA

SOUTH AMERICA

AUSTRALIA

ANTARCTICA

Map © 2008 Richard W. Hughes/ruby-sapphire.com

Figure 6.24

The landmass called Gondwanaland over 100 million years ago before the continents of the southern hemisphere were separated by the movement of tectonic plates.

Organisms which find themselves in an ecosystem with unoccupied niches may, in time, evolve into a number of different species which occupy the different niches. Natural selection favours any mutation which enables an individual to take advantage of the untapped food sources, shelter or other features of the unused niches. In Lake Victoria, for example, over 500 species of cichlid fish evolved over the past 15 000 years from one parent species to fill different niches within the lake.

Extinction has an important role in the evolution of new species. Species which survived the mass extinctions evolved into many new species as they adapted to fill the gaps. Flowering plants evolved in the early Cretaceous, starting in the tropics, then spreading right across towards both poles. Climate changes in the late Jurassic and Cretaceous saw further new bird and mammal species, as existing species evolved to adapt to the new environment.

Question

36 Lake Victoria is the largest tropical lake in the world. It is the source of the Nile. Suggest reasons why evolution in the lake gave rise to so many species of cichlid fish.

6.4 Ecosystems and biodiversity

Ecosystems

Ecosystems contain large numbers of niches, each normally occupied by just one species. Species which are highly adapted to live in a very specialised niche may have little competition from other species. On the other hand, they tend to be less able to adapt to new conditions that arise if the environment changes. When a species is lost from an ecosystem, it leaves the niche it was occupying free. Other species may adapt to fill

Figure 6.25

A green turtle on a coral reef. The green turtle lives in warm seas throughout the world. It stays close to coasts for most of its life, eating plants.

the vacant niche. Circumstances which mean that a niche is left open can have a devastating effect, upsetting the balance of the entire ecosystem.

When Christopher Columbus arrived in the Caribbean in 1492, he found so many manatees and shoals of sea turtles that he thought he was in danger of being shipwrecked by the animals. Columbus and his men immediately began the large-scale hunting of turtles and sea mammals for food, that continued for many years.

As the numbers of turtles and other sea mammals declined, the sea grass, on which these animals normally grazed, increased in abundance. As the competition from large herbivores was removed, sea urchins gradually stepped in as the main grazers controlling the sea grass populations. Then, in 1983, a virus killed off the sea urchins. Within 20 years, the sea grass had completely dominated the ecosystem. Its decaying remains tainted the water, killing off the coral. Ninety per cent of Caribbean coral reefs are now dead, shaded by the mass of plant life which grows unchecked.

No matter how well a species seems to be adapted to its niche, there is always the chance that it will be out-competed by another species. Competition for a niche is a popular theory for the demise of the Neanderthals; their niche was too similar to that of modern humans.

Sometimes introduced species compete for niches with native species. If their natural predators are absent, the introduced species may compete unfairly, becoming pests. If the balance of interactions between species is upset in this way, the ecosystem disruption may be temporary or permanent.

The balance of ecosystems

A stable ecosystem is one which maintains its species diversity over time, recovering from periodic disruptions to return to its steady state. Ecosystems vary in their ability to recover from large-scale changes

Questions

37 In 1954, the Nile perch was first introduced into Lake Victoria (see page 190) in the hope of improving the yield from the lake. The species was present in small numbers until the early to mid-1980s, when there was a very large population expansion. Suggest what consequences this may have had for the diversity of cichlids in the lake.

38 Rabbits were introduced by early settlers landing in Australia in the nineteenth century. Australia has no natural predator for the rabbit. Suggest what the consequences have been for the ecology of the country.

Key term

Species diversity refers to the number and distribution of different species in an area.

39 a) Describe the changes in the populations of moose and wolves on Isle Royale from 1960–2008.
b) Suggest an explanation for the changes you describe.
c) Do the data plotted in Figure 6.26 suggest that this is an ecosystem showing long-term stability?

40 A comparison of different rainforest areas in Sumatra and Borneo shows that the biodiversity of plant and animal species is at its highest when orang-utans are present. Suggest what evidence there is to support the hypothesis that there is a causal relationship here.

due to effects such as climate change, extinctions and human activities. Many connections exist between organisms in an ecosystem, based on food chains, reproduction and shelter. If, for example, a particular plant becomes rare, the herbivores that rely on that plant for food will also become rare. Less grazing then allows the plant population to grow, followed by an increase in the populations of other animals higher in the food chain. This type of negative feedback, where any change produces a further change in the opposite direction, is characteristic of a stable system (Figure 6.26).

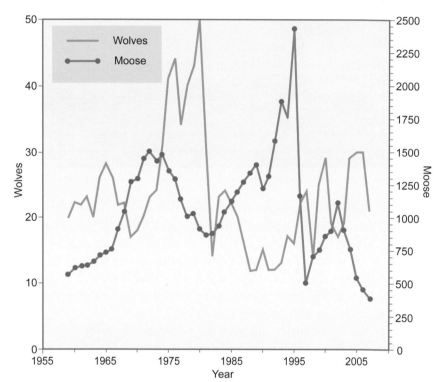

Figure 6.26

This graph shows the population numbers over time of wolf (predator) and moose (prey) populations on Isle Royale over 40 years. The relative position of peaks and troughs in both populations show their interdependence, and the negative feedback effects which contribute to long-term stability.

Keystone species
Figure 6.27

Keystone species are those which link many other species in a community together through interactions such as food webs and shelter. Removal of a keystone species has wide ranging effects on food webs and habitats, greatly affecting the health of other species, even in a complex ecosystem.

The orang-utan is a keystone species in the lowland rainforests of Sumatra and Borneo. As roaming fruit eaters, orang-utans play a large part in dispersing seeds widely, maintaining the diversity of rainforest trees.

An orang-utan photographed at the Sepilok Orang-utan Sanctuary in Malaysian Borneo. Protection of orang-utans is vital to the overall health of the lowland forest ecosystem. The species is extremely endangered. The orang-utan population can only flourish if their forest home is conserved.

Small populations are vulnerable in the face of disruption; a few individuals dying off or migrating can completely remove certain genes from the population. Genetic diversity in a population enables a species to adapt to a changing environment, and contributes to its ability to survive over time.

Other factors linked with resistance to disruption are a less stable climate and a wide variety of habitats within an ecosystem. Simple ecosystems with only a few species are extremely vulnerable. Most of the individuals in a field containing a single crop species are likely to be susceptible to the same pests and diseases. In an agricultural ecosystem, the plants are also likely to have low genetic diversity, increasing their vulnerability. On the other hand, simple ecosystems can be easily rebuilt – this only takes recolonisation by one or two species.

Large, complex ecosystems with high species diversity are most resilient against disruptions. If one species dies out, their predators are likely to be able to find alternative prey. Fluctuations in the numbers of one or two species are balanced by other species, which expand their range to fill the vacant niches. Complex systems have a large capacity to return to a stable state after change, but their destruction can be irreversible. A destroyed tropical rainforest or a destroyed coral reef may be lost forever.

Ecosystems naturally change over time. Clear ground, for example, is colonised by pioneer species. Then, gradually, other species arrive and help to build up a complex, stable community such as a forest. Grazing, high salinity, poor soil or high altitudes are examples of natural factors which may affect the type of ecosystem that develops. In the UK, urbanisation, pollution and agriculture are the main human activities preventing a natural succession to forest. There was widespread woodland cover in the UK 3000 years ago, before the Bronze Age. By 1900 only 5% of the UK land area was forested, but this has now risen to 11.6% as a result of tree planting and forest management. A small proportion of existing UK woodland dates back to 1600 AD. This ancient woodland, which includes Sherwood Forest where Robin Hood is believed to have lived, has never been cleared or replanted. As a result, it is very diverse, and contains many native species.

What is biodiversity?

The term 'biodiversity' refers to the species diversity, diversity of habitats and the genetic diversity within an ecosystem. The species diversity in an area depends on the number of different species, and the abundance of each species. Ecologists use their data to calculate a measure of diversity.

Key term

The **genetic diversity** of a population includes the diversity of alleles (allelic diversity) and the number of organisms that have a combination of two different alleles (heterozygosity). Genetic diversity is a result of the recombination of alleles during sexual reproduction, mutations, natural selection and chance. It is affected by population effects such as migration, which in small populations can remove or add certain genes to the available pool.

Questions

41 Some starfish act as keystone species by preying on sea urchins, which in turn feed on coral. The starfish also eat mussels and other shellfish that have no other natural predators. Suggest what happens if the starfish is removed from the ecosystem.

42 Why is genetic diversity important in determining whether a population of a species can adapt to a changing environment?

43 Suggest why an unstable climate might lead to ecosystems with greater resilience to disturbance.

44 Why do farmers on intensive farms have to use fertilisers, pesticides and herbicides to maintain good crop yields?

45 In the UK, the Woodland Trust campaigns to protect ancient trees and ancient woods. The trust has 150 000 paying members. Why do people support an organisation of this kind?

Figure 6.28

Tropical rainforest in Queensland, Australia. Tropical rainforests are areas of high biodiversity, with huge numbers of species in every hectare. Tropical rainforests have high species evenness, which means all the species present are represented by an approximately equal number of individuals – no single species dominates. Other climax ecosystems do not have such high species evenness. For example, coniferous forest tends to be dominated by a few tree species, with a limited understorey of plants. Agricultural monocultures, where a single crop species dominates, are an extreme example of an ecosystem with low species diversity.

Questions

46 Which of the two meadows in Figure 6.29 has:
a) greater species evenness
b) greater species diversity?

47 What is the effect on the value of the species diversity index, D, if the total number of species, N, increases?

48 What is the effect on the value of the species diversity index, D, of having a few dominant species rather than a more even spread of species numbers in the community?

Species diversity index
Figure 6.29

There are various methods for calculating species diversity in an ecosystem. A commonly used equation is Simpson's diversity index:

$$D = \frac{N(N-1)}{\Sigma n(n-1)}$$

D = diversity index
N = total number of organisms of all species found
n = number of individuals of a particular species
Σ means 'the sum of' – in this case the sum of all the values of $n(n-1)$

Flower species	Numbers of individuals	
	Meadow 1	Meadow 2
Daisy	315	22
Dandelion	324	45
Buttercup	361	933
Total	1000	1000

This table shows the species represented when 1000 individual flower species were sampled from two different meadows. One meadow has a more even species distribution than the other.

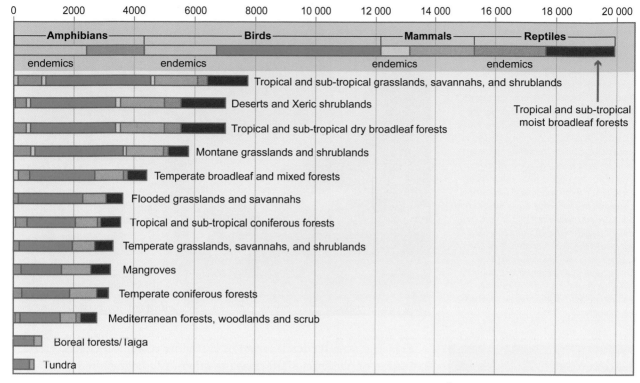

Figure 6.30

The number of endemic and non-endemic species of animals in different ecosystems. An endemic species is one that is only found in a particular area.

Ecosystems with higher values of species diversity tend to be more stable. A very low value for a species diversity index could suggest (i) a polluted site where only certain tolerant species can survive; (ii) recent colonisation, for example on a building site; or (iii) agricultural land. Some ecosystems, such as estuaries and hot springs, have a naturally low diversity index.

A gradient of species richness, declining from the tropics to the poles, is seen in land, marine and freshwater ecosystems (Figure 6.30). Exceptions to this trend are frequently seen, as land biodiversity is affected by local climate and altitude. Scientists still debate the various theories which attempt to explain this observation. One well-supported theory is based on the idea that the species diversity in a region depends on the amount of time that the ecosystem has existed under relatively unchanged conditions.

6.5 Protecting biodiversity

Most zoos in the UK do not have a bonobo for you to visit. This closest relative of human beings only occurs in the wild in the Congo basin. It is now near extinction due to destruction of its habitat and being hunted by humans as bush meat (Figure 6.31). Living on the front line in a long-term civil war has resulted in mass killing of the bonobo and other great apes for bush meat, much of which travels down the Congo river to supply soldiers, or is poached by local people living in poverty.

Questions

49 To what extent does Figure 6.30 support the generalisation that species richness declines from the tropics to the poles?

50 The trend of species diversity up a mountain is similar to that seen between low and high latitudes (it decreases). Suggest why this is the case.

51 Tundra is found in the Arctic where the subsoil is permanently frozen. Explain why the tundra has low species diversity.

52 Use your knowledge of how species evolve to suggest why a higher species diversity is usually found in more stable environments.

Figure 6.31

A stall selling monkeys and pieces of antelope at Oyen in the Republic of Congo. Bushmeat is readily available, with a variety of game from the rainforest including many rare and protected species. Conservation efforts have to work within the context of the local situation. Issues of social justice and international relations affect the future of species, as do other human activities such as use of fossil fuels. The failure to conserve the great apes is mainly due to human crises of poverty, illness, war, commercial greed, political corruption and lawlessness. In addition to knowledge about species and their habitats, people working to conserve animals threatened with extinction need expertise in the local human factors of welfare and health, peacekeeping and conflict resolution, crime prevention and law enforcement, commercial contract negotiation, food production, political ethics and morality.

Question

53 Explain why conservation of wildlife cannot be separated from the local political and social situations in areas of threatened species.

Evidence from the fossil record of cascading ecological effects, where extinction of one species affects many others, can be used to draw inferences about possible modern day effects, such as extinction of keystone species. The removal of species hunted by humans, such as the mastodon and mammoth, had large effects on vegetation, which may in turn explain the disappearance of many other vertebrates during the Pleistocene period. Entire ecosystems need to be protected in order to protect the species which live in them.

The fossil record shows that widespread species are less vulnerable to disaster than geographically restricted groups. If a rare, top carnivore becomes locally extinct in an area of tropical savannah, the area can be repopulated from an adjacent area. Repopulation is less likely on an island far from the mainland.

On the other hand, groups which are well-adapted and able to survive background extinctions, do not necessarily have the geographical distribution or environmental tolerance to withstand the large disruptions which lead to the mass extinctions.

Human impacts on ecosystems

Human activities such as farming, atmospheric pollution, transport, wars and urbanisation affect the habitats of a large number of species. Evidence from the fossil record of mass extinctions, along with evidence from modern ecological disasters, suggests that large-scale extinction in a particular area generally leaves ecosystems with low biodiversity. Post-disaster areas are populated by small numbers of generalist species which are better able to adapt to new conditions. These 'winner' species tend to be species that humans classify as 'weeds' and 'pests'. These species are able to take advantage of the niches freed up due to extinctions.

Following a period of worldwide destruction and extinction, human activities might act as a filter, selecting for those species best able to survive within the modified ecosystems. The biosphere would then have relatively few species and be much more similar from place to place than it is now. It would, very likely, be dominated by rats, ragweed and cockroaches rather than the large number of more vulnerable species that are useful to humans as food, medicines and genetic resources.

Why should biodiversity be protected?

Estimates of the current rate of extinctions ranges between 50 000 and 100 000 species a year. This represents a rate previously seen only during the five mass extinctions, and about 1500 times the natural background rate.

Conserving species protects the genetic resource they represent; a wide range of genes provides the potential to breed plants and animals for human requirements such as agriculture and sources of chemicals for medicines.

Ecosystems with high levels of biodiversity help to sustain human life by providing essential resources. They also have the potential to provide solutions to help alleviate the destruction brought about by human activities. Plant products such as fuels and recyclable materials can contribute to sustainable living. Carbon dioxide is absorbed during photosynthesis by land and aquatic plants, buffering the effects of greenhouse gas emissions. Corals and other marine organisms make their hard parts from calcium carbonate, absorbing large amounts of carbon dioxide from the oceans.

Regulation to protect biodiversity

Effective regulation protecting biodiversity relies on good communication between scientists and policymakers. A number of international and local laws protect individual species and ecosystems through regulation of activities such as hunting, trading and pollution. Government and non-governmental organisations (NGOs) work together to prioritise actions for conservation and to agree the most appropriate legislation for protection of biodiversity.

The Convention on Biological Diversity (1992) was signed at the United Nations Earth Summit in Rio in 1992. It requires countries to produce national action plans for the conservation of biodiversity.

Questions

54 What distinguishes the current, widespread extinction of species from previous mass extinctions?

55 Suggest reasons why the extinction of species is a threat to the future well-being and health of humans with reference to:
a) plants
b) animals.

56 Why is it important to conserve the genetic diversity of plants closely related to the crops we grow for food?

57 Suggest reasons why sustaining biodiversity is important to ensure that people have enough water to drink in future.

58 Suggest reasons why highly diverse ecosystems can help to boost tourism and the economy of a country.

59 Give examples of technologies that bring benefits which people value, while at the same time having undesirable impacts that threaten biodiversity.

Figure 6.32

In the 1930s, overgrazing of the Great Plains in eastern America transformed parts of this area into a dust bowl. Dust storms such as this one which took place near Kansas in 1935 'turned day into night'. People had to protect themselves from the silt, which even forced its way into buildings. Greatly improved methods of agriculture, along with land and water management in the Great Plains, have prevented a similar disaster from recurring, but desertification presently affects millions of people in almost every continent. Desertification results in the loss of habitats, and this is often irreversible.

Commitments to the original Rio principles were strongly reaffirmed at the World Summit on Sustainable Development held in Johannesburg in 2002.

The programme for local implementation of sustainable development agreed at Rio is called Agenda 21. People can ask to see how local authorities and organisations are implementing Agenda 21 in their area. Local initiatives to decrease the impact of humans on the environment include recycling schemes, transport schemes and commuter plans, environmental education and energy-efficiency schemes.

The World Wide Fund for Nature (WWF) coordinates a project called The Living Planet Index. This index follows trends in nearly 4000 populations of 1477 vertebrate species to track human impact on the Earth. The 2008 data show that between 1970 and 2005, the value of the global planet index fell by 27%. This suggests that the world will fail to meet the target of reducing the rate of biodiversity loss set by the 2002 Convention on Biological Diversity.

The Convention on International Trade in Endangered Species of Wild Fauna and Flora (CITES) is an international agreement between governments to ensure that international trade in specimens of wild animals and plants does not threaten their survival.

In the UK, the Wildlife and Countryside Act 1981 provides varying degrees of protection for listed species of animals and plants. The act includes comprehensive protection of wild birds, their nests and their eggs, and designates Marine Nature Reserves. A system of Sites of Special Scientific Interest (SSSIs) is detailed in the act, awarding powers for their protection and the introduction of management agreements.

Questions

60 a) Why does society need rules and regulations to protect biodiversity?
b) Why are national and international regulatory bodies needed to oversee the regulations?

61 Why is it not surprising that countries worldwide are failing to meet agreed targets to reduce the rate of loss of biodiversity?

An interview with a biologist who studies and conserves wetlands

What is a wetland?

"Technically, a wetland is any place where the water table is less than 30 cm below the ground surface and not more than 2 m above the surface. However, in practice, just remember that 'if you need wellies, you're standing in a wetland.'

"There are lots of different types of wetlands including lakes, rivers, marshes, peat bogs, estuaries, salt marshes (in temperate regions), mangroves (in tropical regions) and flooded forests.

"One of the few things wetlands have in common is that they are all very productive ecosystems and they tend to occur on relatively flat terrain. These two factors make the land very valuable to people. Wetlands are also characterised by a relatively high diversity of plants, amphibians, fish and birds.

"Wetlands are important because of the biodiversity they contain, and also for the benefits they provide. Wetlands are important because they help to provide clean drinking water, fisheries, means of transport, flood defences, dilution of pollutants and opportunities for recreation."

Figure 6.33

Peter Long is a biologist studying wetlands both in Britain and in Madagascar. Here Peter is returning from a hard day's work in the Madagascar wetlands.

What are the main global threats to wetlands? Are people to blame?

"The most serious threat to wetlands from people worldwide is conversion to other land uses. For example, in Britain, the fens in East Anglia have been drained to create highly fertile and productive farmland. In Madagascar where I work, wetlands have been turned into shrimp farms. Water abstraction for agriculture is also a major threat. Irrigation of cotton is largely responsible for the contraction of the Aral Sea in the Soviet Union.

"The pollution of rivers by industry and agriculture is also serious. These are examples of how human activities can have seriously detrimental effects on wetland biodiversity and human livelihoods. Another danger arises from introducing a new species into an ecosystem such as Nile perch into Lake Victoria.

"We describe climate change as a meta-threat. What we mean is that it causes other threats to become more severe."

Is it always necessary to intervene to conserve wetlands under threat, or will the ecosystem return to stability if detrimental factors can be removed?

"The nice thing about wetlands is that, if the hydrological conditions are right, they can restore themselves or be created from scratch relatively quickly. Some threats, such as excessive water abstraction, are much easier to deal with than others, particularly invasive species. However, it may not be possible to make less severe some of the consequences arising from other threats such as climate change."

Do you always work in a team?

"My work is very collaborative. To address global questions requires huge amounts of data that no one person could ever collect by themselves. I use remotely sensed data from satellites quite a lot, and I rely hugely upon monitoring data (using the Internet) about observations of particular species in particular places at particular times.

"Much of the observational data is collected by volunteers. I have several colleagues in Madagascar with whom I work very closely (Figure 6.34). We undertake fieldwork and analyse data together, and publish our results jointly.

Figure 6.34

Sama Zefania, Marc Rabenandrasana, Hery Andrianandrasana and Sam Seing work closely with Peter.

Questions

65 Explain the importance of 'conservation capacity building' among the people who live near to a wetland to reduce over-exploitation of valuable biological resources.

66 Why is it necessary to set priorities for scientific research into biodiversity?

"The team identifies and trains local people to observe wildlife and work with communities to help them value their natural environments and wildlife. This way of engaging local people we call 'conservation capacity building'."

What are the aims of your work?

"The overall aim of my work is to conserve biodiversity without compromising the livelihoods of people who depend on wetlands. The actual research I do is shaped by current hot topics in conservation science, such as community genetics, systematic conservation planning, species distribution and modelling, then applying the findings to the ecosystems where I work.

"Effective conservation involves management of a species or habitat which results in increased probability of its persistence. Scientists working in conservation have research questions they need to answer. The findings of conservation practitioners must then be communicated back to the people who have the power to make decisions about actions on the ground.

"For example, Madagascar has been identified as a biodiversity hotspot (see page 207) by Conservation International but it is still necessary to have people observing and monitoring the detail at individual sites. This science then helps to identify the issues that need more research.

"We have to take into account the interests of the agencies that award grants to fund research. These agencies help to define the broad priorities for conservation work. International legislation such as the Convention on Biological Diversity (CBD), signed at the Earth Summit in Rio de Janeiro in 1992, provides a framework which helps to set the priorities for research to understand biodiversity and projects to conserve precious ecosystems."

Coral – the canary of the oceans

Coral reefs are home to more biodiversity than anywhere else in the seas. They also help to protect coastlines from waves. Coral responds quickly to environmental changes. Coloured algae living in the coral's tissues and essential for the coral's health are killed by temperature rises, or by rapid rises in sea level which prevent photosynthesis. As the algae are expelled, the coral loses its colour, becoming 'bleached'.

The bar chart in Figure 6.35 shows data collected from coral reefs around the Fiji islands. A decline in coral cover started in 2000, with a loss of between 40 and 80% nationwide. Since then there has been a rebound effect where hard coral coverage is back to pre-bleaching levels.

In late 2005, NASA recorded satellite images of severe and widespread bleaching of coral reefs in the Caribbean that has resulted in extensive coral death in much of the region. The death of coral exposes the islands to flooding and wave action. Loss of coral also removes a popular tourist attraction, the nursery grounds for marine fisheries, and a habitat for many specialised marine species.

All around the world the corals are dying, mainly due to global warming. Both sea level rises and warmer seas contribute to coral destruction. As the seas rise, the more unpredictable global climate produces storms which flood the lower lying marginal land claimed by poorer human populations.

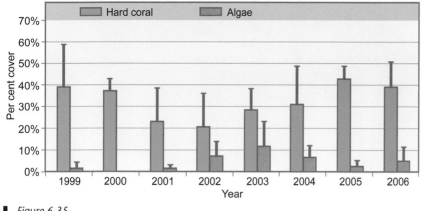

Figure 6.35

Changes in coral and algal (seaweed) cover in the Fiji Islands, caused by cyclones and bleaching.

Questions

67 a) Describe the changes in coral and algal (seaweed) cover in Figure 6.35.
b) What evidence is there in the data to suggest that there has been some regeneration of the coral?

68 Measurements are made of a single characteristic in two separate populations of organisms.
a) Give two measures that can be used to measure the spread of the data.
b) When trying to decide whether or not the differences in the data show that the populations are two different species, what additional information might be necessary?

69 Some islanders use the stone from their surrounding living coral reefs to build flood defence walls, either from the raw rock, or from cement made from the coral limestone. Why is this a particularly misguided thing to do?

On 26th December 2004, the destruction caused by a massive tsunami was much greater in the areas of reef destruction off the south-west coast of Sri Lanka than in nearby areas where the coral reefs were intact.

A team of researchers from the United States and Sri Lanka published their findings in a report several months after the tsunami. Eyewitnesses described a visible reduction in the height of the water wall and its deflection as it approached the coral reef. The research team noted that the low-lying Maldives islands directly in the path of the tsunami escaped destruction. The suggestion is that healthy coral reefs protected the islands.

Islanders who destroy their reefs through destructive fishing, pollution or through silting due to deforestation not only remove their protection from an effect of global warming, but also exacerbate the global warming by reducing carbon fixation. Coral helps to offset the effects of CO_2 emissions as it removes carbon from the sea to build the calcium carbonate reef structure.

6.6 How should conservation efforts be directed?

The role of zoos

Humans have been making collections of wild animals since ancient civilisation. Records of the Shang dynasty (c. 1500 BC) show that the rulers and wealthy classes in China built animal reserves, and ancient Greek and Roman *vivaria* existed as public spectacles.

In the nineteenth century, the role of zoos was mainly entertainment and education of the public. Zoos were a drain on the wild populations, as the methods of capture were often brutal. For example, several adults might be killed to capture a baby gorilla. Animals were not kept in conditions that allowed them to survive for very long, or to breed. Some animals were even mistreated, with sticks available for the public to poke the animals.

Key terms

Ex situ means off-site, so *ex situ*
conservation is where organisms are
taken from their natural habitat to be
protected in a zoo, botanical garden
or wildlife enclosure.

In situ (on-site) **conservation** is
where an endangered plant or
animal species is protected in its
natural habitat.

However, the serious study of taxonomy and anatomy were also
important, and it is during this period that Charles Darwin shocked the
world by suggesting a relationship between humans and animals based
on common ancestry.

Modern zoos (Figure 6.36) emphasise education, scientific research and
conservation of endangered species.

With a blend of *ex situ* research and breeding, and *in situ* conservation
and reintroduction programmes, zoos aim to conserve endangered
animals and habitats.

Organisations such as The World Association of Zoos and Aquariums
(WAZA) and the European Association of Zoos and Aquaria (EAZA)
promote cooperation in collecting and wildlife conservation between
member countries.

These organisations also coordinate information on species in captivity
across the world. Carefully kept studbooks allow breeding to be organised
between pairs of animals in captivity, to avoid inbreeding between
closely related animals. Inbreeding is to be avoided, because it reduces
genetic diversity in the species and emphasises genetic weaknesses in
rare, recessive genetic traits. The same recessive allele is more likely to be
present in two closely related individuals. If these individuals interbreed
and both pass on the allele to their offspring, the recessive genetic
trait will be expressed. Maintaining genetic diversity through breeding
programmes is particularly important if animals are to be returned to
their natural habitat.

Critics of zoos point out that only a very small number of species have
been returned to the wild successfully as a result of captive breeding
programmes. Reintroduction risks contamination of wild species by
disease-causing microorganisms carried from other zoo animals, and
captive-bred animals have little resistance to infections present in wild
populations. The majority of animals displayed in zoos are not on the
endangered list, so in these cases the claims for conservation are not

justified. Increasingly, conservation programmes focus on protecting ecosystems rather than individual species, improving the survival chances of many species in endangered habitats.

Reintroducing the peregrine falcon

Peregrine falcon populations throughout North America crashed in the 1960s due to widespread contamination of the environment with the pesticide dichlorodiphenyltrichloroethane (DDT).

When first discovered and used in the 1940s and 1950s, DDT was thought to be a safe and effective insecticide. It was widely used as an insecticide by farmers, and to combat lice and mosquitoes and other organisms responsible for the spread of diseases. At the time, there were no known harmful effects to either animal or human health.

In time it became clear that DDT is harmful. It does not break down easily and it accumulates in the fat reserves of animals. Animals at the top of a food chain accumulate particularly high concentrations in their tissues.

DDT causes female peregrines to lay thin-shelled eggs that dry out or break under the weight of the nesting adults. A ban on DDT in the USA in 1972 improved the situation, but it is taking many years to clear the residues completely from the environment.

From 1976 to 1997, a captive breeding programme operated from the University of California and other institutions (Figure 6.37). Peregrine chicks were raised by captive adult falcons for about five weeks and then released. Researchers took the young birds into the wild where they were fed and taught to fly until they were able to hunt for themselves.

This programme released more than 6000 peregrine falcons into the wild across 34 states. Brought back from near extinction as a result of the banning of DDT and protection under the Endangered Species Act, the peregrine now occupies all its former range, and is no longer on the protected species list.

Question

70 Give two reasons why conservation should focus on the preservation of whole ecosystems rather than on particular species.

Questions

71 What lessons can be learnt about the introduction of new technologies from the experience with DDT?

72 What features of the approach to the conservation of peregrine falcons in the USA meant that it was successful?

Figure 6.37

Fragile eggs can be removed from nests and hatched in incubators. As long as the eggs are replaced with dummies to keep the parents on the nest, hatchlings could be slipped back into foster peregrine nests in the wild. This is an alternative approach to raising and releasing older chicks.

The gentle lemur: a conflict between people and wildlife

Around 80% of Madagascar's species are found nowhere else in the world. They are endemic to this large island lying off the coast of Africa in the Indian Ocean. Few large predators made it to the island when it broke off from the land mass that became India 100 million years ago, so new species evolved to fill different niches. The gentle lemur, for example, adapted for life in the reed beds surrounding Lake Alaotra (Figure 6.38). Its small size allows it to jump through the reed beds and its soft, gripping fingers enable it to target the young shoots which it feeds on.

Today Madagascar is a relatively poor country and its population is growing fast. This puts pressure on its rich natural resources. The local villagers remove the reeds that grow in the shallows of Lake Alaotra by burning, and replace them with rice plants which they grow for food. This artificial 'ecosystem' produces a monoculture unable to support the large variety of wildlife found in a varied reed bed system.

The local people also use the reeds for building materials and textiles. But the reeds are important to the natural ecosystem of Lake Alaotra. They filter silt from water entering the lake as it flows through the reed beds. As reeds are removed, the lake silts up and fish die. Denied the food from fishing, villagers turn to other food sources. They hunt the gentle lemur by burning the reeds and driving the animals out into the open.

The Durrell Wildlife Conservation Trust has worked with locally trained people in its efforts to bring back the gentle lemur from the brink of extinction. Simply trying to stop rice cultivation is not a realistic option. By developing a local understanding of sustainable agriculture, the people and the wildlife are now able to co-exist on the land they both need for survival.

In Madagascar, beliefs and traditions are passed from generation to generation in song and dance. So this has been the medium used to convey the message that conserving the lake ecosystem is vital to long-term productivity of the surrounding land. More efficient ways of using the land for rice have been developed, and some villagers have gone as far as to plant new reed beds, holding a reed planting ceremony each year, thereby giving the process of succession a helping hand.

Figure 6.38

A gentle lemur of Madagascar.

Questions

73 Draw a diagram to show the positive feedback cycle around Lake Alaotra that threatens extinction for the gentle lemur.

74 a) Why is conservation of the reed beds around Lake Alaotra in the long-term interests of the people who live near the lake?
b) How can short-term necessities be reconciled with longer term interests?

Conservation strategies and sustainable development

Complementary conservation strategies blend *ex situ* research, breeding and reintroduction programmes with *in situ* habitat protection. Research is still needed to determine the best balance between the two approaches for different species. Successful strategies are responsive to changing needs and priorities, and to the rapidly developing genetic sciences and new technologies which can support conservation work.

Modern conservation programmes aim to optimise sustainable use of biodiversity with reference to the particular species being conserved, the geographic and ecological nature of the habitat, the local human culture, infrastructures and human resources.

Sustainable development acknowledges that land is shared by humans and wildlife, and that maintenance of ecosystems is essential for long-term human health and well-being.

A United Nations report written by the World Commission on Economic Development (WCED) first introduced the term 'sustainability'. The 1987 report, *Our Common Future*, prepared the ground for the Rio Earth Summit of 1992 and Agenda 21. It described an integrated framework in which the international economy, resource depletion and environmental degradation are all linked. A new kind of sustainable economic development was proposed, with all nations having a stake in bringing this about. The element of social justice acknowledges that the wealthiest nations consume more than their fair share of resources, and that the poorest third of human society are frequently forced to use resources unsustainably in order to survive. The wealthy nations have the freedom to make choices for more sustainable development, while the poorest nations generally do not.

People argue for the idea of sustainability from a number of different frameworks.

- Holists, or ecocentrics, would argue that human beings are part of nature and have no right to cause disproportionate damage to ecosystems and the global environment.
- Anthropocentric or 'human'-centred views see humans at the centre of the universe, arguing that human concerns override any others. Protection of biodiversity is justified by its usefulness to humans.
- Technocentrics argue that use of resources and economic growth are only possible along with technological advancement. Biodiversity is a resource to be exploited, being the source of raw materials, food and wealth. This view is optimistic that technology will be able to solve the problems of resource management, and that a free market economy will work to protect species by making rare resources more valuable.

Technocentrism contrasts with the pessimism of Malthus. Malthus' ideas influenced Darwin's thinking about the competition for rare resources, leading to the theory of natural selection. Malthus realised that population growth poses a trap for development, as the fixed land area of the Earth will not be able to supply adequate food and resources infinitely into the future.

Setting the priorities for conservation

A major choice for conservation is between saving as many individual species as possible, or maintaining the Earth's capacity for evolving new species. In the past, tropical forests and wetlands have evolved the majority of new species. These are the very ecosystems under threat from the current effects of climate change and human activities.

Key term

A common definition of **sustainable development** is meeting the needs of the present generation without compromising the ability of future generations to meet their needs.

Question

75 Is it realistic to think that economic development in the UK can be genuinely sustainable? State your opinion on this question and present arguments to support your point of view.

Key term

Scientists use **logarithms** to handle values which range over several orders of magnitude. Logarithms to base 10 are defined in such a way that, for example, log 1000 = 3, log 100 = 2 and log 10 = 1. This means that on a logarithmic scale a change of one unit corresponds to a ×10 change in the value of the data point.

Question

76 Give one example of scientific data with a large range which is commonly represented using a logarithmic scale.

Conservation biologists measure the number of species found in a given area. For example, starting with an area of about 10 m² in a forest, there might be a single species of tree. As the area being sampled is expanded there are more and more trees and the probability of finding more species increases.

Scientists have found a recurring pattern in the data when species number and area are measured.

Area in square miles	Number of species
4	5
40	10
400	20
4000	40
40 000	80

Figure 6.39

These data on the number of species of amphibians and reptiles in the Antilles Islands show that both the numbers measuring the area and the number of species form geometric series. In a geometric series, each number relates to the previous number by the same ratio. In this case, the area increases by ×10 each time, and the number of species increases by ×2.

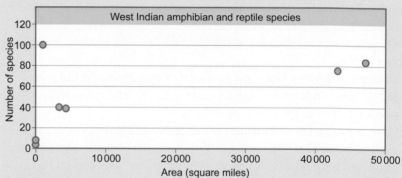

Figure 6.40

A species–area curve for amphibians and reptiles in the West Indies. If the data are plotted on axes with arithmetic scales (where any two successive numbers in the scale are separated by the same difference e.g. 2, 4, 6, 8), the pattern in the relationship between species number and area is not clear.

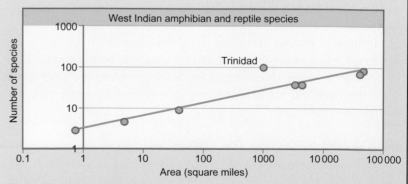

Figure 6.41

When both the variables of the data shown in Figure 6.41 are plotted on logarithmic scales, the relationship between area and species number becomes clear. Logarithmic scales are used in this way to bring out patterns in data. They are also used when the range of the data is very large, as a log scale compresses the range on an axis.

If the Earth is about to experience the sixth mass extinction, as some scientists think, destruction of these evolutionary power houses could remove the Earth's capacity to recover. Continued reduction of tropical forests and wetlands could delay the recovery of biodiversity by millions of years.

Much of the Earth's species diversity is concentrated into a few relatively small areas. In a 2000 paper by Norman Myers, the scientist who originally defined hotspots, 34 biodiversity hotspots were identified. Several international organisations collaborate to define biodiversity hotspots as areas where conservation efforts should be concentrated (Figure 6.42). If an organisation such as Conservation International defines a new biodiversity hotspot, this will be accepted by the scientific community if the appropriate evidence is provided, and this is presented in a peer-reviewed journal or scientific conference.

The 34 recognised hotspots cover only 2.3% of the Earth's surface, but support nearly 77% of the world's terrestrial vertebrate species, with a very high share of endemic species.

If conservation efforts were directed at species with the most potential to evolve and produce new species, worms, insects and other invertebrates would be saved before the pandas, whales and tigers whose plight appeals to most people. With their huge capacity for reproduction, invertebrates provide the raw material for natural selection.

Conservation efforts need the background information on where the threats exist. The work of monitoring species and habitat changes and cataloguing biodiversity must continue and accelerate if the key species, habitats and ecosystems are to be targeted for attention. Collection of climate data is important, in order to be able to predict effects on local ecosystems. Much of this data can be collected by

Questions

77 Decisions about which species and habitats to maintain involves a cost-benefit analysis. Describe some of the 'costs' to human beings if steps are not taken to protect tropical rainforests.

78 Explain why efforts to conserve the hotspots can only be successful if they are long term, global and inter-organisational.

Key term

A **biodiversity hotspot** is an area identified as containing at least 1500 species of higher plants which are endemic to that area. The ecosystem must have lost at least 70% of its original habitat.

Figure 6.42

Map showing the world's biodiversity hotspots in orange.

Key
■ Hotspots

remote sensing (from satellite imaging), but scientists are needed in the locations to do the work of monitoring and cataloguing.

There are limited resources available for conservation work, so priority setting must take place to direct efforts for maximum effect. Conservation of key species which significantly influence surrounding ecosystems is appropriate. Rare ecosystems or communities are also prioritised, as the threat of extinction is greater for these communities. Intact and distinct ecosystems which display the full range of habitats and biodiversity for these regions should be maintained, as these provide a model for comparison with degraded ecosystems, allowing degradation to be assessed. These may be represented by small regions such as National Parks, or large-scale areas which may be entire countries.

Review Questions

79 The same set of objects can be classified in different ways; the classification used depends on the purpose of classifying and is often based on underlying theoretical ideas. Explain and illustrate this statement in the context of the biological classification of species.

80 The 'tragedy of the commons' is a term which refers to the way that communal resources (such as common land for grazing animals) are degraded due to the selfish self-interest of people who use or destroy more than their fair share of the common resources. Discuss, with examples, whether or not this term can be rightly applied to the impacts of human activity on the Earth's biodiversity.

81 Give examples to illustrate the following statements about policy and practice in the context of sustaining the variety of life on Earth:
   a) Much of the evidence available to the people who organise schemes to conserve biodiversity is often uncertain because the systems involved are not well understood.
   b) Decisions about policies to bring about sustainable development have to take account of international agreements.
   c) Policymakers are influenced by the mass media, special interest groups and public opinion.
   d) Vested interests can affect the interpretation and evaluation of evidence by the people involved in making decisions.

82 Give your reasoned answer to this question: "What is the point in preserving endangered species that have no practical use to humans, apart from their aesthetic appeal or their intellectual interest to biologists?"